THE ODYSSEY

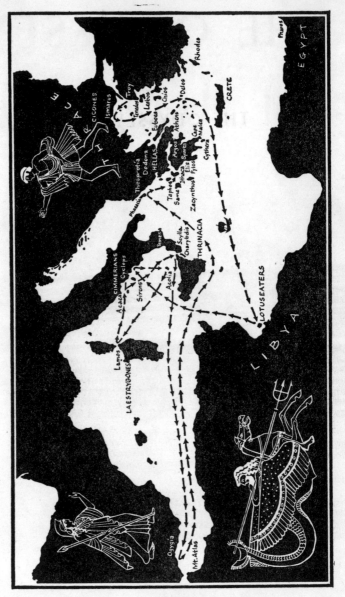

The Wanderings of Odysseus from Troy to Ithaca

THE ODYSSEY
OF HOMER

TRANSLATED BY SAMUEL BUTLER

EDITED BY LOUISE ROPES LOOMIS

Published for the Classics Club by

WALTER J. BLACK · ROSLYN, NEW YORK

The decorative panels at the beginning of each book of the Odyssey were designed by Lucy Cores. The individual figures were taken from authentic reproductions of paintings on Greek vases of the fifth and sixth century B.C., and combined to illustrate an episode in each book.

The frontispiece map of the Mediterranean, illustrating Odysseus' wanderings, was executed by Philip Grushkin. It is based on a map in Victor Bérard's Les Navigations d'Ulysse, Volume IV.

CONTENTS

PREFACE

This translation is intended to supplement a work entitled *The Authoress of the Odyssey*, which I published in 1897. I could not give the whole *Odyssey* in that book without making it unwieldy, I therefore epitomized my translation, which was already completed and which I now publish in full.

I shall not here argue the two main points dealt with in the work just mentioned; I have nothing either to add to, or to withdraw from, what I have there written. The points in question are:

(1) that the *Odyssey* was written entirely at, and drawn entirely from, the place now called Trapani on the west coast of Sicily, alike as regards the Phaeacian and the Ithaca scenes; while the voyages of Ulysses,[1] when once he is within easy reach of Sicily, resolve themselves into a periplus of the island, practically from Trapani back to Trapani, via the Lipari islands, the Straits of Messina, and the island of Pantellaria;

(2) that the poem was entirely written by a very young woman, who lived at the place now called Trapani, and introduced herself into her work under the name of Nausicaa.

The main arguments on which I base the first of these somewhat startling contentions, have been prominently and repeatedly before the English and Italian public ever since they appeared (without rejoinder) in the *Athenaeum* for 30th January and 20th February 1892. Both contentions were urged (also without rejoinder) in the Johnian *Eagle* for the Lent and October Terms of the same year. Nothing to which I should reply has reached me from any quarter, and knowing how anxiously I have endeavored to learn the existence of any flaws in my argument, I begin to feel

---

[1] In this edition of Butler's translation the name Ulysses has been restored to its Greek form, Odysseus.

some confidence that, did such flaws exist, I should have heard, at any rate about some of them, before now. Without, therefore, for a moment pretending to think that scholars generally acquiesce in my conclusions, I shall act as thinking them little likely so to gainsay me as that it will be incumbent upon me to reply, and shall confine myself to translating the *Odyssey* for English readers, with such notes as I think will be found useful. . . .

In the preface to my translation of the *Iliad* [2] I have given my views as to the main principles by which a translator should be guided, and need not repeat them here, beyond pointing out that the initial liberty of translating poetry into prose involves the continual taking of more or less liberty throughout the translation; for much that is right in poetry is wrong in prose, and the exigencies of readable prose are the first things to be considered in a prose translation. That the reader, however, may see how far I have departed from strict construe, I will print here Messrs. Butcher and Lang's translation of the first lines of the *Odyssey*. Their translation runs:

"Tell me, Muse, of that man, so ready at need, who wandered far and wide, after he had sacked the sacred citadel of Troy, and many were the men whose towns he saw and whose mind he learnt, yea, and many the woes he suffered in his heart on the deep, striving to win his own life and the return of his company. Nay, but even so he saved not his company, though he desired it sore. For through the blindness of their own hearts they perished, fools, who devoured the oxen of Helios Hyperion: but the god took from them their days of returning. Of these things, goddess, daughter of Zeus, whencesoever thou hast heard thereof, declare thou even unto us.

"Now all the rest, as many as fled from sheer destruction, were at home, and had escaped both war and sea, but Odysseus only, craving for his wife and his homeward path, the lady nymph Calypso held, that fair goddess, in her hollow caves, longing to have him for her lord. But when now the year had come in the courses

[2] See Classics Club *Iliad*, xxix.

of the seasons, wherein the gods had ordained that he should return home to Ithaca, not even there was he quit of labours, not even among his own; but all the gods had pity on him save Poseidon, who raged continually against god-like Odysseus, till he came to his own country. Howbeit Poseidon had now departed for the distant Ethiopians, the Ethiopians that are sundered in twain, the uttermost of men, abiding some where Hyperion sinks and some where he rises. There he looked to receive his hecatomb of bulls and rams, there he made merry, sitting at the feast, but the other gods were gathered in the halls of Olympian Zeus. Then among them the father of men and gods began to speak, for he bethought him in his heart of noble Aegisthus, whom the son of Agamemnon, far-famed Orestes, slew. Thinking upon him he spake out among the Immortals:

" 'Lo you now, how vainly mortal men do blame the gods! For of us they say comes evil, whereas they even of themselves, through the blindness of their own hearts, have sorrows beyond that which is ordained. Even as of late Aegisthus, beyond that which was ordained, took to him the wedded wife of the son of Atreus and killed her lord on his return, and that with sheer doom before his eyes, since we had warned him by the embassy of Hermes the keen-sighter, the slayer of Argos, that he should neither kill the man, nor woo his wife. . . .' "

The *Odyssey* (as everyone knows) abounds in passages borrowed from the *Iliad;* I had wished to print these in a slightly different type, with marginal references to the *Iliad,* and had marked them to this end in my MS. I found, however, that the translation would be thus hopelessly scholasticized, and abandoned my intention. I would nevertheless again urge on those who have the management of our University presses, that they would render a great service to students if they would publish a Greek text of the *Odyssey* with the Iliadic passages printed in a different type, and with marginal references. I have given the British Museum a copy of the *Odyssey* with the Iliadic passages underlined and referred to in MS.; I have also given an *Iliad* marked with all the Odyssean passages, and their references; but copies of both the *Iliad* and *Odyssey* so marked ought to be within easy reach of all students.

Anyone who at the present day discusses the questions that have arisen round the *Iliad* since Wolf's[3] time, without keeping it well before his reader's mind that the *Odyssey* was demonstrably written from one single neighborhood, and hence (even though nothing else pointed to this conclusion) presumably by one person only—that it was written certainly before 750, and in all probability before 1000 B.C.—that the writer of this very early poem was demonstrably familiar with the *Iliad* as we now have it, borrowing as freely from those books whose genuineness has been most impugned, as from those which are admitted to be by Homer—anyone who fails to keep these points well before his readers, is hardly dealing equitably by them. Anyone, on the other hand, who will mark his *Iliad* and his *Odyssey* from the copies in the British Museum above referred to, and who will draw the only inference that common sense can draw from the presence of so many identical passages in both poems, will, I believe, find no difficulty in assigning their proper value to a large number of books here and on the Continent that at present enjoy considerable reputations. Furthermore, and this perhaps is an advantage better worth securing, he will find many puzzles of the *Odyssey* cease to puzzle him on the discovery that they arise from over-saturation with the *Iliad*.

Other difficulties will also disappear as soon as the development of the poem in the writer's mind is understood. I have dealt with this at some length in *The Authoress of the Odyssey*. Briefly, the *Odyssey* consists of two distinct poems: (1) The Return of Ulysses, which alone the Muse is asked to sing in the opening lines of the poem. This poem includes the Phaeacian episode, and the account of Ulysses' adventures as told by himself in Books ix-xii. It consists of lines 1-79 (roughly) of Book i, of line 28 of Book v, and thence

---

[3] The German scholar, Wolf, was the founder of a school of modern higher critics who denied that Homer was the author of the *Iliad* and the *Odyssey*. He broke both poems up into separate folk lays, which he claimed had been composed at different times and only at a much later period united as we have them.

without intermission to the middle of line 187 of Book xiii, at which point the original scheme was abandoned.

(2) The story of Penelope and the suitors, with the episode of Telemachus' voyage to Pylos. This poem begins with line 80 (roughly) of Book i, is continued to the end of Book iv, and not resumed till Ulysses wakes in the middle of line 187, Book xiii, from whence it continues to the end of Book xxiv.

In *The Authoress of the Odyssey* I wrote:

"The introduction of lines xi, 115-137, and of line ix, 535, with the writing a new council of the gods at the beginning of Book v, to take the place of the one that was removed to Book i, 1-79, were the only things that were done to give even a semblance of unity to the old scheme and the new, and to conceal the fact that the Muse, after being asked to sing of one subject, spent two-thirds of her time in singing a very different one, with a climax for which no one has asked her. For roughly the Return occupies eight books, and Penelope and the Suitors sixteen."

I believe this to be substantially correct. . . .

25th July 1900.   S. BUTLER

PRINCIPAL PERSONAGES OF THE ODYSSEY

(The names by which they were known to the Romans, when different from the Greek, are given in parentheses.)

Gods and Goddesses

ZEUS (Jupiter, Jove), son of Cronus (Saturn); king of the gods and ruler of the sky.

POSEIDON (Neptune), son of Cronus; king of the sea.

HADES, son of Cronus; ruler of the house of the dead.

ATHENE (Minerva), daughter of Zeus; goddess of skill and intelligence.

APOLLO, son of Zeus and Leto; archer god of light.

ARTEMIS (Diana), daughter of Zeus and Leto; huntress goddess of the woods.

APHRODITE (Venus), daughter of Zeus and Dione; goddess of love.

ARES (Mars), son of Zeus; god of war.

HEPHAESTUS (Vulcan), son of Zeus and Hera; god of metalworking and handicraft.

HERMES (Mercury), son of Zeus; messenger of the gods.

PERSEPHONE (Proserpina), daughter of Demeter; wife of Hades and queen of the underworld.

Lesser Divinities

PROTEUS, old man of the sea, one of the gods deposed by Zeus.

EIDOTHEA, daughter of Proteus; sea-nymph.

CALYPSO, daughter of Atlas; island nymph on Ogygia.

AEOLUS, son of Hippotas; keeper of the winds.

CIRCE, daughter of the Sun; goddess of the wild, enchantress.

Family and Household of Odysseus

ODYSSEUS (Ulysses), son of Laertes; king of Ithaca.

LAERTES, son of Arceisius; aged father of Odysseus.

PENELOPE, daughter of Icarius; wife of Odysseus.

TELEMACHUS, son of Odysseus and Penelope.

MENTOR, friend and steward of Odysseus.

PHEMIUS, son of Terpes; minstrel in the house.

MEDON, herald.

EUMAEUS, son of Ctesius; keeper of Odysseus' swine.

MELANTHIUS, son of Dolius; keeper of the goats.

PHILOETIUS, keeper of the cattle.

DOLIUS, aged gardener and field worker.

EURYCLEA, daughter of Ops; old nurse of Odysseus and Telemachus.

EURYNOME, head maid and housekeeper.

MELANTHO, daughter of Dolius; favored maid of Penelope.

EURYLOCHUS, husband of Odysseus' sister, sailor with Odysseus.

ELPENOR, youngest sailor with Odysseus.

Men of Ithaca and Suitors for the Hand of Penelope

AEGYPTIUS, aged lord in Ithaca.

HALITHERSES, son of Mastor; seer and prophet.

NOEMON, son of Phromius; shipowner.

PIRAEUS, son of Clytius; trusty friend of Telemachus.

EUPEITHES, lord in Ithaca.

IRUS, town beggar.

ANTINOUS, son of Eupeithes; leader of the suitors.

EURYMACHUS, son of Polybus;
LEIOCRITUS, son of Evenor; } suitors from Ithaca.
AGELAUS, son of Damastor;
AMPHIMEDON, son of Melanus;

CTESIPPUS, son of Polytherses; suitor from Same.

AMPHINOMUS, son of Nisus; suitor from Dulichium.

LEIODES, son of Oenops; soothsayer for the suitors.

Persons met by Telemachus on his Trip to the Mainland

NESTOR, son of Neleus; aged king of Pylos, returned from Troy.

PISISTRATUS, son of Nestor.

MENELAUS, son of Atreus; king of Sparta, returned from Troy.

HELEN, daughter of Zeus and Leda; wife of Menelaus, brought back from Troy.

THEOCLYMENUS, son of Polypheides; fugitive seer from Argos, received by Telemachus.

Dwellers in the Land of the Phaeacians

ALCINOUS, son of Nausithous; king of the Phaeacians in Scheria.

ARETE, daughter of Rhexenor; wife of Alcinous and queen of the Phaeacians.

LAODAMAS, eldest son of Alcinous and Arete.

NAUSICAA, young daughter of Alcinous and Arete.

DEMODOCUS, blind bard at Alcinous' court.

EURYALUS, son of Naubolus; Phaeacian noble.

Monsters and Other Inhuman Beings

POLYPHEMUS, son of Poseidon; giant Cyclops and ogre.

ANTIPHATES, king of the cannibal Laestrygonians.

Two SIRENS, fatal beguilers of men with their singing.

SCYLLA, daugther of Crataiis; six-headed monster and man-eater.

CHARYBDIS, a whirlpool which draws vessels to their doom.

Spirits of the Dead in the House of Hades

TEIRESIAS, blind prophet of Thebes.

ANTICLEIA, daughter of Autolycus; wife of Laertes and mother of Odysseus.

TYRO, daughter of Salmoneus; mother by Poseidon of Pelias and Neleus.

EPICASTE, also called Jocasta, mother and wife of Oedipus, king of Thebes.

AGAMEMNON, son of Atreus; king of the Greeks at Troy.

ACHILLES, son of Peleus; hero of the *Iliad*.

PATROCLUS, son of Menoetius; comrade of Achilles.

AJAX, son of Telamon; great warrior at Troy.

TITYUS
TANTALUS } spirits tormented in punishment.
SISYPHUS

SHADE OF HERACLES (Hurcules), son of Zeus; heroic laborer for mankind.

NEW ARRIVALS, spirits of Elpenor and of the suitors.

Scene of Action

Island of Ithaca.

Nestor's home at Pylos.

Palace of Menelaus in Sparta.

Calypso's island of Ogygia in the West.

River mouth in Scheria, land of the Phaeacians, and palace of the king, Alcinous.

> *The names of the gods and goddesses and of the hero Odysseus, which our translator, Samuel Butler, turned into Latin forms, have in this edition been restored to the Greek.*

INTRODUCTION

The *Iliad* of Homer is a tragedy of youth, a tale of irreparable woe brought on himself and the whole Greek host by the wrath of one young captain in the camp before Troy. The *Odyssey* is a romance of middle age, a tale of an older man's long and perilous wanderings in the years after Troy fell, and his final victorious homecoming. "Tell me, O muse," it begins, "of that man so ready of resource, who voyaged far and wide after he had sacked the sacred city of Troy. Many were the men whose cities he saw and whose minds he learned, and many the griefs he suffered in his heart on the sea, striving to keep his own life and bring his men safely home." When the *Odyssey* opens, Troy has been ashes, Priam and his sons slain, and the Greek camp on the shore empty for ten years.

Many of the Greeks, both young and old, who played famous parts in the *Iliad,* are dead also. Achilles, the greater Ajax, and countless others were left behind in tombs on Trojan soil, when their comrades took ship at last for home. Others on their voyage across the Aegean were blown out of their course and wrecked on unfriendly coasts. The winds and currents in those waters are notoriously tricky and dangerous to this day. And the Greeks by their arrogant and blasphemous behavior when they took Troy drew down on themselves the anger even of those gods that had hitherto befriended them. For his boastful impiety the lesser Ajax was swept by a blow from Poseidon's trident off his high crag and drowned. The king of kings, Agamemnon, reached his home in Argos only to find treachery and murder waiting for him there, a wife conniving with a guilty steward to stab him as he sat at the welcoming banquet table. His shameful fate is still a horrifying memory in everyone's mind, even though his son, Orestes, has since avenged him by killing his mother and her base accomplice. Few, indeed, of the greater chiefs are back in their longed-for homes in peace. Valiant Diomed is one of them, old Nestor another. Menelaus, with his lovely Helen, is ensconced again in the palace at Sparta, almost as if nothing had ever happened. The miraculous beauty of Helen has always set her apart from the pains of ordinary mortals.

But one of the greatest chiefs has disappeared. No one has seen the hero of the *Odyssey* since he and his men sailed away from their companions at Troy ten years ago. At his home, on the wooded, craggy island of Ithaca, his wife, Penelope, and his twenty-year-old son Telemachus, whom he left a baby when he went to Troy, have until now clung desperately to a failing hope that he might yet some day return. A few of his trusty serfs still save the best wine and the tenderest pork for the master on the chance that he may yet come to enjoy them. But for years now a gang of uninvited visitors from the neighboring estates and islands have been feasting in his house, loudly declaring him dead and calling on his wife to admit herself a widow and take one of them for a new husband. Steadily, on one excuse or another, she has put them off. For three years she played the trick of the shroud, which must be woven for Odysseus' aged father before she left his roof. All day she wove industriously at it but each night pulled out what she had done by day. However, a traitorous maid at last betrayed her secret. The shroud has had to be finished. The suitors grow more threatening and insistent. Telemachus is still too young to know how to deal with a crowd of ugly-tempered men, and watches miserably while they bully his mother, demoralize his home and consume his father's substance.

Archaeologists disagree as to which of several small islands off the west coast of Greece was Odysseus' Ithaca. It may have been one that modern Greeks call Thiaki. It may have been one close to it. The little harbor, the tree-clad mountain, the shadowy cave consecrated to the nymphs, that Homer describes, can be found on any one of them, as also traces of ancient occupation. Whichever Ithaca was, it lay on the edge of that partially enclosed eastern end of the Mediterranean which in Homer's day made all the world his Greeks or Achaeans knew.

The ancestors of these Greeks, who some centuries earlier had moved down from the northern mountains of Thrace to settle in Greece and along the shores of Asia Minor, had quickly learned enough of the seafarers' art to put out in boats to fish, or to raid neighboring lands for slaves and booty, or to traffic with the more civilized peoples of Crete, Phoenicia, and Egypt. By Homer's time, eight or nine hundred years, that is, before Christ, it has become nothing unusual for an enterprising trader to load a few ships with casks of sweet Greek wine and oil, and, when the wind is favorable, sail with them down the Syrian coast or across the wide water to Egypt. There he may join the fleet that daily makes its way up the great river he knows as the Egyptus, to the golden city of Thebes, to exchange his wares for rare objects of art and luxury. From Thebes, Helen has brought back to Sparta a workbasket of silver, edged with gold and mounted on wheels, and a marvelous drug that, mixed with wine, makes the drinker forgetful of pain.

To the west, however, of Ithaca and Egypt lies a far wider waste of unknown water into which the Greeks as yet have not dared to penetrate. Only the Phoenicians, much older and more experienced navigators, have pushed on and on into the sunset, founding a trading post here and a colony there until they reached the straits leading into the Western Ocean, where the sun drops at night. They have perhaps by now made out sea charts or sailing directions, to list the natural landmarks along the route, the danger spots to be avoided and the safe landing places where one may call for supplies of food and water. But to the Greeks everything beyond the familiar shores and islands is still a world of blank and utter mystery. When no trace of the vanished Odysseus can be found in the known, enclosed world of the East, he is given up as irretrievably lost.

In the settled Greek countries of the East, the civilization that modern historians call the late Mycenean is now well established. Petty chiefs and kings, not unlike the feudal lords of the Middle Ages, rule their lands and estates from strong, walled houses of stone or timber, served and defended by slaves, serfs, and free retainers. A greater king or overlord of a whole region may live in a palace whose walls and pillars are overlaid with copper, silver, and colored enamels, "shining like the sheen of sun or moon." The island boy, Telemachus, is astounded at the palace of Menelaus in Sparta, "blazing with copper and gold, silver and ivory," like the mansions of Olympian Zeus. Even the traveled Odysseus is amazed at first sight of the palace of Alcinous, king of the wealthy Phaeacians, its entrance door guarded by watchdogs of gold and silver, its great hall lit by torches, borne by gold statues of boys standing on fine wrought pedestals.

Though Odysseus is the acknowledged chief king of Ithaca and sends the overflow of his flocks and herds to the mainland for pasture, his house is no such palace. Yet it is substantial, spacious and opulent enough. A large forecourt, closed by a heavy gate, contains the necessary outbuildings and quarters for menservants. In the center stands a massive altar for sacrifices to Zeus. Thence, through a covered portico and second strong gateway, one steps into the great hall with its roof supported by tall pillars. On the wide hearth a fire is always burning, the smoke of which makes its way out through an opening in the rafters of the roof. Chimneys, of course, are still to be invented. A line of chairs with high decorated backs stands against the wall. Soft robes are thrown over them and footstools placed in front, that the sitters may take their ease. Long polished tables are set before the chairs when the time comes to eat, for not yet has arisen the custom of later Greeks and Romans of reclining on divans at meals.

From the great hall one may pass in one direction to the serving rooms and kitchens, from which the waiting maids and men bring gold and silver ewers and basins to wash the guests' hands, platters and baskets of meat, bread and fruit, and cups and pitchers of wine. On another side are the rooms where the mistress sits and spins and directs her women at their work. Overhead are the family bedrooms. Only Odysseus has a special room of his own attached to the house, with a bedstead built by himself around an olive tree trunk that chanced to be growing there. Nearby is the bathing room, where water is heated and poured into a huge, burnished cauldron and a maid rubs and anoints the bather with smooth olive oil. Down a long corridor, leading to the rear of the house, lie the armory, holding a store of helmets, shields, spears, swords, and other weapons of war, and a locked treasure room, where stand chests of jewels and embroidered robes, heaps of precious vessels, jars of the choicest wine, and bars of unworked silver and gold. Coined money has not yet been invented and values are computed in weights of metal.

Though Odysseus' wife Penelope has her own withdrawing room, she appears among the men in the great hall and speaks her mind to them as often as she pleases. In the absence of her husband, however, and before this boisterous crowd of importunate suitors, she keeps two maids with her always, draws her veil before her face and never lingers long. But in a house where the master is at hand to protect his wife from insolence, she sits by his side in the place of dignity beside the hearth. There Helen graciously receives Telemachus when he comes to Sparta and there Arete, the revered queen of the Phaeacians, hears the appeal of the shipwrecked Odysseus. The women of the *Odyssey,* both the goddesses and their mortal sisters, are singularly free and forceful personalities, not like the wives of later Athenians, compelled to remain out of sight in the women's quarters. An unmarried daughter of a great house, like the girl, Nausicaa, does not indeed show herself among the throng in the hall, but about the rest of the house and out of doors she comes and goes as she likes. When she wants a word with Odysseus she waylays him frankly in an inner room.

Outside and around the house lie the gardens, orchards, and vineyards. The perfect garden in front of Alcinous' palace is four acres in size and walled about by a hedge. Tall pears, pomegranates, apples, figs, and olives grow in profusion, while on one side of the fertile vineyard tiny green grapes are dropping their flower petals and on the other rich clusters are purpling to sweetness. Beyond the trees are plots of flowers that bloom all the year through. The whole is irrigated by streams from a spring carried up and down in little shining channels. When Odysseus at length comes home, he finds his father, Laertes, hoeing in the orchard and proves his own identity to the grieving old man by recalling the trees Laertes gave him when he was a child. "Thirteen pear trees," he says, "you gave me, ten apples, forty figs; and you described the fifty rows of vines you would give me, each one ripening in its season, so that always there would be bunches of grapes on them."

Beyond Odysseus' garden lie his barns, sheds and styes for the animals, and his pastures, fields, and woods. Cattlemen, goatherds, shepherds, and swineherds look after the stock. Ithaca, being a rough and rocky island, has no smooth grazing grounds for horses or roads suited to chariot driving. So Odysseus boasts no swift and beautiful chargers as King Menelaus on the mainland does. Instead of horses as their companions, his men have dogs. His lonely son, Telemachus, has two shining dogs ever at his heels. The only creature to recognize Odysseus on his return by the mere sound of his voice is the old hound Argos, whom he left a half-trained pup when he sailed for Troy. Now lying weak, forlorn, and neglected on a dung heap outside the court, he hears his master speak as he passes by. He pricks up his ears, thumps his tail, and struggles to drag himself forward. But the joy and the effort are too much for him. Down he sinks into the blackness of death, having known his master after twenty years.

A king at home has plenty of occupation. The suitors who for years now have been doing nothing but persecute Penelope are abhorred for their idleness as well as for their gluttonous feasting on a defenseless man's bread and wine. Kings and nobles have a right, of course, to sit sometimes and feast, listen to minstrels singing, watch the young lads toss their balls and dance, or take a hand themselves in a contest of boxing, racing, or pitching weights, but only as a rest between labors. Like any great ranch owners, the more they and their wives possess in the way of practical skills, the more their affairs are likely to prosper. The lady Penelope is renowned not only for her beauty but for her weaving and competence as a housewife. Odysseus has the reputation of having in the past done every job on the place better than anyone else could do it. Those who remember him are forever telling stories of his accomplishments. He could drive the straightest furrow with the plow, mow the biggest stretch of meadow in a day, breed the best strains of oxen and swine. He was adept at carpentry, too. There stand his room and the unique bed he built that no one has touched since he went away. Hunting the woods for wild boar, he was the surest marksman with his great bow, that was too heavy for an ordinary man even to draw.

But a king is not only master of his lands, he is ruler of the people on them. He has power of life and death over his slaves. In a case of dispute involving other free landowners he sends out his heralds to call an assembly of the neighbors. When all are gathered, the aggrieved one presents his complaint, the accused replies, and the matter is fully discussed. Anyone who wishes to speak may get in his turn from the herald the scepter or baton that gives him momentarily the floor. An attending augur or priest interprets whatever omens may appear as indicating the judgment of the gods. There are no written laws to follow but the authority of established custom and the priest's word is strong. A decision is reached eventually by the majority and enforced by the winning party and his friends.

Justice like this, depending on the custom and the priest and the power of individuals to execute it, is inevitably limited and local in its application. When the injured man is dead or too weak or too distant to appear against his injurer, there is no redress. All the dwellers in Argos were outraged by the murder of Agamemnon, but his false wife and her steward reigned on unmolested in the palace, until Orestes, whose peculiar duty it was to avenge his father, appeared and performed it. So pirate raids on foreign shores are permissible and right, for stranger populations are outside the boundaries of Greek justice. Odysseus can speak with pride of sacking the unoffending city of Ismarus on the Thracian coast, killing the men, and dividing their wives and wealth "justly" among himself and his crew, sparing only the priest of Apollo piously in return for seven talents of gold, a mixing bowl of silver, and twelve jars of mellow wine. But this is part of the universal custom of the time. The idea of justice is everywhere primitive yet and applies not to man as man but only to members of one's own community.

The Homeric chief, however, like the hero of a Norse saga or a medieval *chanson,* has his personal, chivalrous code of honor, as the *Iliad* shows. He is, first of all, a strong and courageous fighter, fierce to destroy an enemy in the heat of battle, but not coldly or maliciously cruel. At all costs he is true to his friends, fair and loyal to his followers, hospitable and courteous to his guests. He keeps his pledged word. He reverences the gods. He is compassionate also to any poor suppliant who comes for protection to his hearth. Zeus, the Father of men and gods, hears, he believes, the prayers of such humble ones, who have no earthly defender, and punishes the arrogant and hard of heart who forget they too are mortals. All these knightly virtues have been characteristic of Odysseus. He has won fame both as a warrior and as a friend. His slaves speak of him as a humane master and the relationship between his family and their faithful, old servants is intimate and affectionate. The rule of generous hospitality to strangers, no matter how lowly, is observed by his wife and son as part of the changeless tradition of the house.

But the special virtue of Odysseus, the one that from his youth up raised him conspicuously above other brave and chivalrous men, was, everyone agrees, his intelligence. He had a keen man's love of daring plans and zest for unusual adventures. He was quick to read other men's minds, grasp the meaning of a situation, exceedingly fertile in resource and persuasive in counsel. Withal he was canny, cool-headed, able to keep his own excitement under control. He never let a good scheme be spoiled for lack of a little caution and patience in carrying it through. In the ambush of the wooden horse, that was the undoing of Troy, he kept Menelaus and Diomed from betraying themselves when Helen called them, and gripped another man's mouth shut with his hands until the temptation to answer her was past. When the occasion required, he could lie magnificently. "Even a god," says Athene to him once, approvingly, "to keep pace with you, must be cunning and sharp at every trick, you deceiving, crafty wretch!" "You were always," Penelope tells him tenderly, "an understanding man."

The *Odyssey* opens with the picture of Odysseus' home in the twentieth year since he left it to go to Troy. Penelope has at last reached the point of telling herself firmly that her husband must be dead and that in fairness to Telemachus she must accept a second husband and so relieve the boy of the presence of the lawless mob of suitors in what should be his house, and stop the drain upon his resources. As yet, however, she has not been able to bring herself to select any one of them and at night lies sobbing on her bed, thinking of the man who has never come back or sent her any word.

But of all who grieve for Odysseus' loss, the one who needs him most is his son, Telemachus. He has grown up dreaming of the famous father, of whom men said such wonderful things, and now he hears on every hand that his father has perished in some dark, inexplicable way, leaving behind no message nor token of remembrance. And he, who should be filling that father's place as head of the house and his mother's protector, has no idea how to assert his authority over the rioting bedlam in the hall. He is in despair over his disgraceful failure to measure up to his father's standard.

But Zeus does not intend to leave a man like Odysseus languishing in exile forever. Though in the past he angered Poseidon, he has suffered enough for his offense and should now be allowed to return home. First, Athene is sent in the guise of a family friend to Telemachus, to lift him out of his mood of hopeless humiliation. His father, she tells him, is alive and will some day be back. Meanwhile there is something he can do—call an assembly of the neighbors and in their presence formally demand that the suitors leave his house, then go himself to the mainland to find whether Odysseus' old associates, King Nestor and King Menelaus, have any tidings of him.

Encouraged and resolved to play the man, Telemachus sends out the heralds to proclaim the assembly, describes to it the plight of his house and demands the withdrawal of the suitors. But at the end, a flood of mortification and rage suddenly surges over him, he bursts into tears and dashes the speaker's baton to the ground. The assembly breaks up with the suitors more insolent than ever, contriving a plot to murder Telemachus, who is evidently getting out of hand.

Again he must be heartened by Athene and helped to get his boat and crew together, to slip away by night without the suitors' knowledge. Once, however, on the mainland, he receives the warmest of welcomes from Nestor and Menelaus and the eternally fascinating Helen. Their affectionate and flattering treatment of him and reminiscences of his father's greatness go far to put strength into him and cure his boyish misery and self-distrust. No one has seen his father, but Menelaus has a tale of catching off guard a slippery and oracular sea god on the way back from Egypt, who assured him that Odysseus was living, even though a prisoner on an unnamed island. Thus when, after two weeks' stay, Telemachus leaves for home again, though anxious still for his father's safety, he has the steadiness and the pride that will fit him to stand by Odysseus' side without flinching when the day of reckoning comes.

As for the long-lost Odysseus himself, the gods know where he is, even though to his friends and family he has been as dead, ever since a great storm drove him and his ships westward and southward over the edge of the known, habitual world into the region of terrors and enchantments. Now, the lone survivor of all his company, he is a prisoner on the remote island of Ogygia, where seven years ago he was cast up and where the fair nymph, Calypso, keeps him with her in her wooded paradise, trying to make him forget the world of men and become an immortal. But never has he succumbed to her wiles or tasted of her divine food, the ambrosia and nectar that would make him deathless. Always has he kept the will to return to his human Penelope, and chafed and mourned at his inability to escape. And now comes Zeus' messenger, Hermes, to bid Calypso let him go.

Dextrous as ever, Odysseus builds a stout, high-railed raft with the tools and lumber Calypso gives him and jubilantly sets sail, steering his course by the stars directly East. On the eighteenth day he is almost home, when the vindictive Poseidon spies him and crashes down upon him with one last tempestuous blow. His raft is broken in pieces, for two days he drifts near to drowning, until at length Athene guides him to a quiet river's mouth on the island of the Phaeacians. It is not Ithaca, but it is a home of merciful human beings. The king's daughter, the charming girl Nausicaa, is moved with pity at sight of him and takes him to her father's palace. And there before Alcinous and his wife, Queen Arete, and a hushed and astounded audience he tells the tale of his ten years' sufferings and adventures.

The tale of Odysseus told in the hall of Alcinous is the first travelers' yarn in European literature, and for thrill and variety and imaginative power it never has been surpassed. How much of the material Homer took from the sagas of Trojan heroes that older generations of minstrels had sung before him and how much was his personal invention, no one now can say. He tells us himself that not more than ten years after the events, the bards were already chanting stories of the wooden horse and the downfall of Troy and the dire fate that overtook so many of her conquerors. The opening lines of the *Odyssey*, previously quoted, show that Odysseus particularly was celebrated as one who voyaged far and wide before reaching home. So the idea of his journey into the magical world of the West and encounters with supernatural danger there may have been part of the Odysseus legend when Homer took it for his theme. But to Homer is certainly due the inimitable form in which it has come down to us.

Strabo, a Greek geographer, who lived near the time of Christ and to whom the whole Mediterranean area was familiar ground, thought that Homer got his knowledge of the West, his notions of the spots his hero visited, from the Phoenicians. His place names, it seems, appear sometimes like Greek translations of known Semitic names. His descriptions of local features, such as the whirlpool of Charybdis in the Messenian straits, the windswept island of Aeolus off the Sicilian coast, the jutting headlands that block the harbor of Lamos in northern Sardinia, the meadows of parsley near the straits of Gibraltar, might well have been taken from the log of some pilot of Sidon or of Tyre. The mountain which Italians still call Monte Circeo, standing up from the low marshland to the north of the Bay of Naples, might easily have been mistaken by passing mariners for an island. And Aeaea, Homer's name for it, in a Semitic tongue means "sea hawk," which is likewise the meaning of the Greek word Circe, the name of the glittering enchantress Odysseus found there.

What, however, a matter-of-fact seaman might regard as a casual phenomenon of the physical landscape, Homer might see as a living, malignant creature. The dangerous rock of Scylla, across from Charybdis, is for him a six-headed devil, that reaches out to snatch six screaming wretches from Odysseus' boat in spite of all his puny efforts to prevent her. The huge mountainous shape with the round fiery eye, from which rocks fly hurtling into the sea, is to him no plain volcanic peak, one of the many craters at present extinct around Vesuvius, but a gigantic ogre, maddened with pain, whose single eye Odysseus has just put out with his blazing stake. On a perilous reef, covered with human bones, Sirens are singing to lure more unwary men to destruction. So Odysseus' exploits take place in a setting compounded, apparently, of a few facts, gathered, perhaps, from some Phoenician's nautical guide, and an abundance of tale-teller's fancies. A recent French scholar's attempt to separate Homer's facts from his fancies is recounted in Victor Bérard's interesting little book, *Did Homer Live?*

But whatever unforseeable perils or horrors Odysseus encounters, lost and wandering through this world of lurking poisons, man-eating savages, and perverse divinities, he remains the unconquerable, audacious one that he ever was back in the common world of men. His hatred of being baffled, his explorer's curiosity still compel him to find out what manner of being inhabits each new country, what sort of house a distant smoke rises from. Thereby he is caught in fearful traps, but until he is washed up on Calypso's isle he always contrives to extricate himself and his men, as long as they obey and follow him. Only when Circe sends him to the house of Hades to consult the dead prophet Teiresias, does he go, shrinking and in dread.

The house of Hades did not probably figure on any Phoenician navigator's chart. But lying on the western verge of the earth, it may

drunken suitors, while Telemachus by a plausible excuse removes all arms from the hall to the storeroom in the rear. It needs now only the opportunity that Penelope puts into Odysseus' hand by bringing out his own great bow to test, she says, the marksmanship of her wooers. No one of them, in the condition they are in, can even string it. In time it comes to Odysseus. His long-pent wrath and indignation now break out. Like a lion he stands, glaring at a herd of panic-struck, befuddled oxen. With the help of Telemachus, Eumaeus and a trusty cattleman, he kills them all, there in the hall, among the upturned tables and the spilt wine cups. The maids they have corrupted are called in to remove the mass of blood and gore, and scrub and sweeten the place with sulphur. Then they are taken out and hanged. But when the old nurse Euryclea would raise a noisy chant of triumph over the piles of bodies, Odysseus checks her. "An unholy thing," he says, "it is to boast over slain men. By the doom of the gods they fell, for the wickedness they wrought." He knows what death means.

All is now over but the scenes of recognition and rejoicing. The old nurse has already known her master by the long white scar on his leg he got as a boy, which she discovered while washing his feet at Penelope's bidding, as part of the courtesy to be shown a stranger. The doubting, fearing Penelope herself is slowly convinced that here is in truth the husband she thought never to see again. She spends most of the night listening to the tale he told Alcinous. The next day the old father is found and learns the glad news. Finally the relatives of the dead suitors, who gather to exact vengeance for their killing, are pacified by the intervention of Athene and Zeus, who will that peace shall come to Odysseus and to Ithaca at last.

In the century or two after Homer, six more epics were composed by different poets to form with the *Iliad* and the *Odyssey* a continuous cycle, covering the entire story of Troy from the fateful judgment of Paris and his abduction of Helen down through the sack of the city and the returns and deaths of all the Greek survivors, including Odysseus. But none of these later six epics seem to have been preserved for more than a few hundred years. We know of their contents only from rare allusions to them by ancient authors. But the two great poems that were persistently called Homer's came more and more to be regarded as sacred, and to be recited in public all over Greece on solemn occasions. Plato, Aristotle, and many other Greek writers before and after quote from them. In the third and second centuries before Christ, Greek scholars, working in the great library of Alexandria, went painstakingly through the Homeric manuscripts then current, weeding out what they judged were errors and spurious additions and establishing a text they thought authentic. This Alexandrian text is essentially what we use today. Our two oldest complete copies of it, however, were written, one in the tenth and one in the eleventh century of our era. They are preserved in the beautiful Laurentian Library, designed by Michelangelo, to receive the books of the Medici family in Florence.

These manuscripts were brought from the East to Italy during the period of the Renaissance, for from the fall of Rome to the time of the revival of Greek studies in the fourteenth and fifteenth centuries, Homer, like most other Greek authors, was lost to the West. The tale of Troy and of Odysseus, the far traveler, had, however, been retold in part by Vergil, and in much cruder form by later poets and prose writers. So the minstrels of the Middle Ages had their versions of the story, derived from the Latins and differing freely from Homer's. But in 1488, the first edition of the genuine *Iliad* and *Odyssey* in Greek was printed in Florence. Once they were known and read again, the Latin fabrications were discarded and the blind bard, "whom the Muse loved above all other men," came into his own in that Western world which he had sent his most courageous hero to explore. His Sirens, his Cyclops, his Scylla and Charybdis, his Lotus-eaters, his Circe, seem now to belong as much to our Western imagination and literature as if they had been ours from the first. One of our most modern writers has called his finest novel *Ulysses*—using the Latin form of the name—because, though the scene is laid in a twentieth-century Dublin slum and the two chief characters are an elderly Jew and a youthful Irish poet, the relationship between them is in essence that between a wandering father and a troubled son, who needs him, and the experiences through which they pass are translations into terms of present-day living of the episodes of the *Odyssey*.

But the whole story of Odysseus Homer never told. He brought him home to his own country and left him there. What became of him afterward? Was he content to settle down and become a prosperous king like Menelaus and spend his evenings with Penelope by the fire in the great hall? On his visit to the house of Hades he had had his future briefly forecast to him by the spirit of the seer Teiresias. From Ithaca he would take one more journey, this time far inland, to offer a final propitiatory sacrifice to Poseidon in a place so remote from the sea that an inhabitant would not know what was the ship's oar he carried on his shoulder. Afterwards he would live on in his Ithaca, until when he was full of years, death would come gently to him from the sea. The author of the last poem of the Trojan cycle, called the *Telegonia,* invented a young hero, Telegonus, purported to be the son of Odysseus and Circe, who in the course of his rambling visited Ithaca and by chance killed his father with a lance barbed with a fish bone, thus fulfilling Teiresias' prophecy. But other ancients had a story according to which Odysseus presently grew tired of domesticity, left Penelope again, and crossed to wild Thesprotia on the mainland, where he conquered a new kingdom and another bride.

Other poets since have taken Odysseus as a symbol of the unresting spirit in man, that is always on a quest for new knowledge and new experience, "strong in will to strive, to seek, to find and not to yield." Their Odysseus cannot be satisfied with merely one more kingdom and a fresh, new wife. He is possessed by thoughts of the seas he did not sail, the lands he did not reach, lying still farther westward. He must have one more voyage before he dies, out beyond any world he ever knew. "My purpose holds," Tennyson makes him say,

> "To sail beyond the sunset and the baths
> Of all the western stars, until I die.

> *It may be that the gulfs will wash us down:*
> *It may be we shall touch the Happy Isles*
> *And see the great Achilles whom we knew."*

A greater poet than Tennyson has drawn the picture of Odysseus' death. Writing at the beginning of the fourteenth century, Dante knew of him only what had been related by Vergil and other Latins. Such a crafty old pagan, he who had engineered the ruse of the wooden horse, must be set in the fiery chasm of Hell where burn all lying and unscrupulous counselors. But even in Hell Dante recognizes a heroic spirit when he sees it. On his way through, he insists upon stopping to hear from Odysseus how and where he died. All the love I bore my son, my aged father and Penelope, answers Odysseus, could not quench in me "the ardor that I had to gain yet more experience of the world and of men's faults and valor."

> *"I put forth on the deep and open sea*
> *With but one ship and that small company*
> *Which until then had not forsaken me . . .*
>
> *Both I and they were growing old and slow*
> *When we were come unto that narrow strait*
> *Where Hercules once set his landmarks*
>
> *To warn men not to venture farther . . .*
>
> *'O brothers,' cried I, 'through a hundred thousand*
> *Perils have ye driven to the West!*
> *Now in the brief and tiny span*
>
> *That still remains to you of waking life,*
> *Refuse not to explore whatever lies*
> *Behind the sun, the world where no man is.*
>
> *Recall from what ye sprang! Ye were not made*

To live as do the brutes but to pursue
And follow stoutly after knowledge!'

With these few words I made my company
So keen and eager for the voyage that scarcely
Then could I have held them back.

We kept our poop straight turned toward the morning
And in our oars had wings for our mad flight."

Five times the light of the moon was kindled over them and disappeared. The southern stars shone in the sky,

"When there appeared to us a mountain dim
In the distance; to me it looked the highest
I had on any shore beheld.

We hailed the sight with joy, but soon our joy
Was turned to grief. From that strange land there came
A blast that struck the forepart of our ship.

Three times it whirled her round in all the waves,
The fourth, it lifted her stern high aloft
And sank her prow down,—at some power's behest,—

So deep the sea closed over us."

LOUISE ROPES LOOMIS

THE ODYSSEY

BOOK I

The gods in council agree that the time has come for Odysseus to be brought home to avenge himself on Penelope's suitors and to recover his kingdom. Hermes is sent to Calypso's isle to bid her release the captive Odysseus. Athene, disguised as Mentes, appears to Telemachus, advising him to call an assembly of the men of Ithaca, to complain of the behavior of the suitors; then to go himself in quest of his father to Pylos and Sparta.

TELL ME, O MUSE, OF THAT INGENIOUS HERO who traveled far and wide after he had sacked the famous town of Troy. Many cities did he visit, and many were the nations with whose manners and customs he was acquainted; moreover he suffered much by sea while trying to save his own life and bring his men safely home; but do what he might he could not have his men, for they perished through their own sheer folly in eating the cattle of the Sun-god Hyperion; so the god prevented them from ever reaching home. Tell me, too, about all these things, O daughter of Zeus, from whatsoever source you may know them.

So now all who escaped death in battle or by shipwreck had got safely home except Odysseus, and he, though he was longing to return to his wife and country, was detained by the goddess Calypso, who had got him into a large cave and wanted to marry him. But as

3

years went by, there came a time when the gods settled that he should go back to Ithaca; even then, however, when he was among his own people, his troubles were not yet over. Nevertheless, all the gods had now begun to pity him except Poseidon, who still persecuted him without ceasing and would not let him go home.

Now Poseidon had gone off to the Ethiopians, who are at the world's end, and lie in two halves, the one looking west and the other east.[1] He had gone there to accept a hecatomb of sheep and oxen, and was enjoying himself at his festival; but the other gods met in the house of Olympian Zeus, and the sire of gods and men spoke first. At that moment he was thinking of Aegisthus, who had been killed by Agamemnon's son Orestes;[2] so he said to the other gods:

"See now, how men lay blame upon us gods for what is after all nothing but their own folly. Look at Aegisthus; he must needs make love to Agamemnon's wife unrighteously and then kill Agamemnon, though he knew it would be the death of him; for I sent Hermes to warn him not to do either of these things, inasmuch as Orestes would be sure to take his revenge when he grew up and wanted to return home. Hermes told him this in all good will but he would not listen, and now he has paid for everything in full."

Then Athene said: "Father, son of Cronus, king of kings, it served Aegisthus right, and so it would anyone else who does as he did; but Aegisthus is neither here nor there; it is for Odysseus that my heart bleeds, when I think of his sufferings in that lonely sea-girt island, far away, poor man, from all his friends. It is an island covered with forest, in the very middle of the sea, and a goddess lives there, daughter of the magician Atlas, who looks after the bottom of the ocean, and carries the great columns that keep heaven and earth asunder. This daughter of Atlas has got hold of poor un-

---

[1] Black races are evidently known to the writer as stretching all across Africa, one half looking west on to the Atlantic, and the other east on to the Indian Ocean. (B.)
[2] Zeus refers here to the terrible homecoming of Agamemnon, king of Argos and chief of the Greeks at Troy, and his murder by the slave Aegisthus, whom Queen Clytemnestra had taken as her lover. Since then Agamemnon's and Clytemnestra's son, Orestes, had killed both his mother and Aegisthus to avenge his father's death. For fuller accounts of the same dreadful deed, see Books III, p. 32, IV, p. 50, and XI, pp. 140-1.

happy Odysseus, and keeps trying by every kind of blandishment to make him forget his home, so that he is tired of life, and thinks of nothing but how he may once more see the smoke of his own chimneys. You, sir, take no heed of this, and yet when Odysseus was before Troy did he not propitiate you with many a burnt sacrifice? Why then should you keep on being so angry with him?"

And Zeus said: "My child, what are you talking about? How can I forget Odysseus than whom there is no more capable man on earth, nor more liberal in his offerings to the immortal gods that live in heaven? Bear in mind, however, that Poseidon is still furious with Odysseus for having blinded an eye of Polyphemus, king of the Cyclopes. Polyphemus is son to Poseidon by the nymph Thoosa, daughter to the sea-king Phorcys; therefore though he will not kill Odysseus outright, he torments him by preventing him from getting home. Still, let us lay our heads together and see how we can help him to return; Poseidon will then be pacified, for if we are all of a mind he can hardly stand out against us."

And Athene said: "Father, son of Cronus, king of kings, if, then, the gods now mean that Odysseus should get home, we should first send Hermes to the Ogygian island to tell Calypso that we have made up our minds and that he is to return. In the meantime I will go to Ithaca, to put heart into Odysseus' son Telemachus; I will embolden him to call the Achaeans in assembly, and speak out to the suitors of his mother Penelope, who persist in eating up any number of his sheep and oxen; I will also conduct him to Sparta and to Pylos, to see if he can hear anything about the return of his dear father—for this will make people speak well of him."

So saying she bound on her glittering golden sandals, imperishable, with which she can fly like the wind over land or sea; she grasped the redoubtable bronze-shod spear, so stout and sturdy and strong, wherewith she quells the ranks of heroes who have displeased her, and down she darted from the topmost summits of Olympus, whereon forthwith she was in Ithaca, at the gateway of Odysseus' house, disguised as a visitor, Mentes, chief of the Taphians, and she held a bronze spear in her hand. There she found the lordly suitors seated on hides of the oxen which they had killed and eaten, and playing draughts in front of the house. Menservants and pages were bustling about to wait upon them, some mixing wine with water in the mixing-bowls, some cleaning down the tables with wet sponges and laying them out again, and some cutting up great quantities of meat.

Telemachus saw her long before anyone else did. He was sitting moodily among the suitors thinking about his brave father, and how he would send them flying out of the house, if he were to come to his own again and be honored as in days gone by. Thus brooding as he sat among them, he caught sight of Athene and went straight to the gate, for he was vexed that a stranger should be kept waiting for admittance. He took her right hand in his own, and bade her give him her spear. "Welcome," said he, "to our house, and when you have partaken of food you shall tell us what you have come for."

He led the way as he spoke, and Athene followed him. When they were within he took her spear and set it in the spear-stand against a strong bearing-post along with the many other spears of his unhappy father, and he conducted her to a richly decorated seat under which he threw a cloth of damask. There was a footstool also for her feet,[3] and he set another seat near her for himself, away from the suitors, that she might not be annoyed while eating by their noise and insolence, and that he might ask her more freely about his father.

A maidservant brought them water in a beautiful golden ewer and poured it into a silver basin for them to wash their hands, and she drew a clean table beside them. An upper servant brought them bread, and offered them many good things of what there was in the house, the carver fetched them plates of all manner of meats and set cups of gold by their side, and a manservant brought them wine and poured it out for them.

Then the suitors came in and took their places on the benches and seats. Forthwith menservants poured water over their hands,

---

[3] The original use of the footstool was probably less to rest the feet than to keep them (especially when bare) from a floor which was often wet and dirty. (B.)

maids went round with the bread-baskets, pages filled the mixing-bowls with wine and water, and they laid their hands upon the good things that were before them. As soon as they had had enough to eat and drink they wanted music and dancing, which are the crowning embellishments of a banquet, so a servant brought a lyre to Phemius, whom they compelled perforce to sing to them. As soon as he touched his lyre and began to sing, Telemachus spoke low to Athene, with his head close to hers that no man might hear.

"I hope, sir," said he, "that you will not be offended with what I am going to say. Singing comes cheap to those who do not pay for it, and all this is done at the cost of one whose bones lie rotting in some wilderness or grinding to powder in the surf. If these men were to see my father come back to Ithaca they would pray for longer legs rather than a longer purse, for money would not serve them; but he, alas, has fallen on an ill fate, and even when people do sometimes say that he is coming, we no longer heed them; we shall never see him again. And now, sir, tell me and tell me true, who you are and where you come from. Tell me of your town and parents, what manner of ship you came in, how your crew brought you to Ithaca, and of what nation they declared themselves to be—for you cannot have come by land. Tell me also truly, for I want to know, are you a stranger to this house, or have you been here in my father's time? In the old days we had many visitors for my father went about much himself."

And Athene answered: "I will tell you truly and particularly all about it. I am Mentes son of Anchialus, and I am king of the Taphians. I have come here with my ship and crew, on a voyage to men of a foreign tongue being bound for Temesa[4] with a cargo of iron, and I shall bring back copper. As for my ship, it lies over yonder off the open country away from the town, in the harbor Rheithron under the wooded mountain Neritum. Our fathers were friends before us, as old Laertes will tell you, if you will go and ask him. They say, however, that he never comes to town now, and lives by

---

[4] Temesa was on the West Coast of the toe of Italy, in what is now the gulf of Sta Eufemia. It was famous in remote times for its copper mines. (B.)

himself in the country, faring hardly, with an old woman to look after him and get his dinner for him, when he comes in tired from pottering about his vineyard. They told me your father was at home again, and that is why I came, but it seems the gods are still keeping him back, for he is not dead yet—not on the mainland. It is more likely he is on some sea-girt island in mid-ocean, or a prisoner among savages who are detaining him against his will. I am no prophet, and know very little about omens, but I speak as it is borne in upon me from heaven, and assure you that he will not be away much longer; for he is a man of such resource that even though he were in chains of iron he would find some means of getting home again. But tell me, and tell me true, can Odysseus really have such a fine looking fellow for a son? You are indeed wonderfully like him about the head and eyes, for we were close friends before he set sail for Troy where the flower of all the Argives went also. Since that time we have never either of us seen the other."

"My mother," answered Telemachus, "tells me I am son to Odysseus, but it is a wise child that knows his own father. Would that I were son to one who had grown old upon his own estates, for, since you ask me, there is no more ill-starred man under heaven than he who they tell me is my father."

And Athene said: "There is no fear of your race dying out yet, while Penelope has such a fine son as you are. But tell me, and tell me true, what is the meaning of all this feasting, and who are these people? What is it all about? Have you some banquet, or is there a wedding in the family—for no one seems to be bringing any provisions of his own? And the guests—how atrociously they are behaving; what riot they make over the whole house; it is enough to disgust any respectable person who comes near them."

"Sir," said Telemachus, "as regards your question, so long as my father was here it was well with us and with the house, but the gods in their displeasure have willed it otherwise, and have hidden him away more closely than mortal man was ever yet hidden. I could have borne it better even though he were dead, if he had fallen with his men before Troy, or had died with friends around

him when the days of his fighting were done; for then the Achaeans would have built a mound over his ashes, and I should myself
have been heir to his reknown; but now the storm-winds have spirited him away we know not whither; he is gone without leaving so
much as a trace behind him, and I inherit nothing but dismay. Nor
does the matter end simply with grief for the loss of my father;
heaven has laid sorrows upon me of yet another kind; for the chiefs
from all our islands, Dulichium, Same, and the woodland island of
Zacynthus, as also all the principal men of Ithaca itself, are eating
up my house under the pretext of paying court to my mother, who
will neither pointblank say that she will not marry, nor yet bring
matters to an end; so they are making havoc of my estate, and before long will do so also with myself."

"Is that so?" exclaimed Athene. "Then you do indeed want Odysseus home again. Give him his helmet, shield, and a couple of
lances, and if he is the man he was when I first knew him in our
house, drinking and making merry, he would soon lay his hands
about these rascally suitors, were he to stand once more upon his
own threshold. He was then coming from Ephyra, where he had
been to beg poison for his arrows from Ilus son of Mermerus. Ilus
feared the ever-living gods and would not give him any, but my
father let him have some, for he was very fond of him. If Odysseus
is the man he then was, these suitors will have a short shrift and
a sorry wedding.

"But there! It rests with heaven to determine whether he is to
return, and take his revenge in his own house or no; I would, however, urge you to set about trying to get rid of these suitors at once.
Take my advice, call the Achaean heroes in assembly tomorrow
morning—lay your case before them, and call heaven to bear you
witness. Bid the suitors take themselves off, each to his own place,
and if your mother's mind is set on marrying again, let her go back
to her father, who will find her a husband and provide her with all
the marriage gifts that so dear a daughter may expect. As for yourself, let me prevail upon you to take the best ship you can get, with
a crew of twenty men, and go in quest of your father who has so

long been missing. Someone may tell you something, or (and people often hear things in this way) some heaven-sent message may
direct you. First go to Pylos and ask Nestor; thence go on to Sparta
and visit Menelaus, for he got home last of all the Achaeans; if you
hear that your father is alive and on his way home, you can put up
with the waste these suitors will make for yet another twelve
months. If on the other hand you hear of his death, come home at
once, celebrate his funeral rites with all due pomp, build a barrow
to his memory, and make your mother marry again. Then, having
done all this, think it well over in your mind how, by fair means or
foul, you may kill these suitors in your own house. You are too old
to plead infancy any longer; have you not heard how people are
singing Orestes' praises for having killed his father's murderer Aegisthus? You are a fine, smart-looking fellow; show your mettle,
then, and make yourself a name in story. Now, however, I must go
back to my ship and to my crew, who will be impatient if I keep
them waiting longer; think the matter over for yourself, and remember what I have said to you."

"Sir," answered Telemachus, "it has been very kind of you to talk
to me in this way, as though I were your own son, and I will do all
you tell me. I know you want to be getting on with your voyage, but
stay a little longer till you have taken a bath and refreshed yourself.
I will then give you a present, and you shall go on your way rejoicing; I will give you one of great beauty and value—a keepsake
such as only dear friends give to one another."

Athene answered, "Do not try to keep me, for I would be on my
way at once. As for any present you may be disposed to make me,
keep it till I come again, and I will take it home with me. You shall
give me a very good one, and I will give you one of no less value in
return."

With these words she flew away like a bird into the air, but she
had given Telemachus courage, and had made him think more than
ever about his father. He felt the change, wondered at it, and knew
that the stranger had been a god, so he went straight to where the
suitors were sitting.

Phemius was still singing, and his hearers sat rapt in silence as he told the sad tale of the return from Troy, and the ills Athene had laid upon the Achaeans. Penelope daughter of Icarius heard his song from her room upstairs, and came down by the great staircase, not alone, but attended by two of her handmaids. When she reached the suitors she stood by one of the bearing posts that supported the roof of the cloisters,[5] with a staid maiden on either side of her. She held a veil, moreover, before her face, and was weeping bitterly.

"Phemius," she cried, "you know many another feat of gods and heroes, such as poets love to celebrate. Sing the suitors some one of these, and let them drink their wine in silence, but cease this sad tale, for it breaks my sorrowful heart, and reminds me of my lost husband whom I mourn ever without ceasing, and whose name was great over all Hellas and middle Argos."

"Mother," answered Telemachus, "let the bard sing what he has a mind to; bards do not make the ills they sing of; it is Zeus, not they, who makes them, and who sends weal or woe upon mankind according to his own good pleasure. This fellow means no harm by singing the ill-fated return of the Danaans, for people always applaud the latest songs most warmly. Make up your mind to it and bear it; Odysseus is not the only man who never came back from Troy, but many another went down as well as he. Go, then, within the house and busy yourself with your daily duties, your loom, your distaff, and the ordering of your servants; for speech is man's matter, and mine above all others—for it is I who am master here."

She went wondering back into the house, and laid her son's saying in her heart. Then, going upstairs with her handmaids into her room, she mourned her dear husband till Athene shed sweet sleep over her eyes. But the suitors were clamorous throughout the covered cloisters,[6] and prayed each one that he might be her bedfellow.

Then Telemachus spoke. "Shameless," he cried, "and insolent suitors, let us feast at our pleasure now, and let there be no brawl-

[5] See note on these cloisters, Book XVIII, p. 231.
[6] The whole inner court that made the forepart of the house had a covered cloister running around it. This covered part was distinguished by being called "shady" or "shadow-giving." It was in this part that the tables for the suitors were laid. The arrangement is still common in Sicily and the Greek islands.

ing, for it is a rare thing to hear a man with such a divine voice as Phemius has; but in the morning meet me in full assembly that I may give you formal notice to depart, and feast at one another's houses, turn and turn about, at your own cost. If, on the other hand, you choose to persist in sponging upon one man, heaven help me, but Zeus shall reckon with you in full, and when you fall in my father's house there shall be no man to avenge you."

The suitors bit their lips as they heard him, and marveled at the boldness of his speech. Then, Antinous son of Eupeithes said, "The gods seem to have given you lessons in bluster and tall talking; may Zeus never grant you to be chief in Ithaca as your father was before you."

Telemachus answered: "Antinous, do not chide with me, but, god willing, I will be chief too if I can. Is this the worst fate you can think of for me? It is no bad thing to be a chief, for it brings both riches and honor. Still, now that Odysseus is dead there are many great men in Ithaca both old and young, and some other may take the lead among them. Nevertheless, I will be chief in my own house, and will rule those whom Odysseus has won for me."

Then Eurymachus son of Polybus answered: "It rests with heaven to decide who shall be chief among us, but you shall be master in your own house and over your own possessions; while there is a man in Ithaca no one shall do you violence or rob you. And now, my good fellow, I want to know about this stranger. What country does he come from? Of what family is he, and where is his estate? Has he brought you news about the return of your father, or was he on business of his own? He seemed a well-to-do man, but he hurried off so suddenly that he was gone in a moment before we could get to know him."

"My father is dead and gone," answered Telemachus, "and even if some rumor reaches me I put no more faith in it now. My mother does indeed sometimes send for a soothsayer and question him, but I give his prophesyings no heed. As for the stranger, he was Mentes son of Anchialus, chief of the Taphians, an old friend of my father's." But in his heart he knew that it had been the goddess.

The suitors then returned to their singing and dancing until the evening; but when night fell upon their pleasuring they went home to bed each in his own abode.[7] Telemachus' room was high up in a tower that looked on to the outer court; hither, then, he hied, brooding and full of thought. A good old woman, Euryclea, daughter of Ops the son of Pisenor, went before him with a couple of blazing torches. Laertes had bought her with his own money when she was quite young; he gave the worth of twenty oxen for her, and showed as much respect to her in his household as he did to his own wedded wife, but he did not take her to his bed for he feared his wife's resentment. She it was who now lighted Telemachus to his room, and she loved him better than any of the other women in the house did, for she had nursed him when he was a baby. He opened the door of his bedroom and sat down upon the bed; as he took off his shirt he gave it to the good old woman, who folded it tidily up, and hung it for him over a peg by his bedside, after which she went out, pulled the door to by a silver catch, and drew the bolt home by means of the strap. But Telemachus as he lay covered with a woolen fleece kept thinking all night of his intended voyage and of the counsel that Athene had given him.

[7] The reader will note that none of the suitors were allowed to sleep in Odysseus house. (B.)

BOOK II

Telemachus manfully calls an assembly and presents his grievances, appealing to the suitors to stop wasting his substance and to quit his house. Disregarding his appeal, the suitors taunt him. Telemachus prays to Athene and hastens his preparations for the journey, aided by the goddess and the old nurse Euryclea. At nightfall Athene causes the suitors to fall into a deep slumber, and herself sets sail with Telemachus for Pylos.

NOW WHEN THE CHILD OF MORNING, ROSY-fingered Dawn, appeared, Telemachus rose and dressed himself. He bound his sandals on to his comely feet, girded his sword about his shoulder, and left his room looking like an immortal god. He at once sent the criers round to call the people in assembly, so they called them and the people gathered thereon. Then, when they were got together, he went to the place of assembly spear in hand—not alone, for his two hounds went with him. Athene endowed him with a presence of such divine comeliness that all marveled at him as he went by, and when he took his place in his father's seat even the oldest councilors made way for him.

Aegyptius, a man bent double with age, and of infinite experience, was the first to speak. His son Antiphus had gone with Odys-

14

seus to Ilium, land of noble steeds, but the savage Cyclops had killed him when they were all shut up in the cave, and had cooked his last dinner for him.[1] He had three sons left, of whom two still worked on their father's land, while the third, Eurynomus, was one of the suitors. Nevertheless, their father could not get over the loss of Antiphus, and was still weeping for him when he began his speech.

"Men of Ithaca," he said, "hear my words. From the day Odysseus left us there has been no meeting of our councilors until now. Who then can it be, whether old or young, that finds it so necessary to convene us? Has he got wind of some host approaching, and does he wish to warn us, or would he speak upon some other matter of public moment? I am sure he is an excellent person, and I hope Zeus will grant him his heart's desire."

Telemachus took this speech as of good omen and rose at once, for he was bursting with what he had to say. He stood in the middle of the assembly and the good herald Pisenor brought him his staff. Then, turning to Aegyptius, "Sir," said he, "it is I, as you will shortly learn, who have convened you, for it is I who am the most aggrieved. I have not got wind of any host approaching about which I would warn you, nor is there any matter of public moment on which I would speak. My grievance is purely personal, and turns on two great misfortunes which have fallen upon my house. The first of these is the loss of my excellent father, who was chief among all you here present, and was like a father to every one of you; the second is much more serious, and ere long will be the utter ruin of my estate. The sons of all the chief men among you are pestering my mother to marry them against her will. They are afraid to go to her father Icarius, asking him to choose the one he likes best, and to provide marriage gifts for his daughter, but day by day they keep hanging about my father's house, sacrificing our oxen, sheep, and fat goats for their banquets, and never giving so much as a thought to the quantity of wine they drink. No estate can stand such reck-

---

[1] Aegyptius cannot of course know of the fate Antiphus had met with, for there had as yet been no news of or from Odysseus. (B.)

lessness. We have now no Odysseus to ward off harm from our doors, and I cannot hold my own against them. I shall never all my days be as good a man as he was; still I would indeed defend myself if I had power to do so, for I cannot stand such treatment any longer; my house is being disgraced and ruined. Have respect, therefore, to your own consciences and to public opinion. Fear, too, the wrath of heaven, lest the gods should be displeased and turn upon you. I pray you by Zeus and Themis, who is the beginning and the end of councils, do not hold back, my friends, and leave me single-handed—unless it be that my brave father Odysseus did some wrong to the Achaeans which you would now avenge on me, by aiding and abetting these suitors. Moreover, if I am to be eaten out of house and home at all, I had rather you did the eating yourselves, for I could then take action against you to some purpose, and serve you with notices from house to house till I got paid in full, whereas now I have no remedy." [2]

With this Telemachus dashed his staff to the ground and burst into tears. Everyone was very sorry for him, but they all sat still and no one ventured to make him an angry answer, save only Antinous, who spoke thus:

"Telemachus, insolent braggart that you are, how dare you try to throw the blame upon us suitors? It is your mother's fault, not ours, for she is a very artful woman. This three years past, and close on four, she has been driving us out of our minds by encouraging each one of us, and sending him messages without meaning one word of what she says. And then there was that other trick she played us. She set up a great tambour frame in her room, and began to work on an enormous piece of fine needlework. 'Sweet hearts,' said she, 'Odysseus is indeed dead, still do not press me to marry again immediately, wait—for I would not have my skill in needlework perish unrecorded—till I have completed a pall for the hero Laertes, to be in readiness against the time when death shall take him. He is very

---

[2] That is, you have money, and could pay when I got judgment, whereas the suitors are men of straw. (B.)

rich, and the women of the place will talk if he is laid out without a pall.'

"This was what she said, and we assented; whereon we could see her working on her great web all day long, but at night she would unpick the stitches again by torchlight. She fooled us in this way for three years and we never found her out, but as time wore on and she was now in her fourth year, one of her maids who knew what she was doing told us, and we caught her in the act of undoing her work, so she had to finish it whether she would or no. The suitors, therefore, make you this answer, that both you and the Achaeans may understand: 'Send your mother away, and bid her marry the man of her own and of her father's choice'; for I do not know what will happen if she goes on plaguing us much longer with the airs she gives herself on the score of the accomplishments Athene has taught her, and because she is so clever. We never yet heard of such a woman; we know all about Tyro, Alcmena, Mycene, and the famous women of old, but they were nothing to your mother, any one of them. It was not fair of her to treat us in that way, and as long as she continues in the mind with which heaven has now endowed her, so long shall we go on eating up your estate; and I do not see why she should change, for she gets all the honor and glory, and it is you who pay for it, not she. Understand, then, that we will not go back to our lands, neither here nor elsewhere, till she has made her choice and married some one or other of us."

Telemachus answered: "Antinous, how can I drive the mother who bore me from my father's house? My father is abroad and we do not know whether he is alive or dead. It will be hard on me if I have to pay Icarius the large sum which I must give him if I insist on sending his daughter back to him. Not only will he deal rigorously with me, but heaven will also punish me; for my mother when she leaves the house will call on the Furies to avenge her; besides, it would not be a creditable thing to do, and I will have nothing to say to it. If you choose to take offense at this, leave the house and feast elsewhere at one another's house at your own cost, turn and turn about. If, on the other hand, you elect to persist in sponging upon one man, heaven help me, but Zeus shall reckon with you in full, and when you fall in my father's house there shall be no man to avenge you."

As he spoke Zeus sent two eagles from the top of the mountain, and they flew on and on with the wind, sailing side by side in their own lordly flight. When they were right over the middle of the assembly they wheeled and circled about, beating the air with their wings and glaring death into the eyes of them that were below; then, fighting fiercely and tearing at one another, they flew off towards the right over the town. The people wondered as they saw them, and asked each other what all this might be; whereon Halitherses, who was the best prophet and reader of omens among them, spoke to them plainly and in all honesty, saying:

"Hear me, men of Ithaca, and I speak more particularly to the suitors, for I see mischief brewing for them. Odysseus is not going to be away much longer; indeed he is close at hand to deal out death and destruction, not on them alone, but on many another of us who live in Ithaca. Let us then be wise in time, and put a stop to this wickedness before he comes. Let the suitors do so of their own accord; it will be better for them, for I am not prophesying without due knowledge; everything has happened to Odysseus as I foretold when the Argives set out for Troy, and he with them. I said that after going through much hardship and losing all his men he should come home again in the twentieth year and that no one would know him; and now all this is coming true."

Eurymachus son of Polybus then said: "Go home, old man, and prophesy to your own children, or it may be worse for them. I can read these omens myself much better than you can; birds are always flying about in the sunshine somewhere or other, but they seldom mean anything. Odysseus has died in a far country, and it is a pity you are not dead along with him, instead of prating here about omens and adding fuel to the anger of Telemachus which is fierce enough as it is. I suppose you think he will give you something for your family, but I tell you—and it shall surely be—when an old man like you, who should know better, talks a young one over till he becomes troublesome, in the first place his young friend will only fare so much the worse—he will take nothing by it, for the suitors will prevent this—and in the next, we will lay a heavier fine, sir, upon yourself than you will at all like paying, for it will bear hardly upon you. As for Telemachus, I warn him in the presence of you all to send his mother back to her father, who will find her a husband and provide her with all the marriage gifts so dear a daughter may expect. Till then we shall go on harassing him with our suit; for we fear no man, and care neither for him, with all his fine speeches, nor for any fortune-telling of yours. You may preach as much as you please, but we shall only hate you the more. We shall go back and continue to eat up Telemachus' estate without paying him, till such time as his mother leaves off tormenting us by keeping us day after day on the tiptoe of expectation, each vying with the other in his suit for a prize of such rare perfection. Besides, we cannot go after the other women whom we should marry in due course, but for the way in which she treats us."

Then Telemachus said: "Eurymachus, and you other suitors, I shall say no more, and entreat you no further, for the gods and the people of Ithaca now know my story. Give me, then, a ship and a crew of twenty men to take me hither and thither, and I will go to Sparta and to Pylos in quest of my father who has so long been missing. Someone may tell me something, or (and people often hear things in this way) some heaven-sent message may direct me. If I can hear of him as alive and on his way home I will put up with the waste you suitors will make for yet another twelve months. If, on the other hand, I hear of his death, I will return at once, celebrate his funeral rites with all due pomp, build a barrow to his memory, and make my mother marry again."

With these words he sat down, and Mentor, who had been a friend of Odysseus and had been left in charge of everything with full authority over the servants, rose to speak. He, then, plainly and in all honesty addressed them thus:

"Hear me, men of Ithaca, I hope that you may never have a kind and well-disposed ruler any more, nor one who will govern you equitably; I hope that all your chiefs henceforward may be cruel and unjust, for there is not one of you but has forgotten Odysseus, who ruled you as though he were your father. I am not half so angry with the suitors, for if they choose to do violence in the naughtiness of their hearts, and wager their heads that Odysseus will not return, they can take the high hand and eat up his estate, but as for you others I am shocked at the way in which you all sit still without even trying to stop such scandalous goings on—which you could do if you chose, for you are many and they are few."

Leiocritus son of Evenor answered him saying: "Mentor, what folly is all this, that you should set the people to stay us? It is a hard thing for one man to fight with many about his victuals. Even though Odysseus himself were to set upon us while we are feasting in his house and do his best to oust us, his wife, who wants him back so very badly, would have small cause for rejoicing, and his blood would be upon his own head if he fought against such great odds. There is no sense in what you have been saying. Now, therefore, do you people go about your business, and let his father's old friends, Mentor and Halitherses, speed this boy on his journey, if he goes at all—which I do not think he will, for he is more likely to stay where he is till someone comes and tells him something."

On this he broke up the assembly, and every man went back to his own abode, while the suitors returned to the house of Odysseus.

Then Telemachus went all alone by the seaside, washed his hands in the gray waves, and prayed to Athene.

"Hear me," he cried, "you god who visited me yesterday, and bade me sail the seas in search of my father who has so long been missing. I would obey you, but the Achaeans, and more particularly the wicked suitors, are hindering me that I cannot do so."

As he thus prayed, Athene came close up to him in the likeness and with the voice of Mentor. "Telemachus," said she, "if you are made of the same stuff as your father, you will be neither fool nor coward henceforward, for Odysseus never broke his word nor left his work half done. If, then, you take after him, your voyage will not be fruitless, but unless you have the blood of Odysseus and of Penelope in your veins I see no likelihood of your succeeding. Sons are seldom as good men as their fathers; they are generally worse, not better. Still, as you are not going to be either fool or coward henceforward, and are not entirely without some share of your father's wise discernment, I look with hope upon your undertaking. But mind you never make common cause with any of those foolish suitors, for they have neither sense nor virtue, and give no thought to death and to the doom that will shortly fall on one and all of them, so that they shall perish on the same day. As for your voyage, it shall not be long delayed. Your father was such an old friend of mine that I will find you a ship and will come with you myself. Now, however, return home, and go about among the suitors; begin getting provisions ready for your voyage; see everything well stowed, the wine in jars, and the barley meal, which is the staff of life, in leathern bags, while I go round the town and beat up volunteers at once. There are many ships in Ithaca both old and new; I will run my eye over them for you and will choose the best; we will get her ready and will put out to sea without delay."

Thus spoke Athene daughter of Zeus, and Telemachus lost no time in doing as the goddess told him. He went moodily home, and found the suitors flaying goats and singeing pigs in the outer court.[3] Antinous came up to him at once and laughed as he took his hand in his own, saying, "Telemachus, my fine fire-eater, bear no more ill blood neither in word nor deed, but eat and drink with us as you used to do. The Achaeans will supply you with everything a ship and a picked crew to boot—so that you can set sail for Pylos at once and get news of your noble father."

"Antinous," answered Telemachus, "I cannot eat in peace, nor take pleasure of any kind with such men as you are. Was it not enough that you should waste so much good property of mine while I was yet a boy? Now that I am older and know about it, I am also stronger, and whether here among this people, or by going to Pylos,

[3] The walled outer court, closed by a great gateway, formed the approach to the house. Around it stood the barns, storehouses, and other outbuildings, and in the center a large altar.

I will do you all the harm I can. I shall go, and my going will not be in vain—though, thanks to you suitors, I have neither ship nor crew of my own, and must be passenger not captain."

As he spoke he snatched his hand from that of Antinous. Meanwhile the others went on getting dinner ready about the buildings, jeering at him tauntingly as they did so.

"Telemachus," said one youngster, "means to be the death of us. I suppose he thinks he can bring friends to help him from Pylos, or again from Sparta, where he seems bent on going. Or will he go to Ephyra as well, for poison to put in our wine and kill us?"

Another said: "Perhaps if Telemachus goes on board ship, he will be like his father and perish far from his friends. In this case we should have plenty to do, for we could then divide up his property amongst us. As for the house, we can let his mother and the man who marries her have that."

This was how they talked. But Telemachus went down into the lofty and spacious storeroom where his father's treasure of gold and bronze lay heaped up upon the floor, and where the linen and spare clothes were kept in oaken chests. Here, too, there was a store of fragrant olive oil, while casks of old well-ripened wine, unblended and fit for a god to drink, were ranged against the wall in case Odysseus should come home again after all. The room was closed with well-made doors opening in the middle; moreover, the faithful old housekeeper Euryclea, daughter of Ops the son of Pisenor, was in charge of everything both night and day. Telemachus called her to the storeroom and said:

"Nurse, draw me off some of the best wine you have, after what you are keeping for my father's own drinking, in case, poor man, he should escape death, and find his way home again after all. Let me have twelve jars, and see that they all have lids; also fill me some well-sewn leathern bags with barley meal—about twenty measures in all. Get these things put together at once, and say nothing about it. I will take everything away this evening as soon as my mother has gone upstairs for the night. I am going to Sparta and to Pylos to see if I can hear anything about the return of my dear father."

When Euryclea heard this she began to cry, and spoke fondly to him, saying: "My dear child, what ever can have put such a notion as that into your head? Where in the world do you want to go to—you, who are the one hope of the house? Your poor father is dead and gone in some foreign country nobody knows where, and as soon as your back is turned these wicked ones here will be scheming to get you put out of the way, and will share all your possessions among themselves; stay where you are among your own people, and do not go wandering and worrying your life out on the barren ocean."

"Fear not, nurse," answered Telemachus, "my scheme is not without heaven's sanction; but swear that you will say nothing about all this to my mother, till I have been away some ten or twelve days, unless she hears of my having gone, and asks you; for I do not want her to spoil her beauty by crying."

The old woman swore most solemnly that she would not, and when she had completed her oath, she began drawing off the wine into jars, and getting the barley meal into the bags, while Telemachus went back to the suitors.

Then Athene bethought her of another matter. She took his shape, and went round the town to each one of the crew, telling them to meet at the ship by sundown. She went also to Noemon son of Phronius, and asked him to let her have a ship—which he was very ready to do. When the sun had set and darkness was over all the land, she got the ship into the water, put all the tackle on board her that ships generally carry, and stationed her at the end of the harbor. Presently the crew came up, and the goddess spoke encouragingly to each of them.

Furthermore, she went to the house of Odysseus, and threw the suitors into a deep slumber. She caused their drink to fuddle them, and made them drop their cups from their hands, so that instead of sitting over their wine, they went back into the town to sleep, with their eyes heavy and full of drowsiness. Then she took the form and voice of Mentor, and called Telemachus to come outside.

"Telemachus," said she, "the men are on board and at their oars, waiting for you to give orders, so make haste and let us be off."

On this she led the way, while Telemachus followed in her steps. When they got to the ship they found the crew waiting by the water side, and Telemachus said, "Now my men, help me to get the stores on board; they are all put together in the cloister, and my mother does not know anything about it, nor any of the maidservants except one."

With these words he led the way and the others followed after. When they had brought the things as he told them, Telemachus went on board, Athene going before him and taking her seat in the stern of the vessel, while Telemachus sat beside her. Then the men loosed the hawsers and took their places on the benches. Athene sent them a fair wind from the west that whistled over the deep blue waves, whereon Telemachus told them to catch hold of the ropes and hoist sail, and they did as he told them. They set the mast in its socket in the cross plank, raised it, and made it fast with the forestays; then they hoisted their white sails aloft with ropes of twisted oxhide. As the sail bellied out with the wind, the ship flew through the deep blue water, and the foam hissed against her bows as she sped onward. Then they made all fast throughout the ship, filled the mixing-bowls to the brim, and made drink offerings to the immortal goods that are from everlasting, but more particularly to the gray-eyed daughter of Zeus.

Thus, then, the ship sped on her way through the watches of the night from dark till dawn.

BOOK III

Telemachus is warmly welcomed by Nestor in Pylos and joins in celebrating the festival of Poseidon. Nestor tells stories of the return of himself and the other heroes from Troy, but knows nothing of the fate of Odysseus. The next day sacrifices are offered for Telemachus' success. Nestor sends his son Pisistratus with Telemachus, as he continues his journey to Sparta by land.

A S THE SUN WAS RISING FROM THE FAIR SEA INTO the firmament of heaven to shed light on mortals and immortals, they reached Pylos, the city of Neleus. Now the people of Pylos were gathered on the seashore to offer sacrifice of black bulls to Poseidon lord of the earthquake. There were nine guilds with five hundred men in each, and there were nine bulls to each guild. As they were eating the inward meats[1] and burning the thighbones [on the embers] in the name of Poseidon, Telemachus and his crew arrived, furled their sails, brought their ship to anchor, and went ashore.

---

[1] The heart, liver, lights, kidneys, etc., were taken out from the inside and eaten first as being more readily cooked; the bone meat was cooking while the inward meats were being eaten. I imagine that the thighbones made a kind of gridiron, while at the same time the marrow inside them got cooked. (B.)

Athene led the way and Telemachus followed her. Presently she said, "Telemachus, you must not be in the least shy or nervous. You have taken this voyage to try and find out where your father is buried and how he came by his end; so go straight up to Nestor that we may see what he has got to tell us. Beg of him to speak the truth, and he will tell no lies, for he is an excellent person."

"But how, Mentor," replied Telemachus, "dare I go up to Nestor, and how am I to address him? I have never yet been used to holding long conversations with people, and am ashamed to begin questioning one who is so much older than myself."

"Some things, Telemachus," answered Athene, "will be suggested to you by your own instinct, and heaven will prompt you further; for I am assured that the gods have been with you from the time of your birth until now."

She then went quickly on, and Telemachus followed in her steps till they reached the place where the guilds of the Pylian people were assembled. There they found Nestor sitting with his sons, while his company round him were busy getting dinner ready, and putting pieces of meat on to the spits[2] while other pieces were cooking. When they saw the strangers they crowded round them, took them by the hand and bade them take their places. Nestor's son Pisistratus at once offered his hand to each of them, and seated them on some soft sheepskins that were lying on the sands near his father and his brother Thrasymedes. Then he gave them their portions of the inward meats and poured wine for them into a golden cup, handing it to Athene first, and saluting her at the same time.

"Offer a prayer, sir," said he, "to King Poseidon, for it is his feast that you are joining. When you have duly prayed and made your drink offering, pass the cup to your friend that he may do so also. I doubt not that he too lifts his hands in prayer, for man cannot live without God in the world. Still he is younger than you are, and is

---

[2] The meat would be pierced with the skewer, and laid over the ashes to grill—the two ends of the skewer being supported in whatever way might be found convenient. Meat so cooking may be seen in any eating house in Smyrna, or any Eastern town. When I rode across the Troad from the Dardanelles to Hissarlik and Mount Ida, I noticed that my dragoman and his men did all our outdoor cooking exactly in the Odyssean and Iliadic fashion. (B.)

much of an age with myself, so I will give you the precedence."

As he spoke he handed her the cup. Athene thought it very right and proper of him to have given it to herself first; she accordingly began praying heartily to Poseidon. "O thou," she cried, "that encirclest the earth, vouchsafe to grant the prayers of thy servants that call upon thee. More especially we pray thee send down thy grace on Nestor and on his sons; thereafter also make the rest of the Pylian people some handsome return for the goodly hecatomb they are offering you. Lastly, grant Telemachus and myself a happy issue, in respect of the matter that has brought us in our ship to Pylos."

When she had thus made an end of praying, she handed the cup to Telemachus and he prayed likewise. By and by, when the outer meats were roasted and had been taken off the spits, the carvers gave every man his portion and they all made an excellent dinner. As soon as they had had enough to eat and drink, Nestor, knight of Gerene, began to speak.

"Now," said he, "that our guests have done their dinner, it will be best to ask them who they are. Who, then, sir strangers, are you, and from what port have you sailed? Are you traders? or do you sail the seas as rovers with your hand against every man, and every man's hand against you?"

Telemachus answered boldly, for Athene had given him courage to ask about his father and get himself a good name.

"Nestor," said he, "son of Neleus, honor to the Achaean name, you ask whence we come, and I will tell you. We come from Ithaca under Neritum, and the matter about which I would speak is of private not public import. I seek news of my unhappy father Odysseus, who is said to have sacked the town of Troy in company with yourself. We know what fate befell each one of the other heroes who fought at Troy, but as regards Odysseus heaven has hidden from us the knowledge even that he is dead at all, for no one can certify us in what place he perished, nor say whether he fell in battle on the mainland or was lost at sea amid the waves of Amphitrite. Therefore I am suppliant at your knees, if haply you may be pleased to tell me of his melancholy end, whether you saw it with your own eyes, or heard it from some other traveler, for he was a man born to trouble. Do not soften things out of any pity for me, but tell me in all plainness exactly what you saw. If my brave father Odysseus ever did you loyal service, either by word or deed, when you Achaeans were harassed among the Trojans, bear it in mind now as in my favor and tell me truly all."

"My friend," answered Nestor, "you recall a time of much sorrow to my mind, for the brave Achaeans suffered much both at sea, while privateering under Achilles, and when fighting before the great city of King Priam. Our best men all of them fell there—Ajax, Achilles, Patroclus, peer of gods in counsel, and my own dear son Antilochus, a man singularly fleet of foot and in fight valiant. But we suffered much more than this; what mortal tongue indeed could tell the whole story? Though you were to stay here and question me for five years, or even six, I could not tell you all that the Achaeans suffered, and you would turn homeward weary of my tale before it ended. Nine long years did we try every kind of stratagem, but the hand of heaven was against us; during all this time there was no one who could compare with your father in subtlety—if indeed you are his son—I can hardly believe my eyes—and you talk just like him too—no one would say that people of such different ages could speak so much alike. He and I never had any kind of difference from first to last neither in camp nor council, but in singleness of heart and purpose we advised the Argives how all might be ordered for the best.

"When, however, we had sacked the city of Priam, and were setting sail in our ships as heaven had dispersed us, then Zeus saw fit to vex the Argives on their homeward voyage; for they had not all been either wise or understanding, and hence many came to a bad end through the displeasure of Zeus' daughter Athene, who brought about a quarrel between the two sons of Atreus.[3]

"The sons of Atreus called a meeting which was not as it should be, for it was sunset and the Achaeans were heavy with wine. When they explained why they had called the people together, it seemed

[3] That is, the brothers, Agamemnon and Menelaus.

that Menelaus was for sailing homeward at once, and this displeased Agamemnon, who thought that we should wait till we had offered hecatombs to appease the anger of Athene. Fool that he was, he might have known that he would not prevail with her, for when the gods have made up their minds they do not change them lightly. So the two stood bandying hard words, whereon the Achaeans sprang to their feet with a cry that rent the air, and were of two minds as to what they should do.

"That night we rested and nursed our anger, for Zeus was hatching mischief against us. But in the morning some of us drew our ships into the water and put our goods with our women on board, while the rest, about half in number, stayed behind with Agamemnon. We—the other half—embarked and sailed; and the ships went well, for heaven had smoothed the sea. When we reached Tenedos we offered sacrifices to the gods, for we were longing to get home. Cruel Zeus, however, did not yet mean that we should do so, and raised a second quarrel in the course of which some among us turned their ships back again, and sailed away under Odysseus to make their peace with Agamemnon; but I, and all the ships that were with me pressed forward, for I saw that mischief was brewing. The son of Tydeus⁴ went on also with me, and his crews with him. Later on Menelaus joined us at Lesbos, and found us making up our minds about our course—for we did not know whether to go outside Chios by the island of Psyra, keeping this to our left, or inside Chios, over against the stormy headland of Mimas. So we asked heaven for a sign, and were shown one to the effect that we should be soonest out of danger if we headed our ships across the open sea to Euboea. This we therefore did, and a fair wind sprang up which gave us a quick passage during the night to Geraestus, where we offered many sacrifices to Poseidon for having helped us so far on our way. Four days later Diomed and his men stationed their ships in Argos, but I held on for Pylos, and the wind never fell light from the day when heaven first made it fair for me.

"Therefore, my dear young friend, I returned without hearing

⁴ Diomed.

anything about the others. I know neither who got home safely nor who were lost but, as in duty bound, I will give you without reserve the reports that have reached me since I have been here in my own house. They say the Myrmidons returned home safely under Achilles' son Neoptolemus; so also did the valiant son of Poias, Philoctetes. Idomeneus, again, lost no men at sea, and all his followers who escaped death in the field got safe home with him to Crete. No matter how far out of the world you live, you will have heard of Agamemnon and the bad end he came to at the hands of Aegisthus—and a fearful reckoning did Aegisthus presently pay. See what a good thing it is for a man to leave a son behind him to do as Orestes did, who killed false Aegisthus, the murderer of his noble father. You too, then—for you are a tall, smart-looking fellow—show your mettle and make yourself a name in story."

"Nestor son of Neleus," answered Telemachus, "honor to the Achaean name, the Achaeans applaud Orestes and his name will live through all time for he has avenged his father nobly. Would that heaven might grant me to do like vengeance on the insolence of the wicked suitors, who are ill treating me and plotting my ruin; but the gods have no such happiness in store for me and for my father, so we must bear it as best we may."

"My friend," said Nestor, "now that you remind me, I remember to have heard that your mother has many suitors, who are ill disposed towards you and are making havoc of your estate. Do you submit to this tamely, or are public feeling and the voice of heaven against you? Who knows but what Odysseus may come back after all, and pay these scoundrels in full, either single-handed or with a force of Achaeans behind him? If Athene were to take as great a liking to you as she did to Odysseus when we were fighting before Troy (for I never yet saw the gods so openly fond of anyone as Athene then was of your father), if she would take as good care of you as she did of him, these wooers would soon some of them forget their wooing."

Telemachus answered: "I can expect nothing of the kind; it would be far too much to hope for. I dare not let myself think of it.

Even though the gods themselves willed it no such good fortune
could befall me."

On this Athene said: "Telemachus, what are you talking about?
Heaven has a long arm if it is minded to save a man; and if it were
me, I should not care how much I suffered before getting home,
provided I could be safe when I was once there. I would rather
this than get home quickly, and then be killed in my own house as
Agamemnon was by the treachery of Aegisthus and his wife. Still,
death is certain, and when a man's hour is come, not even the gods
can save him, no matter how fond they are of him."

"Mentor," answered Telemachus, "do not let us talk about it any
more. There is no chance of my father's ever coming back; the gods
have long since counseled his destruction. There is something else,
however, about which I should like to ask Nestor, for he knows
much more than anyone else does. They say he has reigned for
three generations so that it is like talking to an immortal. Tell me,
therefore, Nestor, and tell me true, how did Agamemnon come to
die in that way? What was Menelaus doing? And how came false
Aegisthus to kill so far better a man than himself? Was Menelaus
away from Achaean Argos, voyaging elsewhither among mankind,
that Aegisthus took heart and killed Agamemnon?"

"I will tell you truly," answered Nestor, "and indeed you have
yourself divined how it all happened. If Menelaus when he got back
from Troy had found Aegisthus still alive in his house, there would
have been no barrow heaped up for him, not even when he was
dead, but he would have been thrown outside the city to dogs and
vultures, and not a woman would have mourned him, for he had
done a deed of great wickedness. But we were over there, fighting
hard at Troy, while Aegisthus, who was taking his ease quietly in
the heart of Argos, cajoled Agamemnon's wife Clytemnestra with
incessant flattery.

"At first she would have nothing to do with his wicked scheme,
for she was of a good natural disposition; moreover there was a bard
with her, to whom Agamemnon had given strict orders on setting
out for Troy, that he was to keep guard over his wife; but when

heaven had counseled her destruction, Aegisthus carried this bard off to a desert island, and left him there for crows and seagulls to batten upon—after which she went willingly enough to the house of Aegisthus. Then he offered many burnt sacrifices to the gods, and decorated many temples with tapestries and gilding, for he had succeeded far beyond his expectations.

"Meanwhile Menelaus and I were on our way home from Troy, on good terms with one another. When we got to Sunium, which is the point of Athens, Apollo with his painless shafts killed Phrontis, the steersman of Menelaus' ship (and never man knew better how to handle a vessel in rough weather), so that he died then and there with the helm in his hand, and Menelaus, though very anxious to press forward, had to wait in order to bury his comrade and give him his due funeral rites. Presently, when he too could put to sea again, and had sailed on as far as the Malean heads, Zeus counseled evil against him and made it blow hard till the waves ran mountains high. Here he divided his fleet and took the one half towards Crete where the Cydonians dwell round about the waters of the river Iardanus. There is a high headland hereabouts stretching out into the sea from a place called Gortyn, and all along this part of the coast as far as Phaestus the sea runs high when there is a south wind blowing, but after Phaestus the coast is more protected, for a small headland can make a great shelter. Here this part of the fleet was driven on to the rocks and wrecked; but the crews just managed to save themselves. As for the other five ships, they were taken by winds and seas to Egypt, where Menelaus gathered much gold and substance among people of an alien speech. Meanwhile Aegisthus here at home plotted his evil deed. For seven years after he had killed Agamemnon he ruled in Mycene, and the people were obedient under him, but in the eighth year Orestes came back from Athens to be his bane, and killed the murderer of his father. Then he celebrated the funeral rites of his mother and of false Aegisthus by a banquet to the people of Argos, and on that very day Menelaus came home with as much treasure as his ships could carry.

"Take my advice then, and do not go traveling about for long so far from home, nor leave your property with such dangerous people in your house; they will eat up everything you have among them, and you will have been on a fool's errand. Still, I should advise you by all means to go and visit Menelaus, who has lately come off a voyage among such distant peoples as no man could ever hope to get back from, when the winds had once carried him so far out of his reckoning; even birds cannot fly the distance in a twelvemonth, so vast and terrible are the seas that they must cross. Go to him, therefore, by sea, and take your own men with you; or if you would rather travel by land you can have a chariot, you can have horses, and here are my sons who can escort you to Sparta where Menelaus lives. Beg of him to speak the truth, and he will tell you no lies, for he is an excellent person."

As he spoke the sun set and it came on dark, whereon Athene said: "Sir, all that you have said is well; now, however, order the tongues of the victims to be cut, and mix wine that we may drink offerings to Poseidon and the other immortals, and then go to bed, for it is bedtime. People should go away early and not keep late hours at a religious festival."

Thus spoke the daughter of Zeus, and they obeyed her saying. Menservants poured water over the hands of the guests, while pages filled the mixing-bowls with wine and water, and handed it round after giving every man his drink offering; then they threw the tongues of the victims into the fire, and stood up to make their drink offerings. When they had made their offerings and had drunk each as much as he was minded, Athene and Telemachus were for going on board their ship, but Nestor caught them up at once and stayed them.

"Heaven and the immortal gods," he exclaimed, "forbid that you should leave my house to go on board of a ship! Do you think I am so poor and short of clothes, or that I have so few cloaks and rugs as to be unable to find comfortable beds both for myself and for my guests? Let me tell you I have store both of rugs and cloaks, and shall not permit the son of my old friend Odysseus to camp down on the deck of a ship—not while I live—nor yet will my sons after me, but they will keep open house as I have done."

Then Athene answered: "Sir, you have spoken well, and it will be much better that Telemachus should do as you have said. He, therefore, shall return with you and sleep at your house, but I must go back to give orders to my crew, and keep them in good heart. I am the only older person among them. The rest are all young men of Telemachus' own age, who have taken this voyage out of friendship; so I must return to the ship and sleep there. Moreover tomorrow I must go to the Cauconians where I have a large sum of money long owing to me. As for Telemachus, now that he is your guest, send him to Sparta in a chariot, and let one of your sons go with him. Be pleased also to provide him with your best and fleetest horses."

When she had thus spoken, she flew away in the form of an eagle, and all marveled as they beheld it. Nestor was astonished, and took Telemachus by the hand. "My friend," said he, "I see that you are going to be a great hero some day, since the gods wait upon you thus while you are still so young. This can have been none other of those who dwell in heaven than Zeus' redoubtable daughter, the Trito-born, who showed such favor towards your brave father among the Argives. Holy queen," he continued, "vouchsafe to send down thy grace upon myself, my good wife, and my children. In return, I will offer you in sacrifice a broad-browed heifer of a year old, unbroken, and never yet brought by man under the yoke. I will gild her horns, and will offer her up to you in sacrifice."

Thus did he pray, and Athene heard his prayer. He then led the way to his own house, followed by his sons and sons-in-law. When they had got there and had taken their places on the benches and seats, he mixed them a bowl of sweet wine that was eleven years old when the housekeeper took the lid off the jar that held it. As he mixed the wine, he prayed much and made drink offerings to Athene, daughter of aegis-bearing Zeus. Then, when they had made their drink offerings and had drunk each as much as he was minded, the others went home to bed each in his own abode; but Nestor put Telemachus to sleep in the room that was over the gateway along with Pisistratus, who was the only unmarried son now left him. As for himself, he slept in an inner room of the house, with the queen his wife by his side.

Now when the child of morning, rosy-fingered Dawn, appeared, Nestor left his couch and took his seat on the benches of white and polished marble that stood in front of his house. Here aforetime sat Neleus, peer of gods in counsel, but he was now dead, and had gone to the house of Hades; so Nestor sat in his seat, scepter in hand, as guardian of the public weal. His sons as they left their rooms gathered round him, Echephron, Stratius, Perseus, Aretus, and Thrasymedes; the sixth son was Pisistratus, and when Telemachus joined them they made him sit with them. Nestor then addressed them.

"My sons," said he, "make haste to do as I shall bid you. I wish first and foremost to propitiate the great goddess Athene, who manifested herself visibly to me during yesterday's festivities. Go, then, one or other of you to the plain, tell the stockman to look me out a heifer, and come on here with it at once. Another must go to Telemachus' ship, and invite all the crew, leaving two men only in charge of the vessel. Someone else will run and fetch Laerceus the goldsmith to gild the horns of the heifer. The rest, stay all of you where you are; tell the maids in the house to prepare an excellent dinner, and to fetch seats, and logs of wood for a burnt offering. Tell them also to bring me some clear spring water."

On this they hurried off on their several errands. The heifer was brought in from the plain, and Telemachus' crew came from the ship. The goldsmith brought the anvil, hammer, and tongs, with which he worked his gold, and Athene herself came to accept the sacrifice. Nestor gave out the gold, and the smith gilded the horns of the heifer that the goddess might have pleasure in their beauty. Then Stratius and Echephron brought her in by the horns; Aretus fetched water from the house in a ewer that had a flower pattern on it, and in his other hand he held a basket of barley meal; sturdy Thrasymedes stood by with a sharp axe, ready to strike the heifer, while Perseus held a bucket. Then Nestor began with washing his hands and sprinkling the barley meal, and he offered many a prayer to Athene as he threw a lock from the heifer's head upon the fire.

When they had done praying and sprinkling the barley meal Thrasymedes dealt his blow, and brought the heifer down with a stroke that cut through the tendons at the base of her neck, whereon the daughters and daughters-in-law of Nestor, and his venerable wife Eurydice (she was eldest daughter to Clymenus) screamed with delight. Then they lifted the heifer's head from off the ground, and Pisistratus cut her throat. When she had done bleeding and was quite dead, they cut her up. They cut out the thighbones all in due course, wrapped them round in two layers of fat, and set some pieces of raw meat on the top of them; then Nestor laid them upon the wood fire and poured wine over them, while the young men stood near him with five-pronged spits in their hands. When the thighs were burned and they had tasted the inward meats, they cut the rest of the meat up small, put the pieces on the spits and toasted them over the fire.

Meanwhile lovely Polycaste, Nestor's youngest daughter, washed Telemachus. When she had washed him and anointed him with oil, she brought him a fair mantle and shirt, and he looked like a god as he came from the bath and took his seat by the side of Nestor. When the outer meats were done they drew them off the spits and sat down to dinner where they were waited upon by some worthy henchmen, who kept pouring them out their wine in cups of gold. As soon as they had had enough to eat and drink Nestor said, "Sons, put Telemachus' horses to the chariot that he may start at once."

Thus did he speak, and they did even as he had said, and yoked the fleet horses to the chariot. The housekeeper packed them up a provision of bread, wine, and sweetmeats fit for the sons of princes. Then Telemachus got into the chariot, while Pisistratus gathered up the reins and took his seat beside him. He lashed the horses on and they flew forward nothing loath into the open country, leaving the high citadel of Pylos behind them. All that day did they travel, swaying the yoke upon their necks till the sun went down and darkness was over all the land. Then they reached Pherae where Diocles lived, who was son to Ortilochus and grandson to Alpheus. Here they passed the night and Diocles entertained them hospitably. When the child of morning, rosy-fingered Dawn, appeared, they again yoked their horses and drove out through the gateway under the echoing gatehouse. Pisistratus lashed the horses on and they flew forward nothing loath. Presently they came to the corn lands of the open country, and in the course of time completed their journey, so well did their steeds take them.

BOOK IV

At Sparta Telemachus is joyfully received by Menelaus and Helen, who recount stories of Odysseus. Menelaus describes their own many adventures on the return from Troy. He reveals that the god Proteus has told him that Odysseus is a prisoner on Calypso's isle. Back in Ithaca, the suitors, learning of Telemachus' journey, plan to murder him. Penelope hears of it and is terrified. Athene sends a vision to Penelope to assure her that her son will come back safely.

NOW WHEN THE SUN HAD SET AND DARKNESS was over the land, they reached the low-lying city of Sparta, where they drove straight to the abode of Menelaus and found him in his own house, feasting with his many clansmen in honor of the wedding of his son, and also of his daughter, whom he was marrying to the son of that valiant warrior Achilles. He had given his consent and promised her to him while he was still at Troy, and now the gods were bringing the marriage about; so he was sending her with chariots and horses to the city of the Myrmidons over whom Achilles' son was reigning. For his only son he had found a bride from Sparta, the daughter of Alector. This son, Megapenthes, was born to him of a bondwoman, for heaven vouchsafed Helen no more children after she had borne Hermione, who was fair as golden Aphrodite herself.

So the neighbors and kinsmen of Menelaus were feasting and making merry in his house. There was a bard also to sing to them and play his lyre, while two tumblers went about performing in the midst of them when the man struck up with his tune.

Telemachus and the son of Nestor stayed their horses at the gate, whereon Eteoneus, servant to Menelaus, came out, and as soon as he saw them ran hurrying back into the house to tell his master. He went close up to him and said, "Menelaus, there are some strangers come here, two men, who look like sons of Zeus. What are we to do? Shall we take their horses out, or tell them to find friends elsewhere as they best can?"

Menelaus was very angry and said: "Eteoneus son of Boethous, you never used to be a fool, but now you talk like a simpleton. Take their horses out, of course, and show the strangers in that they may have supper. You and I have stayed often enough at other people's houses before we got back here, where heaven grant that we may rest in peace henceforward."

So Eteoneus bustled back and bade the other servants come with him. They took their sweating steeds from under the yoke, made them fast to the mangers, and gave them a feed of oats and barley mixed. Then they leaned the chariot against the end wall of the courtyard, and led the way into the house. Telemachus and Pisistratus were astonished when they saw it, for its splendor was as that of the sun and moon; then, when they had admired everything to their heart's content, they went into the bathroom and washed themselves.

When the servants had washed them and anointed them with oil, they brought them woolen cloaks and shirts, and the two took their seats by the side of Menelaus. A maidservant brought them water in a beautiful golden ewer, and poured it into a silver basin for them to wash their hands; and she drew a clean table beside them. An upper servant brought them bread, and offered them many good things of what there was in the house, while the carver fetched them plates of all manner of meats and set cups of gold by their side.

Menelaus then greeted them saying: "Fall to, and welcome. When you have done supper, I shall ask who you are, for the lineage of such men as you cannot have been lost. You must be descended from a line of scepter-bearing kings, for poor people do not have such sons as you are."

On this he handed them a piece of fat roast loin, which had been set near him as being a prime part, and they laid their hands on the good things that were before them. As soon as they had had enough to eat and drink, Telemachus said to the son of Nestor, with his head so close that no one might hear, "Look, Pisistratus, man after my own heart, see the gleam of bronze and gold—of amber,[1] ivory, and silver. Everything is so splendid that it is like seeing the palace of Olympian Zeus. I am lost in admiration."

Menelaus overheard him and said: "No one, my sons, can hold his own with Zeus, for his house and everything about him is immortal; but among mortal men—well, there may be another who has as much wealth as I have, or there may not. But at all events I have traveled much and have undergone much hardship, for it was nearly eight years before I could get home with my fleet. I went to Cyprus, Phoenicia, and the Egyptians; I went also to the Ethiopians, the Sidonians, and the Erembians, and to Libya where the lambs have horns as soon as they are born, and the sheep lamb down three times a year. Everyone in that country, whether master or man, has plenty of cheese, meat, and good milk, for the ewes yield all the year round. But while I was traveling and getting great riches among these people, my brother was secretly and shockingly murdered through the perfidy of his wicked wife, so that I have no pleasure in being lord of all this wealth.

"Whoever your parents may be, they must have told you about all this, and of my heavy loss in the ruin[2] of a stately mansion fully and magnificently furnished. Would that I had only a third of what I

---

[1] Amber is never mentioned in the *Iliad*. Sicily was probably the only amber-producing country known in the Odyssean age. (B.)
[2] This no doubt refers to the story, told in the lost poem of the *Cypria* of how Paris and Helen robbed Menelaus of the greater part of his treasures, when they sailed together for Troy. (B.)

now have so that I had stayed at home, and all those were living who perished on the plain of Troy, far from Argos. I often grieve, as I sit here in my house, for one and all of them. At times I cry aloud for sorrow, but presently I leave off again, for crying is cold comfort and one soon tires of it. Yet grieve for these as I may, I do so for one man more than for them all. I cannot even think of him without loathing both food and sleep, so miserable does he make me, for no one of all the Achaeans worked so hard or risked so much as he did. He took nothing by it, and has left a legacy of sorrow to myself, for he has been gone a long time, and we know not whether he is alive or dead. His old father, his long-suffering wife Penelope, and his son Telemachus, whom he left behind him an infant in arms, are plunged in grief on his account."

Thus spoke Menelaus, and the heart of Telemachus yearned as he bethought him of his father. Tears fell from his eyes as he heard him thus mentioned, so that he held his cloak before his face with both hands. When Menelaus saw this he doubted whether to let him choose his own time for speaking, or to ask him at once and find what it was all about.

While he was thus in two minds, Helen came down from her high vaulted and perfumed room, looking as lovely as Artemis herself. Adraste brought her a seat, Alcippe a soft woolen rug, while Phylo fetched her the silver work-box which Alcandra wife of Polybus had given her. Polybus lived in Egyptian Thebes, which is the richest city in the whole world; he gave Menelaus two baths, both of pure silver, two tripods, and ten talents of gold; besides all this, his wife gave Helen some beautiful presents, to wit, a golden distaff, and a silver work-box that ran on wheels, with a gold band round the top of it. Phylo now placed this by her side, full of fine spun yarn, and a distaff charged with violet colored wool was laid upon the top of it. Then Helen took her seat, put her feet upon the footstool, and began to question her husband.

"Do we know, Menelaus," said she, "the names of these strangers who have come to visit us? Shall I guess right or wrong?—but I cannot help saying what I think. Never yet have I seen either man or woman so like somebody else (indeed when I look at him I hardly know what to think) as this young man is like Telemachus, whom Odysseus left as a baby behind him, when you Achaeans went to Troy with battle in your hearts, on account of my most shameless self."

"My dear wife," replied Menelaus, "I see the likeness just as you do. His hands and feet are just like Odysseus'; so is his hair, with the shape of his head and the expression of his eyes. Moreover, when I was talking about Odysseus, and saying how much he had suffered on my account, tears fell from his eyes, and he hid his face in his mantle."

Then Pisistratus said: "Menelaus son of Atreus, you are right in thinking that this young man is Telemachus, but he is very modest, and is ashamed to come here and begin opening up discourse with one whose conversation is so divinely interesting as your own. My father, Nestor, sent me to escort him hither, for he wanted to know whether you could give him any counsel or suggestion. A son has always trouble at home when his father has gone away leaving him without supporters; and this is how Telemachus is now placed, for his father is absent, and there is no one among his own people to stand by him."

"Bless my heart," replied Menelaus, "then I am receiving a visit from the son of a very dear friend, who suffered much hardship for my sake. I had always hoped to entertain him with most marked distinction when heaven had granted us a safe return from beyond the seas. I should have founded a city for him in Argos, and built him a house. I should have made him leave Ithaca, with his goods, his son, and all his people, and should have sacked for them some one of the neighboring cities that are subject to me. We should thus have seen one another continually, and nothing but death could have interrupted so close and happy an intercourse. I suppose, however, that heaven grudged us such great good fortune, for it has prevented the poor fellow from ever getting home at all."

Thus did he speak, and his words set them all a-weeping. Helen wept, Telemachus wept, and so did Menelaus, nor could Pisistratus keep his eyes from filling, when he remembered his dear brother

Antilochus whom the son of bright Dawn had killed. Thereon he said to Menelaus:

"Sir, my father Nestor, when we used to talk about you at home, told me you were a person of rare and excellent understanding. If, then, it be possible, do as I would urge you. I am not fond of crying while I am getting my supper. Morning will come in due course, and in the forenoon I care not how much I cry for those that are dead and gone. This is all we can do for the poor things. We can only shave our heads for them and wring the tears from our cheeks. I had a brother who died at Troy; he was by no means the worst man there; you are sure to have known him—his name was Antilochus. I never set eyes upon him myself, but they say that he was singularly fleet of foot and in fight valiant."

"Your discretion, my friend," answered Menelaus, "is beyond your years. It is plain you take after your father. One can soon see when a man is son to one whom heaven has blessed both as regards wife and offspring—and it has blessed Nestor from first to last all his days, giving him a green old age in his own house, with sons about him who are both well disposed and valiant. We will put an end therefore to all this weeping, and attend to our supper again. Let water be poured over our hands. Telemachus and I can talk with one another fully in the morning."

On this Asphalion, one of the servants, poured water over their hands and they laid their hands on the good things that were before them.

Then Zeus' daughter Helen bethought her of another matter. She drugged the wine with an herb that banishes all care, sorrow, and ill humor. Whoever drinks wine thus drugged cannot shed a single tear all the rest of the day, not even though his father and mother both of them drop down dead, or he sees a brother or a son hewn in pieces before his very eyes. This drug, of such sovereign power and virtue, had been given to Helen by Polydamna wife of Thon, a woman of Egypt, where there grow all sorts of herbs, some good to put into the mixing-bowl and others poisonous. Moreover, everyone in the whole country is a skilled physician, for they are of the race of Paeeon.[3] When Helen had put this drug in the bowl and had told the servants to serve the wine round, she said:

"Menelaus son of Atreus, and you my good friends, sons of honorable men (which is as Zeus wills, for he is the giver both of good and evil, and can do what he chooses), feast here as you will, and listen while I tell you a tale in season. I cannot indeed name every single one of the exploits of Odysseus, but I can say what he did when he was before Troy, and you Achaeans were in all sorts of difficulties. He covered himself with wounds and bruises, dressed himself all in rags, and entered the enemy's city looking like a menial or a beggar, and quite different from what he did when he was among his own people. In this disguise he entered the city of Troy, and no one said anything to him. I alone recognized him and began to question him, but he was too cunning for me. When, however, I had washed and anointed him and had given him clothes, and after I had sworn a solemn oath not to betray him to the Trojans till he had got safely back to his own camp and to the ships, he told me all that the Achaeans meant to do. He killed many Trojans and got much information before he reached the Argive camp, for all which things the Trojan women made lamentation, but for my own part I was glad, for my heart was beginning to yearn after my home, and I was unhappy about the wrong that Aphrodite had done me in taking me over there, away from my country, my little girl, and my lawful wedded husband, who is indeed by no means deficient either in person or understanding."

Then Menelaus said: "All that you have been saying, my dear wife, is true. I have traveled much, and have had much to do with heroes, but I have never seen such another man as Odysseus. What endurance too, and what courage he displayed within the wooden horse, wherein all the bravest of the Argives were lying in wait to bring death and destruction upon the Trojans.[4] At that moment you came up to us; some god who wished well to the Trojans must have

[3] Physician to the gods, whose healing skill is described in the *Iliad*.
[4] In the Italian insurrection of 1848, eight young men who were being hotly pursued by the Austrian police hid themselves inside Donatello's colossal wooden horse in the Salone at Padua, and remained there for a week, being fed by their confederates. In 1898 the last survivor was carried round Padua in triumph. (B.)

set you on to it and you had Deiphobus with you. Three times did you go all around our hiding place and pat it; you called our chiefs each by his own name, and mimicked all our wives. Diomed, Odysseus, and I from our seats inside heard what a noise you made. Diomed and I could not make up our minds whether to spring out then and there, or to answer you from inside, but Odysseus held us all in check, so we sat quite still, all except Anticlus, who was beginning to answer you, when Odysseus clapped his two brawny hands over his mouth, and kept them there. It was this that saved us all, for he muzzled Anticlus till Athene took you away again."

"How sad," exclaimed Telemachus, "that all this was of no avail to save him, nor yet his own iron courage. But now, sir, be pleased to send us all to bed, that we may lie down and enjoy the blessed boon of sleep."

On this Helen told the maidservants to set beds in the room that was in the gatehouse, and to make them with good red rugs, and spread coverlets on the top of them with woolen cloaks for the guests to wear. So the maids went out, carrying a torch, and made the beds, to which a manservant presently conducted the strangers. Thus, then, did Telemachus and Pisistratus sleep there in the forecourt, while the son of Atreus lay in an inner room with lovely Helen by his side.

When the child of morning, rosy-fingered Dawn, appeared, Menelaus rose and dressed himself. He bound his sandals on to his comely feet, girded his sword about his shoulders, and left his room looking like an immortal god. Then, taking a seat near Telemachus, he said:

"And what, Telemachus, has led you to take this long sea voyage to Sparta? Are you on public or private business? Tell me all about it."

"I have come, sir," replied Telemachus, "to see if you can tell me anything about my father. I am being eaten out of house and home; my fair estate is being wasted, and my house is full of miscreants who keep killing great numbers of my sheep and oxen, on the pretense of paying their addresses to my mother. Therefore, I am suppliant at your knees if haply you may tell me about my father's melancholy end, whether you saw it with your own eyes, or heard it from some other traveler; for he was a man born to trouble. Do not soften things out of any pity for myself, but tell me in all plainness exactly what you saw. If my brave father Odysseus ever did you loyal service either by word or deed, when you Achaeans were harassed by the Trojans, bear it in mind now as in my favor and tell me truly all."

Menelaus on hearing this was very much shocked. "So," he exclaimed, "these cowards would usurp a brave man's bed? A hind might as well lay her newborn young in the lair of a lion, and then go off to feed in the forest or in some grassy dell; the lion when he comes back to his lair will make short work with the pair of them—and so will Odysseus with these suitors. By father Zeus, Athene, and Apollo, if Odysseus is still the man that he was when he wrestled with Philomeleides in Lesbos, and threw him so heavily that all the Achaeans cheered him—if he is still such and were to come near these suitors, they would have a short shrift and a sorry wedding. As regards your questions, however, I will not prevaricate or deceive you, but will tell you without concealment all that the old man of the sea told me.

"I was trying to come on here, but the gods detained me in Egypt, for my hecatombs had not given them full satisfaction, and the gods are very strict about having their dues. Now off Egypt, about as far as a ship can sail in a day with a good stiff breeze behind her, there is an island called Pharos. It has a good harbor from which vessels can get out into open sea when they have taken in water—and here the gods becalmed me twenty days without so much as a breath of fair wind to help me forward. We should have run clean out of provisions and my men would have starved, if a goddess had not taken pity upon me and saved me in the person of Idothea, daughter to Proteus, the old man of the sea, for she had taken a great fancy to me.

"She came to me one day when I was by myself, as I often was, for the men used to go with their barbed hooks all over the island in the hope of catching a fish or two to save them from the pangs of hunger. 'Stranger,' she said, 'it seems to me that you like starving in this way—at any rate it does not greatly trouble you, for you stick here day after day, without even trying to get away though your men are dying by inches.'

" 'Let me tell you,' said I, 'whichever of the goddesses you may happen to be, that I am not staying here of my own accord, but must have offended the gods that live in heaven. Tell me, therefore, for the gods know everything, which of the immortals it is that is hindering me in this way, and tell me also how I may sail the seas so as to reach my home.'

" 'Stranger,' replied she, 'I will make it all quite clear to you. There is an old immortal who lives under the sea hereabouts and whose name is Proteus. He is an Egyptian, and people say he is my father. He is Poseidon's head man and knows every inch of ground all over the bottom of the sea. If you can snare him and hold him tight, he will tell you about your voyage, what courses you are to take, and how you are to sail the sea so as to reach your home. He will also tell you, if you so will, all that has been going on at your house both good and bad, while you have been away on your long and dangerous journey.'

" 'Can you show me,' said I, 'some stratagem by means of which I may catch this old god without his suspecting it and finding me out? For a god is not easily caught—not by a mortal man.'

" 'Stranger,' said she, 'I will make it all quite clear to you. About the time when the sun shall have reached mid-heaven, the old man of the sea comes up from under the waves, heralded by the west wind that furs the water over his head. As soon as he has come up he lies down, and goes to sleep in a great sea cave, where the seals— Halosydne's chickens as they call them—come up also from the gray sea, and go to sleep in shoals all round him; and a very strong and fish-like smell do they bring with them. Early tomorrow morning I will take you to this place and will lay you in ambush. Pick out, therefore, the three best men you have in your fleet, and I will tell you all the tricks that the old man will play you.

" 'First he will look over all his seals, and count them; then, when he has seen them and tallied them on his five fingers, he will go to sleep among them, as a shepherd among his sheep. The moment you see that he is asleep, seize him; put forth all your strength and hold him fast, for he will do his very utmost to get away from you. He will turn himself into every kind of creature that goes upon the earth, and will become also both fire and water; but you must hold him fast and grip him tighter and tighter, till he begins to talk to you and comes back to what he was when you saw him go to sleep. Then you may slacken your hold and let him go; and you can ask him which of the gods it is that is angry with you, and what you must do to reach your home over the seas.'

"Having so said, she dived under the waves, whereon I turned back to the place where my ships were ranged upon the shore; and my heart was clouded with care as I went along. When I reached my ship we got supper ready, for night was falling, and camped down upon the beach.

"When the child of morning, rosy-fingered Dawn, appeared, I took the three men on whose prowess of all kinds I could most rely, and went along by the seaside, praying heartily to heaven. Meanwhile the goddess fetched me up four sealskins from the bottom of the sea, all of them just skinned, for she meant playing a trick upon her father. Then she dug four pits for us to lie in, and sat down to wait till we should come up. When we were close to her, she made us lie down in the pits one after the other, and threw a sealskin over each of us. Our ambuscade would have been intolerable, for the stench of the fishy seals was most distressing—who would go to bed with a sea monster if he could help it?—but here, too, the goddess helped us, and thought of something that gave us great relief, for she put some ambrosia under each man's nostrils, which was so fragrant that it killed the smell of the seals.

"We waited the whole morning and made the best of it, watching the seals come up in hundreds to bask upon the seashore, till at noon the old man of the sea came up too, and when he had found his fat seals he went over them and counted them. We were among the first he counted, and he never suspected any guile, but laid himself down to sleep as soon as he had done counting. Then we rushed upon him with a shout and seized him; on which he began at once with his old tricks, and changed himself first into a lion with a great mane; then all of a sudden he became a dragon, a leopard, a wild boar; the next moment he was running water, and then again directly he was a tree, but we stuck to him and never lost hold, till at last the cunning old creature became distressed, and said, 'Which of the gods was it, son of Atreus, that hatched this plot with you for snaring me and seizing me against my will? What do you want?'

" 'You know that yourself, old man,' I answered, 'you will gain nothing by trying to put me off. It is because I have been kept so long in this island, and see no sign of my being able to get away. I am losing all heart. Tell me, then, for you gods know everything, which of the immortals it is that is hindering me, and tell me also how I may sail the sea so as to reach my home?'

" 'Then,' he said, 'if you would finish your voyage and get home quickly, you must offer sacrifices to Zeus and to the rest of the gods before embarking; for it is decreed that you shall not get back to your friends and to your own house, till you have returned to the heaven-fed stream of Egypt, and offered holy hecatombs to the immortal gods that reign in heaven. When you have done this they will let you finish your voyage.'

"I was brokenhearted when I heard that I must go back all that long and terrible voyage to Egypt. Nevertheless, I answered, 'I will do all, old man, that you have laid upon me; but now tell me, and tell me true, whether all the Achaeans whom Nestor and I left behind us when we set sail from Troy have got home safely, or whether any one of them came to a bad end, either on board his own ship or among his friends when the days of his fighting were done.'

" 'Son of Atreus,' he answered, 'why ask me? You had better not know what I can tell you, for your eyes will surely fill when you have heard my story. Many of those about whom you ask are dead and gone, but many still remain, and only two of the chief men among the Achaeans perished during their return home. As for what happened on the field of battle—you were there yourself. A third Achaean leader is still at sea, alive, but hindered from returning. Ajax was wrecked, for Poseidon drove him on to the great rocks of Gyrae; nevertheless, he let him get safe out of the water, and in spite of all Athene's hatred he would have escaped death if he had not ruined himself by boasting. He said the gods could not drown him even though they had tried to do so, and when Poseidon heard this large talk, he seized his trident in his two brawny hands, and split the rock of Gyrae in two pieces. The base remained where it was, but the part on which Ajax was sitting fell headlong into the sea and carried Ajax with it; so he drank salt water and was drowned.

" 'Your brother and his ships escaped, for Hera protected him, but when he was just about to reach the high promontory of Malea, he was caught by a heavy gale, which carried him out to sea again sorely against his will, and drove him to the foreland where Thyestes used to dwell, but where Aegisthus was then living. By and by, however, it seemed as though he was to return safely after all, for the gods backed the wind into its old quarter and they reached home; whereon Agamemnon kissed his native soil, and shed tears of joy at finding himself again in his own country.

" 'Now there was a watchman whom Aegisthus kept always on the watch, and to whom he had promised two talents of gold. This man had been looking out for a whole year to make sure that Agamemnon did not give him the slip and prepare war; when, therefore, this man saw Agamemnon go by, he went and told Aegisthus, who at once began to lay a plot for him. He picked twenty of his bravest warriors and placed them in ambuscade on one side of the cloister, while on the opposite side he prepared a banquet. Then he sent his chariots and horsemen to Agamemnon, and invited him to the feast, but he meant foul play. He got him there, all unsuspicious of the doom that was awaiting him, and killed him when the banquet was over as though he were butchering an ox in the shambles; not one of Agamemnon's followers was left alive, nor yet one of Aegisthus', but they were all killed there in the cloisters.'

"Thus spoke Proteus, and I was brokenhearted as I heard him. I sat down upon the sands and wept; I felt as though I could no longer bear to live nor look upon the light of the sun. Presently, when I had had my fill of weeping and writhing upon the ground, the old man of the sea said, 'Son of Atreus, do not waste any more time in crying so bitterly; it can do no manner of good; find your way home as fast as ever you can, for Aegisthus may be still alive, and even though Orestes has been beforehand with you in killing him, you may yet come in for his funeral.'

"On this I took comfort in spite of all my sorrow, and said, 'I know, then, about these two. Tell me, therefore, about the third man of whom you spoke; is he still alive, but at sea, and unable to get home? or is he dead? Tell me, no matter how much it may grieve me.'

" 'The third man,' he answered, 'is Odysseus who dwells in Ithaca. I can see him in an island sorrowing bitterly in the house of the nymph Calypso, who is keeping him prisoner, and he cannot reach his home for he has no ships or sailors to take him over the sea. As for your own end, Menelaus, you shall not die in Argos, but the gods will take you to the Elysian plain, which is at the ends of the world. There fair-haired Rhadamanthus reigns, and men lead an easier life than anywhere else in the world, for in Elysium there falls not rain, nor hail, nor snow, but Oceanus breathes ever with a west wind that sings softly from the sea, and gives fresh life to all men. This will happen to you because you have married Helen, and are Zeus' son-in-law.'

"As he spoke he dived under the waves, whereon I turned back to the ships with my companions, and my heart was clouded with care as I went along. When we reached the ships we got supper ready, for night was falling, and camped down upon the beach. When the child of morning, rosy-fingered Dawn, appeared, we drew our ships into the water, and put our masts and sails within them; then we went on board ourselves, took our seats on the benches, and smote the gray sea with our oars. I again stationed my ships in the heaven-fed stream of Egypt, and offered hecatombs that were full and sufficient. When I had thus appeased heaven's anger, I raised a barrow to the memory of Agamemnon that his name might live forever, after which I had a quick passage home, for the gods sent me a fair wind.

"And now for yourself—stay here some ten or twelve days longer, and I will then speed you on your way. I will make you a noble present of a chariot and three horses. I will also give you a beautiful chalice, that so long as you live you may think of me whenever you make a drink offering to the immortal gods."

"Son of Atreus," replied Telemachus, "do not press me to stay longer; I should be contented to remain with you for another twelve months. I find your conversation so delightful that I should never once wish myself at home with my parents; but my crew whom I have left at Pylos are already impatient, and you are detaining me from them. As for any present you may be disposed to make me, I had rather that it should be a piece of plate. I will take no horses back with me to Ithaca, but will leave them to adorn your own stables, for you have much flat ground in your kingdom, where lotus thrives, and also meadow-sweet and wheat and barley, and oats with their white and spreading ears; whereas in Ithaca we have neither open fields nor racecourses, and the country is more fit for goats than horses, and I like it the better for that. None of our islands have much level ground, suitable for horses, and Ithaca least of all."

Menelaus smiled and took Telemachus' hand within his own. "What you say," said he, "shows that you come of good family. I both can, and will, make this exchange for you, by giving you the finest and most precious piece of plate in all my house. It is a mixing-bowl by Hephaestus' own hand, of pure silver, except the rim, which is inlaid with gold. Phaedimus, king of the Sidonians, gave it me in the course of a visit which I paid him when I returned thither on my homeward journey. I will make you a present of it."

Thus did they converse while guests kept coming to the king's house. They brought sheep and wine, while their wives had put up bread for them to take with them; so they were busy cooking their dinners in the courts.

Meanwhile [in Ithaca] the suitors were throwing discs or aiming with spears at a mark on the leveled ground in front of Odysseus' house, and were behaving with all their old insolence. Antinous and Eurymachus, who were their ringleaders and much the foremost among them all, were sitting together when Noemon son of Phronius came up and said to Antinous:

"Have we any idea, Antinous, on what day Telemachus returns from Pylos? He has a ship of mine, and I want it, to cross over to Elis. I have twelve brood mares there with yearling mule foals by their side not yet broken in, and I want to bring one of them over here and break him."

They were astounded when they heard this, for they had made sure that Telemachus had not gone to the city of Neleus. They thought he was only away somewhere on the farms, and was with the sheep, or with the swineherd; so Antinous said, "When did he go? Tell me truly, and what young men did he take with him? Were they freemen or his own bondsmen—for he might manage that too? Tell me also, did you let him have the ship of your own free will because he asked you, or did he take it without your leave?"

"I lent it him," answered Noemon. "What else could I do when a man of his position said he was in a difficulty, and asked me to oblige him? I could not possibly refuse. As for those who went with him, they were the best young men we have, and I saw Mentor go on board as captain—or some god who was exactly like him. I cannot understand it, for I saw Mentor here myself yesterday morning, and yet he was then setting out for Pylos."

Noemon then went back to his father's house, but Antinous and Eurymachus were very angry. They told the others to leave off playing, and to come and sit down along with themselves. When they came, Antinous son of Eupeithes spoke in anger. His heart was black with rage, and his eyes flashed fire as he said:

"Good heavens, this voyage of Telemachus is a very serious matter! We had made sure that it would come to nothing, but the young fellow has got away in spite of us, and with a picked crew too. He will be giving us trouble presently; may Zeus take him before he is full grown. Find me a ship, therefore, with a crew of twenty men, and I will lie in wait for him in the straits between Ithaca and Same. He will then rue the day that he set out to try and get news of his father."

Thus did he speak, and the others applauded his saying; they then all of them went inside the buildings.

It was not long ere Penelope came to know what the suitors were plotting; for a manservant, Medon, overheard them from outside the outer court as they were laying their schemes within, and went to tell his mistress. As he crossed the threshold of her room, Penelope said: "Medon, what have the suitors sent you here for? Is it to tell the maids to leave their master's business and cook dinner for them? I wish they may neither woo nor dine henceforward, neither here nor anywhere else, but let this be the very last time, for the waste you all make of my son's estate. Did not your fathers tell you when you were children how good Odysseus had been to them—never doing anything high-handed, nor speaking harshly to anybody? Kings may say things sometimes, and they may take a fancy to one man and dislike another, but Odysseus never did an unjust thing by anybody—which shows what bad hearts you have, and that there is no such thing as gratitude left in this world."

Then Medon said: "I wish, madam, that this were all; but they are plotting something much more dreadful now—may heaven frustrate their design! They are going to try and murder Telemachus as he is coming home from Pylos and Sparta, where he has been to get news of his father."

Then Penelope's heart sank within her, and for a long time she was speechless; her eyes filled with tears, and she could find no utterance. At last, however, she said, "Why did my son leave me? What business had he to go sailing off in ships that make long voyages over the ocean like sea-horses? Does he want to die without leaving anyone behind him to keep up his name?"

"I do not know," answered Medon, "whether some god set him on to it, or whether he went on his own impulse to see if he could find out if his father was dead, or alive and on his way home."

Then he went downstairs again,[5] leaving Penelope in an agony of grief. There were plenty of seats in the house, but she had no heart for sitting on any one of them; she could only fling herself on

[5] The rampart or body of the house was two stories high. It contained among other things the women's apartments and the storeroom for valuable treasure.

the floor of her own room and cry; whereon all the maids in the house, both old and young, gathered round her and began to cry too, till at last in a transport of sorrow she exclaimed:

"My dears, heaven has been pleased to try me with more affliction than any other woman of my age and country. First I lost my brave and lion-hearted husband, who had every good quality under heaven, and whose name was great over all Hellas and middle Argos, and now my darling son is at the mercy of the winds and waves, without my having heard one word about his leaving home. You hussies, there was not one of you would so much as think of giving me a call out of my bed, though you all of you very well knew when he was starting! If I had known he meant taking this voyage, he would have had to give it up, no matter how much he was bent upon it, or leave me a corpse behind him—one or other. Now, however, go some of you and call old Dolius, who was given me by my father on my marriage, and who is my gardener. Bid him go at once and tell everything to Laertes, who may be able to hit on some plan for enlisting public sympathy on our side, as against those who are trying to exterminate his own race and that of Odysseus."

Then the dear old nurse Euryclea said: "You may kill me, madam, or let me live on in your house, whichever you please, but I will tell you the real truth. I knew all about it, and gave him everything he wanted in the way of bread and wine, but he made me take my solemn oath that I would not tell you anything for some ten or twelve days, unless you asked or happened to hear of his having gone, for he did not want you to spoil your beauty by crying. And now, madam, wash your face, change your dress, and go upstairs with your maids to offer prayers to Athene, daughter of aegis-bearing Zeus, for she can save him even though he be in the jaws of death. Do not trouble Laertes: he has trouble enough already. Besides, I cannot think that the gods hate the race of the son of Arceisius so much, but there will be a son left to come up after him, and inherit both the house and the fair fields that lie far all round it."

With these words she made her mistress leave off crying, and dried the tears from her eyes. Penelope washed her face, changed her dress, and went upstairs with her maids. She then put some bruised barley into a basket and began praying to Athene.

"Hear me," she cried, "daughter of aegis-bearing Zeus, unweariable. If ever Odysseus while he was here burned you fat thighbones of sheep or heifer, bear it in mind now as in my favor, and save my darling son from the villainy of the suitors."

She cried aloud as she spoke, and the goddess heard her prayer. Meanwhile the suitors were clamorous throughout the covered cloister, and one of them said:

"The queen is preparing for her marriage with one or other of us. Little does she dream that her son has now been doomed to die."

This was what they said, but they did not know what was going to happen. Then Antinous said, "Comrades, let there be no loud talking, lest some of it get carried inside. Let us be up and do that in silence, about which we are all of a mind."

He then chose twenty men, and they went down to their ship and to the seaside. They drew the vessel into the water and got her mast and sails inside her; they bound the oars to the thole-pins with twisted thongs of leather, all in due course, and spread the white sails aloft, while their fine servants brought them their armor. Then they made the ship fast a little way out, came on shore again, got their suppers, and waited until night should fall.

But Penelope lay in her own room upstairs unable to eat or drink, and wondering whether her brave son would escape, or be overpowered by the wicked suitors. Like a lioness caught in the toils with huntsmen hemming her in on every side, she thought and thought till she sank into a slumber, and lay on her bed bereft of thought and motion.

Then Athene bethought her of another matter, and made a vision in the likeness of Penelope's sister Iphthime, daughter of Icarius, who had married Eumelus and lived in Pherae. She told the vision to go to the house of Odysseus, and to make Penelope leave off crying. So it came into her room by the hole through which the thong went for pulling the door to, and hovered over her head, saying,

"You are asleep, Penelope. The gods who live at ease will not suffer you to weep and be so sad. Your son has done them no wrong, so he will yet come back to you."

Penelope, who was sleeping sweetly at the gates of dreamland, answered: "Sister, why have you come here? You do not come very often, but I suppose this is because you live such a long way off. Am I, then, to leave off crying and refrain from all the sad thoughts that torture me? I, who have lost my brave and lion-hearted husband, who had every good quality under heaven, and whose name was great over all Hellas and middle Argos; and now my darling son has gone off on board of a ship—a foolish fellow who has never been used to roughing it, or to going about among gatherings of men. I am even more anxious about him than about my husband. I am all in a tremble when I think of him, lest something should happen to him, either from the people among whom he has gone, or by sea, for he has many enemies who are plotting against him, and are bent on killing him before he can return home."

Then the vision said: "Take heart, and be not so much dismayed. There is one gone with him whom many a man would be glad enough to have stand by his side, I mean Athene; it is she who has compassion upon you, and who has sent me to bear you this message."

"Then," said Penelope, "if you are a god or have been sent here by divine commission, tell me also about that other unhappy one—is he still alive, or is he already dead and in the house of Hades?"

And the vision said, "I shall not tell you for certain whether he is alive or dead, and there is no use in idle conversation."

Then it vanished through the thong-hole of the door and was dissipated into thin air; but Penelope rose from her sleep refreshed and comforted, so vivid had been her dream.

Meantime the suitors went on board and sailed their ways over the sea, intent on murdering Telemachus. Now there is a rocky islet called Asteris, of no great size, in mid-channel between Ithaca and Same, and there is a harbor on either side of it where a ship can lie. Here then the Achaeans placed themselves in ambush.

BOOK V

Hermes, bidden by Zeus, flies to Calypso's isle to charge her to let Odysseus go. Obeying the god, Calypso helps her captive to build a raft and set sail. But after seventeen days of smooth sailing, the raft is wrecked in a storm summoned by Poseidon. Odysseus battles the waves bravely and at length reaches shore on the land of the Phaeacians. Exhausted and naked, he finds shelter in a wood and sleeps.

AND NOW, AS DAWN ROSE FROM HER COUCH beside Tithonus—harbinger of light alike to mortals and immortals—the gods met in council and with them, Zeus the lord of thunder, who is their king. Thereon Athene began to tell them of the many sufferings of Odysseus, for she pitied him away there in the house of the nymph Calypso.

"Father Zeus," said she, "and all you other gods that live in everlasting bliss, I hope there may never be such a thing as a kind and well-disposed ruler any more, nor one who will govern equitably. I hope they will be all henceforth cruel and unjust, for there is not one of his subjects but has forgotten Odysseus, who ruled them as though he were their father. There he is, lying in great pain in an island where dwells the nymph Calypso, who will not let him go; and he cannot get back to his own country, for he can find neither ships nor sailors to take him over the sea. Furthermore, wicked people are now trying to murder his only son Telemachus, who is coming home from Pylos and Sparta, where he has been to see if he can get news of his father."

"What, my dear, are you talking about?" replied her father. "Did you not send him there yourself, because you thought it would help Odysseus to get home and punish the suitors? Besides, you are perfectly able to protect Telemachus, and to see him safely home again, while the suitors have to come hurry-skurrying back without having killed him."

When he had thus spoken, he said to his son Hermes, "Hermes, you are our messenger, go therefore and tell Calypso we have decreed that poor Odysseus is to return home. He is to be convoyed neither by gods nor men, but after a perilous voyage of twenty days upon a raft he is to reach fertile Scheria, the land of the Phaecians, who are near of kin to the gods, and will honor him as though he were one of ourselves. They will send him in a ship to his own country, and will give him more bronze and gold and raiment than he would have brought back from Troy, if he had had all his prize money and had got home without disaster. This is how we have settled that he shall return to his country and his friends."

Thus he spoke, and Hermes, guide and guardian, slayer of Argus, did as he was told. Forthwith he bound on his glittering golden sandals with which he could fly like the wind over land and sea. He took the wand with which he seals men's eyes in sleep or wakes them just as he pleases, and flew holding it in his hand over Pieria. Then he swooped down through the firmament till he reached the level of the sea, whose waves he skimmed like a cormorant that flies fishing every hole and corner of the ocean, and drenching its thick plumage in the spray. He flew and flew over many a weary wave, but when at last he got to the island which was his journey's end, he left the sea and went on by land till he came to the cave where the nymph Calypso lived.

He found her at home. There was a large fire burning on the hearth, and one could smell from far the fragrant reek of burning

cedar and sandalwood. As for herself, she was busy at her loom,
shooting her golden shuttle through the warp and singing beautifully. Round her cave there was a thick wood of alder, poplar, and
sweet-smelling cypress trees, wherein all kinds of great birds had
built their nests—owls, hawks, and chattering sea crows that occupy
their business in the waters. A vine loaded with grapes was trained
and grew luxuriantly about the mouth of the cave; there were also
four running rills of water in channels cut pretty close together, and
turned hither and thither so as to irrigate the beds of violets and
luscious herbage over which they flowed. Even a god could not help
being charmed with such a lovely spot, so Hermes stood still and
looked at it; but when he had admired it sufficiently he went inside
the cave.

Calypso knew him at once—for the gods all know each other, no
matter how far they live from one another—but Odysseus was not
within; he was on the seashore as usual, looking out upon the barren ocean with tears in his eyes, groaning and breaking his heart for
sorrow. Calypso gave Hermes a seat and said: "Why have you come
to see me, Hermes—honored, and ever welcome—for you do not
visit me often? Say what you want; I will do it for you at once if I
can, and if it can be done at all. But come inside, and let me set
refreshment for you."

As she spoke she drew a table loaded with ambrosia beside him
and mixed him some red nectar, so Hermes ate and drank till he had
had enough, and then said:

"We are speaking god and goddess to one another, and you ask
me why I have come here, and I will tell you truly as you would
have me do. Zeus sent me; it was no doing of mine. Who could possibly want to come all this way over the sea where there are no cities
full of people to offer me sacrifices or choice hecatombs? Nevertheless, I had to come, for none of us other gods can cross Zeus, or
transgress his orders. He says that you have here the most ill-starred
of all those who fought nine years before the city of King Priam
and sailed home in the tenth year after having sacked it. On their
way home they sinned against Athene, who raised both wind and

waves against them, so that all his brave companions perished, and he alone was carried hither by wind and tide. Zeus says that you are to let this man go at once, for it is decreed that he shall not perish here, far from his own people, but shall return to his house and country and see his friends again."

Calypso trembled with rage when she heard this. "You gods," she exclaimed, "ought to be ashamed of yourselves! You are always jealous, and hate seeing a goddess take a fancy to a mortal man, and live with him in open matrimony. So when rosy-fingered Dawn made love to Orion, you precious gods were all of you furious till Artemis went and killed him in Ortygia. So again when Demeter fell in love with Iasion, and yielded to him in a thrice-ploughed fallow field, Zeus came to hear of it before so very long and killed Iasion with his thunderbolts. And now you are angry with me too because I have a man here. I found the poor creature sitting all alone astride of a keel, for Zeus had struck his ship with lightning and sunk it in mid-ocean, so that all his crew were drowned, while he himself was driven by wind and waves on to my island. I got fond of him and cherished him, and had set my heart on making him immortal, so that he should never grow old all his days. Still I cannot cross Zeus, or bring his counsels to nothing; therefore, if he insists upon it, let the man go beyond the seas again. But I cannot send him anywhere myself, for I have neither ships nor men who can take him. Nevertheless, I will readily give him such advice, in all good faith, as will be likely to bring him safely to his own country."

"Then send him away," said Hermes, "or Zeus will be angry with you and punish you."

On this he took his leave, and Calypso went out to look for Odysseus, for she had heard Zeus' message. She found him sitting upon the beach with his eyes ever filled with tears, and dying of sheer homesickness; for he had got tired of Calypso, and though he was forced to sleep with her in the cave by night, it was she, not he, that would have it so. As for the daytime, he spent it on the rocks and on the seashore, weeping, crying aloud for his despair, and always looking out upon the sea. Calypso then went close up to him and said:

"My poor fellow, you shall not stay here grieving and fretting your life out any longer. I am going to send you away of my own free will; so go, cut some beams of wood, and make yourself a large raft with an upper deck, that it may carry you safely over the sea. I will put bread, wine, and water on board to save you from starving. I will also give you clothes, and will send you a fair wind to take you home, if the gods in heaven so will it—for they know more about these things, and can settle them better than I can."

Odysseus shuddered as he heard her. "Now, goddess," he answered, "there is something behind all this; you cannot be really meaning to help me home when you bid me do such a dreadful thing as put to sea on a raft. Not even a well-found ship with a fair wind would venture on such a distant voyage: nothing that you can say or do shall make me go on board a raft unless you first solemnly swear that you mean me no mischief."

Calypso smiled at this, and caressed him with her hand. "You know a great deal," said she, "but you are quite wrong here. May heaven above and earth below be my witnesses, with the waters of the river Styx—and this is the most solemn oath which a blessed god can take—that I mean you no sort of harm, and am only advising you to do exactly what I should do myself in your place. I am dealing with you quite straightforwardly; my heart is not made of iron, and I am very sorry for you."

When she had thus spoken she led the way rapidly before him, and Odysseus followed in her steps; so the pair, goddess and man, went on and on till they came to Calypso's cave, where Odysseus took the seat that Hermes had just left. Calypso set meat and drink before him of the food that mortals eat; but her maids brought ambrosia and nectar for herself, and they laid their hands on the good things that were before them. When they had satisfied themselves with meat and drink, Calypso spoke, saying:

"Odysseus, noble son of Laertes, so you would start home to your own land at once? Good luck go with you, but if you could only know how much suffering is in store for you before you get back to your own country, you would stay where you are, keep house along with me, and let me make you immortal, no matter how anxious you may be to see this wife of yours, of whom you are thinking all the time day after day. Yet I flatter myself that I am no whit less tall or well-looking than she is, for it is not to be expected that a mortal woman should compare in beauty with an immortal."

"Goddess," replied Odysseus, "do not be angry with me about this. I am quite aware that my wife Penelope is nothing like so tall or so beautiful as yourself. She is only a woman, whereas you are an immortal. Nevertheless, I want to get home, and can think of nothing else. If some god wrecks me when I am on the sea, I will bear it and make the best of it. I have had infinite trouble both by land and sea already, so let this go with the rest."

Presently the sun set and it became dark, whereon the pair retired into the inner part of the cave and went to bed.

When the child of morning, rosy-fingered Dawn, appeared, Odysseus put on his shirt and cloak, while the goddess wore a dress of a light gossamer fabric, very fine and graceful, with a beautiful golden girdle about her waist and a veil to cover her head. She at once set herself to think how she could speed Odysseus on his way. So she gave him a great bronze axe that suited his hands; it was sharpened on both sides, and had a beautiful olive-wood handle fitted firmly on to it. She also gave him a sharp adze, and then led the way to the far end of the island where the largest trees grew—alder, poplar, and pine, that reached the sky—very dry and well seasoned, so as to sail light for him in the water. Then, when she had shown him where the best trees grew, Calypso went home, leaving him to cut them, which he soon finished doing. He cut down twenty trees in all and adzed them smooth, squaring them by rule in good workmanlike fashion. Meanwhile Calypso came back with some augers, so he bored holes with them and fitted the timbers together with bolts and rivets. He made the raft as broad as a skilled shipwright makes the beam of a large vessel, and he fixed a deck on top of the ribs, and ran a gunwale all around it. He also made a mast with a yard arm, and a rudder to steer with. He fenced the raft all round with wicker hurdles as a protection against the waves, and then he threw on a quantity of wood. By and by Calypso brought him some linen to make the sails, and he made these too, excellently, making them fast with braces and sheets. Last of all, with the help of levers, he drew the raft down into the water.

In four days he had completed the whole work, and on the fifth Calypso sent him from the island after washing him and giving him some clean clothes. She gave him a goatskin full of black wine,[1] and another larger one of water; she also gave him a wallet full of provisions, and supplied him with much good meat. Moreover, she made the wind fair and warm for him, and gladly did Odysseus spread his sail before it, while he sat and guided the raft skillfully by means of the rudder. He never closed his eyes, but kept them fixed on the Pleiads, on late-setting Bootes, and on the Bear—which men also call the wain, and which turns round and round where it is, facing Orion, and alone never dipping into the stream of Oceanus—for Calypso had told him to keep this to his left. Days seven and ten did he sail over the sea, and on the eighteenth the dim outlines of the mountains on the nearest part of the Phaeacian coast appeared, rising like a shield on the horizon.

But King Poseidon, who was returning from the Ethiopians, caught sight of Odysseus a long way off, from the mountains of the Solymi. He could see him sailing upon the sea, and it made him very angry, so he wagged his head and muttered to himself, saying, "Good heavens, so the gods have been changing their minds about Odysseus while I was away in Ethiopia, and now he is close to the land of the Phaeacians, where it is decreed that he shall escape from the calamities that have befallen him. Still, he shall have plenty of hardship yet before he has done with it."

Thereon he gathered his clouds together, grasped his trident, stirred it round in the sea, and roused the rage of every wind that blows till earth, sea, and sky were hidden in cloud, and night sprang

---

[1] That is, very deep red like some of the present Sicilian wines that look more black than anything else. (B.)

forth out of the heavens. Winds from east, south, north, and west fell upon him all at the same time, and a tremendous sea got up, so that Odysseus' heart began to fail him. "Alas," he said to himself in his dismay, "what ever will become of me? I am afraid Calypso was right when she said I should have trouble by sea before I get back home. It is all coming true. How black is Zeus making heaven with his clouds, and what a sea the winds are raising from every quarter at once. I am now safe to perish. Blest and thrice blest were those Danaans who fell before Troy in the cause of the sons of Atreus. Would that I had been killed on the day when the Trojans were pressing me so sorely about the dead body of Achilles, for then I should have had due burial and the Achaeans would have honored my name; but now it seems that I shall come to a most pitiable end."

As he spoke a sea broke over him with such terrific fury that the raft reeled again, and he was carried overboard a long way off. He let go the helm, and the force of the hurricane was so great that it broke the mast half way up, and both sail and yard went over into the sea. For a long time Odysseus was under water, and it was all he could do to rise to the surface again, for the clothes Calypso had given him weighed him down; but at last he got his head above water and spat out the bitter brine that was running down his face in streams. In spite of all this, however, he did not lose sight of his raft, but swam as fast as he could towards it, got hold of it, and climbed on board again so as to escape drowning. The sea took the raft and tossed it about as autumn winds whirl thistledown round and round upon a road. It was as though the south, north, east, and west winds were all playing battledore and shuttlecock with it at once.

When he was in this plight, Ino daughter of Cadmus, also called Leucothea, saw him. She had formerly been a mere mortal, but had been since raised to the rank of a marine goddess. Seeing in what great distress Odysseus now was, she had compassion upon him, and, rising like a sea gull from the waves, took her seat upon the raft.

"My poor good man," said she, "why is Poseidon so furiously

angry with you? He is giving you a great deal of trouble, but for all his bluster he will not kill you. You seem to be a sensible person, do then as I bid you; strip, leave your raft to drive before the wind, and swim to the Phaeacian coast where better luck awaits you. And here, take my veil and put it round your chest; it is enchanted, and you can come to no harm so long as you wear it. As soon as you touch land take it off, throw it back as far as you can into the sea, and then go away again." With these words she took off her veil and gave it him. Then she dived down again like a sea gull and vanished beneath the dark blue waters.

But Odysseus did not know what to think. "Alas," he said to himself in his dismay, "this is only some one or other of the gods who is luring me to ruin by advising me to quit my raft. At any rate I will not do so at present, for the land where she said I should be quit of all my troubles seems to be still a good way off. I know what I will do—I am sure it will be best—no matter what happens, I will stick to the raft as long as her timbers hold together, but when the sea breaks her up I will swim for it. I do not see how I can do any better than this."

While he was thus in two minds, Poseidon sent a terrible great wave that seemed to rear itself above his head till it broke right over the raft, which then went to pieces as though it were a heap of dry chaff tossed about by a whirlwind. Odysseus got astride of one plank and rode upon it as if he were on horseback. He then took off the clothes Calypso had given him, bound Ino's veil under his arms, and plunged into the sea—meaning to swim on shore. King Poseidon watched him as he did so, and wagged his head, muttering to himself and saying, "There now, swim up and down as you best can till you fall in with well-to-do people. I do not think you will be able to say that I have let you off too lightly." On this he lashed his horses and drove to Aegae where his palace is.

But Athene resolved to help Odysseus, so she bound the ways of all the winds except one, and made them lie quite still; but she roused a good stiff breeze from the north that should lay the waters till Odysseus reached the land of the Phaeacians where he would be safe.

Thereon he floated about for two nights and two days in the water, with a heavy swell on the sea and death staring him in the face; but when the third day broke, the wind fell and there was a dead calm without so much as a breath of air stirring. As he rose on the swell he looked eagerly ahead, and could see land quite near. Then, as children rejoice when their dear father begins to get better after having for a long time borne sore affliction sent him by some angry spirit, but the gods deliver him from evil, so was Odysseus thankful when he again saw land and trees, and swam on with all his strength that he might once more set foot upon dry ground. When, however, he got within earshot, he began to hear the surf thundering up against the rocks, for the swell still broke against them with a terrific roar. Everything was enveloped in spray; there were no harbors where a ship might ride, or shelter of any kind, but only headlands, low-lying rocks, and mountain tops.

Odysseus' heart now began to fail him, and he said despairingly to himself: "Alas, Zeus has let me see land after swimming so far that I had given up all hope, but I can find no landing place, for the coast is rocky and surf-beaten, the rocks are smooth and rise sheer from the sea, with deep water close under them so that I cannot climb out for want of foothold. I am afraid some great wave will lift me off my legs and dash me against the rocks as I leave the water—which would give me a sorry landing. If, on the other hand, I swim further in search of some shelving beach or harbor, a hurricane may carry me out to sea again sorely against my will, or heaven may send some great monster of the deep to attack me; for Amphitrite breeds many such, and I know that Poseidon is very angry with me."

While he was thus in two minds a wave caught him and took him with such force against the rocks that he would have been smashed and torn to pieces if Athene had not shown him what to do. He caught hold of the rock with both hands and clung to it groaning with pain till the wave retired, so he was saved that time; but presently the wave came on again and carried him back with it far into the sea—tearing his hands as the suckers of a polypus are torn when someone plucks it from its bed, and the stones come up along with it—even so did the rocks tear the skin from his strong hands, and then the wave drew him deep down under the water.

Here poor Odysseus would have certainly perished, even in spite of his own destiny, if Athene had not helped him to keep his wits about him. He swam seaward again, beyond reach of the surf that was beating against the land, and at the same time he kept looking towards the shore to see if he could find some haven, or a spit that should take the waves aslant. By and by, as he swam on, he came to the mouth of a river, and here he thought would be the best place, for there were no rocks, and it afforded shelter from the wind. He felt that there was a current, so he prayed inwardly and said:

"Hear me, O king, whoever you may be, and save me from the anger of the sea-god Poseidon, for I approach you prayerfully. Anyone who has lost his way has at all times a claim even upon the gods, wherefore in my distress I draw near to your stream, and cling to the knees of your riverhood. Have mercy upon me, O king, for I declare myself your suppliant."

Then the god stayed his stream and stilled the waves, making all calm before him, and bringing him safely into the mouth of the river. Here at last Odysseus' knees and strong hands failed him, for the sea had completely broken him. His body was all swollen, and his mouth and nostrils ran down like a river with sea water, so that he could neither breathe nor speak, and lay swooning from sheer exhaustion. Presently, when he had got his breath and came to himself again, he took off the scarf that Ino had given him and threw it back into the salt[2] stream of the river, whereon Ino received it into her hands from the wave that bore it towards her. Then he left the river, laid himself down among the rushes, and kissed the bounteous earth.

---

[2] The reader will note that the river was flowing with salt water, that is, that was tidal.

"Alas," he cried to himself in his dismay, "what ever will become of me, and how is it all to end? If I stay here upon the river bed through the long watches of the night, I am so exhausted that the bitter cold and damp may make an end of me—for towards sunrise there will be a keen wind blowing from off the river. If, on the other hand, I climb the hillside, find shelter in the woods, and sleep in some thicket, I may escape the cold and have a good night's rest, but some savage beast may take advantage of me and devour me."

In the end he deemed it best to take to the woods, and he found one upon some high ground not far from the water. There he crept beneath two shoots of olive that grew from a single stock—the one an ungrafted sucker, while the other had been grafted. No wind, however squally, could break through the cover they afforded, nor could the sun's rays pierce them, nor the rain get through them, so closely did they grow into one another. Odysseus crept under these and began to make himself a bed to lie on, for there was a great litter of dead leaves lying about—enough to make a covering for two or three men even in hard winter weather. He was glad enough to see this, so he laid himself down and heaped the leaves all round him. Then, as one who lives alone in the country, far from any neighbor, hides a brand as fire-seed in the ashes to save himself from having to get a light elsewhere, even so did Odysseus cover himself up with leaves; and Athene shed a sweet sleep upon his eyes, closed his eyelids, and made him lose all memory of his sorrows.

BOOK VI

Nausicaa, daughter of Alcinous, king of the Phaeacians, drives
with her maidens to the washing pools by the seashore, near
where Odysseus lies sleeping. Awakened, Odysseus appeals to
Nausicaa for aid, who, undaunted by his savage appearance,
generously gives him food and clothing and invites him to her
father's house. She and her maidens precede him into the town.

SO HERE ODYSSEUS SLEPT, OVERCOME BY SLEEP
and toil; but Athene went off to the country and city of the
Phaeacians, a people who used to live in the fair town of
Hypereia, near the lawless Cyclopes. Now the Cyclopes were
stronger than they and plundered them, so their king Nausithous
moved them thence and settled them in Scheria, far from all other
people. He surrounded the city with a wall, built houses and temples, and divided the lands among his people; but he was dead and
gone to the house of Hades, and King Alcinous, whose counsels
were inspired of heaven, was now reigning. To his house, then, did
Athene hie in furtherance of the return of Odysseus.

She went straight to the beautifully decorated bedroom in which
there slept a girl who was as lovely as a goddess, Nausicaa, daughter
of King Alcinous. Two maidservants were sleeping near her, both

very pretty, one on either side of the doorway, which was closed with well-made folding doors. Athene took the form of the famous sea captain Dymas' daughter, who was a bosom friend of Nausicaa and just her own age; then, coming up to the girl's bedside like a breath of wind, she hovered over her head and said:

"Nausicaa, what can your mother have been about, to have such a lazy daughter? Here are your clothes all lying in disorder, yet you are going to be married almost immediately, and should not only be well dressed yourself, but should find good clothes for those who attend you. This is the way to get yourself a good name, and to make your father and mother proud of you. Suppose, then, that we make tomorrow a washing day, and start at daybreak. I will come and help you so that you may have everything ready as soon as possible, for all the best young men among your own people are courting you, and you are not going to remain a maid much longer. Ask your father, therefore, to have a wagon and mules ready for us at daybreak, to take the rugs, robes, and girdles; and you can ride, too, which will be much pleasanter for you than walking, for the washing cisterns are some way from the town."

When she had said this Athene went away to Olympus, which they say is the everlasting home of the gods. Here no wind beats roughly, and neither rain nor snow can fall; but it abides in everlasting sunshine and in a great peacefulness of light, wherein the blessed gods are illumined for ever and ever. This was the place to which the goddess went when she had given instructions to the girl.

By and by morning came and woke Nausicaa, who began wondering about her dream; she therefore went to the other end of the house to tell her father and mother all about it, and found them in their own room. Her mother was sitting by the fireside spinning her purple yarn with her maids around her, and she happened to catch her father just as he was going out to attend a meeting of the town council, which the Phaeacian alderman had convened. She stopped him and said:

"Papa dear, could you manage to let me have a good big wagon? I want to take all our dirty clothes to the river and wash them. You are the chief man here, so it is only right that you should have a clean shirt when you attend meetings of the council. Moreover, you have five sons at home, two of them married, while the other three are good-looking bachelors; you know they always like to have clean linen when they go to a dance, and I have been thinking about all this."

She did not say a word about her own wedding, for she did not like to, but her father knew and said, "You shall have the mules, my love, and whatever else you have a mind for. Be off with you, and the men shall get you a good strong wagon with a body to it that will hold all your clothes."

On this he gave his orders to the servants, who got the wagon out, harnessed the mules, and put them to, while the girl brought the clothes down from the linen room and placed them on the wagon. Her mother prepared her a basket of provisions with all sorts of good things, and a goatskin full of wine. The girl now got into the wagon, and her mother gave her also a golden cruse of oil, that she and her women might anoint themselves. Then she took the whip and reins and lashed the mules on, whereon they set off, and their hoofs clattered on the road. They pulled without flagging, and carried not only Nausicaa and her wash of clothes but the maids also who were with her.

When they reached the water side they went to the washing cisterns, through which there ran at all times enough pure water to wash any quantity of linen, no matter how dirty. Here they unharnessed the mules and turned them out to feed on the sweet juicy herbage that grew by the water side. They took the clothes out of the wagon, put them in the water, and vied with one another in treading them in the pits to get the dirt out. After they had washed them and got them quite clean, they laid them out by the seaside, where the waves had raised a high beach of shingle, and set about washing themselves and anointing themselves with olive oil. Then they got their dinner by the side of the stream, and waited for the sun to finish drying the clothes. When they had done dinner they threw off the veils that covered their heads and began to play at ball, while Nausicaa sang for them. As the huntress Artemis goes forth upon the mountains of Taygetus or Erymanthus to hunt wild boars or deer, and the wood-nymphs, daughters of aegis-bearing Zeus, take their sport along with her (then is Leto[1] proud at seeing her daughter stand a full head taller than the others, and eclipse the loveliest amid a whole bevy of beauties), even so did the girl outshine her handmaids.

When it was time for them to start home, and they were folding the clothes and putting them into the wagon, Athene began to consider how Odysseus should wake up and see the handsome girl who was to conduct him to the city of the Phaeacians. The girl, therefore, threw a ball at one of the maids, which missed her and fell into deep water. On this they all shouted, and the noise they made woke Odysseus, who sat up in his bed of leaves and began to wonder what it might all be.

"Alas," said he to himself, "what kind of people have I come amongst? Are they cruel, savage, and uncivilized, or hospitable and humane? I seem to hear the voices of young women, and they sound like those of the nymphs that haunt mountain tops, or springs of rivers and meadows of green grass. At any rate I am among a race of men and women. Let me try if I cannot manage to get a look at them."

As he said this he crept from under his bush, and broke off a bough covered with thick leaves to hide his nakedness. He looked like some lion of the wilderness that stalks about exulting in his strength and defying both wind and rain; his eyes glare as he prowls in quest of oxen, sheep, or deer, for he is famished, and will dare break even into a well-fenced homestead, trying to get at the sheep—even such did Odysseus seem to the young women, as he drew near to them all naked as he was, for he was in great want. On seeing one so unkempt and so begrimed with salt water, the others scampered off along the spits that jutted out into the sea, but the daughter of Alcinous stood firm, for Athene put courage into her heart and took away all fear from her. She stood right in front of

---

[1] Mother of the goddess Artemis by Zeus.

Odysseus, and he doubted whether he should go up to her, throw himself at her feet, and embrace her knees as a suppliant, or stay where he was and entreat her to give him some clothes and show him the way to the town. In the end he deemed it best to entreat her from a distance, in case the girl should take offense at his coming near enough to clasp her knees, so he addressed her in honeyed and persuasive language.

"O queen," he said, "I implore your aid—but tell me, are you a goddess or are you a mortal woman? If you are a goddess and dwell in heaven, I can only conjecture that you are Zeus' daughter Artemis, for your face and figure resemble none but hers; if, on the other hand, you are a mortal and live on earth, thrice happy are your father and mother—thrice happy, too, are your brothers and sisters. How proud and delighted they must feel when they see so fair a scion as yourself going out to a dance! Most happy, however, of all will he be whose wedding gifts have been the richest, and who takes you to his own home. I never yet saw anyone so beautiful, neither man nor woman, and am lost in admiration as I behold you. I can only compare you to a young palm tree which I saw when I was at Delos growing near the altar of Apollo—for I was there, too, with much people after me, when I was on that journey which has been the source of all my troubles. Never yet did such a young plant shoot out of the ground as that was, and I admired and wondered at it exactly as I now admire and wonder at yourself. I dare not clasp your knees, but I am in great distress; yesterday made the twentieth day that I had been tossing about upon the sea. The winds and waves have taken me all the way from the Ogygian island, and now fate has flung me upon this coast that I may endure still further suffering; for I do not think that I have yet come to the end of it, but rather that heaven has still much evil in store for me.

"And now, O queen, have pity upon me, for you are the first person I have met, and I know no one else in this country. Show me the way to your town, and let me have anything that you may have brought hither to wrap your clothes in. May heaven grant you in all things your heart's desire—husband, house, and a happy, peaceful home; for there is nothing better in this world than that man and wife should be of one mind in a house. It discomfits their enemies, makes the hearts of their friends glad, and they themselves know more about it than anyone."

To this Nausicaa answered: "Stranger, you appear to be a sensible, well-disposed person. There is no accounting for luck; Zeus gives prosperity to rich and poor just as he chooses, so you must take what he has seen fit to send you, and make the best of it. Now, however, that you have come to this our country, you shall not want for clothes or for anything else that a foreigner in distress may reasonably look for. I will show you the way to the town, and will tell you the name of our people. We are called Phaeacians, and I am daughter to Alcinous, in whom the whole power of the state is vested."

Then she called her maids and said: "Stay where you are, you girls. Can you not see a man without running away from him? Do you take him for a robber or a murderer? Neither he nor anyone else can come here to do us Phaeacians any harm, for we are dear to the gods, and live apart on a land's end that juts into the sounding sea, and have nothing to do with any other people. This is only some poor man who has lost his way, and we must be kind to him, for strangers and foreigners in distress are under Zeus' protection, and will take what they can get and be thankful. So, girls, give the poor fellow something to eat and drink, and wash him in the stream at some place that is sheltered from the wind."

On this the maids left off running away and began calling one another back. They made Odysseus sit down in the shelter as Nausicaa had told them, and brought him a shirt and cloak. They also brought him the little golden cruse of oil, and told him to go and wash in the stream. But Odysseus said, "Young women, please to stand a little on one side that I may wash the brine from my shoulders and anoint myself with oil, for it is long enough since my skin has had a drop of oil upon it. I cannot wash as long as you all keep standing there. I am ashamed to strip before a number of good-looking young women."

Then they stood on one side and went to tell the girl, while Odysseus washed himself in the stream and scrubbed the brine from his back and from his broad shoulders. When he had thoroughly washed himself, and had got the brine out of his hair, he anointed himself with oil, and put on the clothes which the girl had given him. Athene then made him look taller and stronger than before; she also made the hair grow thick on the top of his head, and flow down in curls like hyacinth blossoms. She glorified him about the head and shoulders as a skillful workman who has studied art of all kinds under Hephaestus and Athene enriches a piece of silver plate by gilding it—and his work is full of beauty. Then he went and sat down a little way off upon the beach, looking quite young and handsome, and the girl gazed on him with admiration; then she said to her maids:

"Hush, my dears, for I want to say something. I believe the gods who live in heaven have sent this man to the Phaeacians. When I first saw him I thought him plain, but now his appearance is like that of the gods who dwell in heaven. I should like my future husband to be just such another as he is, if he would only stay here and not want to go away. However, give him something to eat and drink."

They did as they were told, and set food before Odysseus, who ate and drank ravenously, for it was long since he had had food of any kind. Meanwhile, Nausicaa bethought her of another matter. She got the linen folded and placed in the wagon, she then yoked the mules, and, as she took her seat, she called Odysseus:

"Stranger," said she, "rise and let us be going back to the town; I will introduce you at the house of my excellent father, where I can tell you that you will meet all the best people among the Phaeacians. But be sure to do as I bid you, for you seem to be a sensible person. As long as we are going past the fields and farm lands, follow briskly behind the wagon, along with the maids and I will lead the way myself. Presently, however, we shall come to the town, where you will find a high wall running all around it, and a good harbor on either side with a narrow entrance into the city, and the ships will be drawn up by the roadside, for everyone has a place where his own ship can lie. You will see the market place with a temple of Poseidon in the middle of it, and paved with large stones bedded in the earth. Here people deal in ship's gear of all kinds, such as cables and sails, and here, too, are the places where oars are made; for the Phaeacians are not a nation of archers—they know nothing about bows and arrows, but are a seafaring folk, and pride themselves on their masts, oars, and ships, with which they travel far over the sea.

"I am afraid of the gossip and scandal that may be set on foot against me later on; for the people here are very ill-natured, and some low fellow, if he met us, might say, 'Who is this fine-looking stranger that is going about with Nausicaa? Where did she find him? I suppose she is going to marry him. Perhaps he is a vagabond sailor whom she has taken from some foreign vessel, for we have no neighbors; or some god has at last come down from heaven in answer to her prayers, and she is going to live with him all the rest of her life. It would be a good thing if she would take herself off and find a husband somewhere else, for she will not look at one of the many excellent young Phaeacians who are in love with her.' This is the kind of disparaging remark that would be made about me, and I could not complain, for I should myself be scandalized at seeing any other girl do the like, and go about with men in spite of everybody, while her father and mother were still alive, and without having been married in the face of all the world.

"If, therefore, you want my father to give you an escort and to help you home, do as I bid you. You will see a beautiful grove of poplars by the roadside dedicated to Athene; it has a well in it and a meadow all round it. Here my father has a field of rich garden ground, about as far from the town as a man's voice will carry. Sit down there and wait for a while till the rest of us can get into the town and reach my father's house. Then, when you think we must have done this, come into the town and ask the way to the house of my father Alcinous. You will have no difficulty in finding it; any child will point it out to you, for no one else in the whole town has anything like such a fine house as he has. When you have got past the gates and through the outer court, go right across the inner court till you come to my mother. You will find her sitting by the fire and spinning her purple wool by firelight. It is a fine sight to see her as she leans back against one of the bearing-posts with her maids all ranged behind her. Close to her seat stands that of my father, on which he sits and topes like an immortal god. Never mind him, but go up to my mother and lay your hands upon her knees, if you would get home quickly. If you can gain her over, you may hope to see your own country again, no matter how distant it may be."

So saying she lashed the mules with her whip and they left the river. The mules drew well, and their hoofs went up and down upon the road. She was careful not to go too fast for Odysseus and the maids who were following on foot along with the wagon, so she plied her whip with judgment. As the sun was going down they came to the sacred grove of Athene, and there Odysseus sat down and prayed to the mighty daughter of Zeus.

"Hear me," he cried, "daughter of aegis-bearing Zeus, unweariable, hear me now, for you gave no heed to my prayers when Poseidon was wrecking me. Now, therefore, have pity upon me and grant that I may find friends and be hospitably received by the Phaeacians."

Thus did he pray, and Athene heard his prayer, but she would not show herself to him openly, for she was afraid of her uncle Poseidon, who was still furious in his endeavors to prevent Odysseus from getting home.

BOOK VII

Athene guides Odysseus to the splendid palace of King Alcinous and Queen Arete. They welcome him kindly and listen while he explains his arrival on their shores and appearance at the palace. Moved by his tale, they promise to send him safely back to his home.

THUS, THEN, DID ODYSSEUS WAIT AND PRAY, BUT the girl drove on to the town. When she reached her father's house she drew up at the gateway, and her brothers—comely as the gods—gathered round her, took the mules out of the wagon, and carried the clothes into the house, while she went to her own room, where an old servant, Eurymedusa of Apeira, lit the fire for her. This old woman had been brought by sea from Apeira, and had been chosen as a prize for Alcinous because he was king over the Phaeacians, and the people obeyed him as though he were a god. She had been nurse to Nausicaa, and had now lit the fire for her, and brought her supper for her into her own room.

Presently Odysseus got up to go towards the town, and Athene shed a thick mist all round him to hide him, in case any of the proud Phaeacians who met him should be rude to him or ask him who he was. Then, as he was just entering the town, she came towards him in the likeness of a little girl carrying a pitcher. She stood right in front of him, and Odysseus said:

"My dear, will you be so kind as to show me the house of King Alcinous? I am an unfortunate foreigner in distress, and do not know anyone in your town and country."

Then Athene said: "Yes, father stranger, I will show you the house you want, for Alcinous lives quite close to my own father. I will go before you and show the way, but say not a word as you go, and do not look at any man, or ask him questions; for the people here cannot abide strangers and do not like men who come from some other place. They are a seafaring folk, and sail the seas by the grace of Poseidon in ships that glide along like thought, or as a bird in the air."

On this she led the way, and Odysseus followed in her steps; but not one of the Phaeacians could see him as he passed through the city in the midst of them, for the great goddess Athene in her good will towards him had hidden him in a thick cloud of darkness. He admired their harbors, ships, places of assembly, and the lofty walls of the city, which, with the palisade on top of them, were very striking, and when they reached the king's house Athene said:

"This is the house, father stranger, which you would have me show you. You will find a number of great people sitting at table, but do not be afraid. Go straight in, for the bolder a man is the more likely he is to carry his point, even though he a stranger. First find the queen. Her name is Arete, and she comes of the same family as her husband Alcinous. They both descend originally from Poseidon, who was father to Nausithous by Periboea, a woman of great beauty. Periboea was the youngest daughter of Eurymedon, who at one time reigned over the giants, but he ruined his ill-fated people and lost his own life to boot.

"Poseidon, however, lay with his daughter, and she had a son by him, the great Nausithous, who reigned over the Phaeacians. Nausithous had two sons, Rhexenor and Alcinous,[1] Apollo killed

[1] Polyphemus was also son to Poseidon, see Book IX, p. 116. He was therefore half-brother to Nausithous, half-uncle to King Alcinous, and half-great-uncle to Nausicaa.

the first of them while he was still a bridegroom and without male issue, but he left a daughter Arete, whom Alcinous married, and honors as no other woman is honored of all those that keep house along with their husbands.

"Thus she both was, and still is, respected beyond measure by her children, by Alcinous himself, and by the whole people, who look upon her as a goddess, and greet her whenever she goes about the city. For she is a thoroughly good woman both in head and heart, and when any women are friends of hers, she will help their husbands also to settle their disputes. If you can gain her good will, you may have every hope of seeing your friends again, and getting safely back to your home and country."

Then Athene left Scheria and went away over the sea. She went to Marathon and to the spacious streets of Athens, where she entered the abode of Erechtheus; but Odysseus went on to the house of Alcinous, and he pondered much as he paused a while before reaching the threshold of bronze, for the splendor of the palace was like that of the sun or moon. The walls on either side were of bronze from end to end, and the cornice was of blue enamel. The doors were gold, and hung on pillars of silver that rose from a floor of bronze, while the lintel was silver and the hook of the door was of gold.

On either side there stood gold and silver mastiffs which Hephaestus, with his consummate skill, had fashioned expressly to keep watch over the palace of King Alcinous; so they were immortal and could never grow old. Seats were ranged all along the wall, here and there from one end to the other, with coverings of fine woven work which the women of the house had made. Here the chief persons of the Phaeacians used to sit and eat and drink, for there was abundance at all seasons; and there were golden figures of young men with lighted torches in their hands, raised on pedestals, to give light by night to those who were at table. There are fifty maidservants in the house, some of whom are always grinding rich yellow grain at the mill, while others work at the loom, or sit and spin, and their shuttles go backwards and forwards like the fluttering of aspen leaves, while the linen is so closely woven that it will turn oil. As the Phaeacians are the best sailors in the world, so their women excel all others in weaving, for Athene has taught them all manner of useful arts, and they are very intelligent.

Outside the gate of the outer court there is a large garden of about four acres with a wall all round it. It is full of beautiful trees —pears, pomegranates, and the most delicious apples. There are luscious figs also, and olives in full growth. The fruits never rot nor fail all the year round, neither winter nor summer, for the air is so soft that a new crop ripens before the old has dropped. Pear grows on pear, apple on apple, and fig on fig, and so also with the grapes, for there is an excellent vineyard. On the level ground of a part of this, the grapes are being made into raisins; in another part they are being gathered; some are being trodden in the wine tubs, others further on have shed their blossom and are beginning to show fruit, others again are just changing color. In the further part of the ground there are beautifully arranged beds of flowers that are in bloom all the year round. Two streams go through it, the one turned in ducts throughout the whole garden, while the other is carried under the ground of the outer court to the house itself, and the townspeople draw water from it. Such, then, were the splendors with which the gods had endowed the house of King Alcinous.

So here Odysseus stood for a while and looked about him, but when he had looked long enough he crossed the threshold and went within the precincts of the house. There he found all the chief people among the Phaeacians making their drink offerings to Hermes, which they always did the last thing before going away for the night. He went straight through the court, still hidden by the cloak of darkness in which Athene had enveloped him, till he reached Arete and King Alcinous; then he laid his hands upon the knees of the queen, and at that moment the miraculous darkness fell away from him and he became visible. Everyone was speechless with surprise at seeing a man there, but Odysseus began at once with his petition.

"Queen Arete," he exclaimed, "daughter of great Phexenor, in

my distress I humbly pray you, as also your husband and these your
guests (whom may heaven prosper with long life and happiness, and
may they leave their possessions to their children, and all the honors
conferred upon them by the state) to help me home to my own
country as soon as possible; for I have been long in trouble and
away from my friends."

Then he sat down on the hearth among the ashes[2] and they all
held their peace, till presently the old hero Echeneus, who was an
excellent speaker and an elder among the Phaeacians, plainly and
in all honesty addressed them thus:

"Alcinous," said he, "it is not creditable to you that a stranger
should be seen sitting among the ashes of your hearth; everyone is
waiting to hear what you are about to say. Tell him, then, to rise
and take a seat on a stool inlaid with silver, and bid your servants
mix some wine and water that we may make a drink offering to
Zeus, the lord of thunder, who takes all well-disposed suppliants
under his protection; and let the housekeeper give him some supper, of whatever there may be in the house."

When Alcinous heard this, he took Odysseus by the hand, raised
him from the hearth, and bade him take the seat of Laodamas, who
had been sitting beside him, and was his favorite son. A maidservant then brought him water in a beautiful golden ewer and poured
it into a silver basin for him to wash his hands, and she drew a
clean table beside him; an upper servant brought him bread and
offered him many good things of what there was in the house, and
Odysseus ate and drank. Then Alcinous said to one of the servants,
"Pontonous, mix a cup of wine and hand it round that we may
drink offerings to Zeus, the lord of thunder, who is the protector
of all well-disposed suppliants."

Pontonous then mixed wine and water, and handed it round
after giving every man his drink offering. When they had made
their offerings, and had drunk each as much as he was minded,
Alcinous said:

"Aldermen and town councilors of the Phaeacians, hear my

[2] The humble place, where any Greek suppliant for mercy and help would sit.

words. You have had your supper, so now go home to bed. Tomorrow morning I shall invite a still larger number of aldermen, and will give a sacrificial banquet in honor of our guest. We can then discuss the question of his escort, and consider how we may at once send him back rejoicing to his own country without trouble or inconvenience to himself, no matter how distant it may be. We must see that he comes to no harm while on his homeward journey, but when he is once at home he will have to take the luck he was born with, for better or worse, like other people. It is possible, however, that the stranger is one of the immortals who has come down from heaven to visit us; but in this case the gods are departing from their usual practice, for hitherto they have made themselves perfectly clear to us when we have been offering them hecatombs. They come and sit at our feasts just like one of our selves, and if any solitary wayfarer happens to stumble upon some one or other of them, they affect no concealment, for we are as near of kin to the gods as the Cyclopes and the savage giants are."

Then Odysseus said: "Pray, Alcinous, do not take any such notion into your head. I have nothing of the immortal about me, neither in body nor mind, and most resemble those among you who are the most afflicted. Indeed, were I to tell you all that heaven has seen fit to lay upon me, you would say that I was still worse off than they are. Nevertheless, let me sup in spite of sorrow, for an empty stomach is a very importunate thing, and thrusts itself on a man's notice no matter how dire is his distress. I am in great trouble, yet it insists that I shall eat and drink, bids me lay aside all memory of my sorrows and dwell only on the due replenishing of itself. As for yourselves, do as you propose, and at break of day set about helping me to get home. I shall be content to die if I may first once more behold my property, my bondsmen, and all the greatness of my house."

Thus did he speak. Everyone approved his saying, and agreed that he should have his escort, inasmuch as he had spoken reasonably. Then when they had made their drink offerings, and had drunk each as much as he was minded, they went home to bed, every man in his own abode, leaving Odysseus in the cloister with Arete and Alcinous while the servants were taking the things away after supper. Arete was the first to speak, for she recognized the shirt, cloak, and good clothes that Odysseus was wearing, as the work of herself and of her maids; so she said, "Stranger, before we go any further, there is a question I should like to ask you. Who, and whence are you, and who gave you those clothes? Did you not say you had come here from beyond the sea?"

And Odysseus answered: "It would be a long story madam, were I to relate in full the tale of my misfortunes, for the hand of heaven has been laid heavy upon me; but as regards your question, there is an island far away in the sea which is called the Ogygian. Here dwells the cunning and powerful goddess Calypso, daughter of Atlas. She lives by herself far from all neighbors, human or divine. Fortune, however, brought me to her hearth all desolate and alone, for Zeus struck my ship with his thunderbolts, and broke it up in mid-ocean. My brave comrades were drowned, every man of them, but I stuck to the keel and was carried hither and thither for the space of nine days, till at last during the darkness of the tenth night the gods brought me to the Ogygian island where the great goddess Calypso lives. She took me in and treated me with the utmost kindness; indeed she wanted to make me immortal that I might never grow old, but she could not persuade me to let her do so.

"I stayed with Calypso seven years straight on end, and watered the good clothes she gave me with my tears during the whole time; but at last when the eighth year came round she bade me depart of her own free will, either because Zeus had told her she must, or because she had changed her mind. She sent me from her island on a raft, which she provisioned with abundance of bread and wine. Moreover she gave me good stout clothing, and sent me a wind that blew both warm and fair. Days seven and ten did I sail over the sea, and on the eighteenth I caught sight of the first outlines of the mountains upon your coast—and glad indeed was I to set eyes upon them. Nevertheless, there was still much trouble in store for me, for at this point Poseidon would let me go no further, and raised a great storm against me. The sea was so terribly high that I could no longer keep to my raft, which went to pieces under the fury of the gale, and I had to swim for it, till wind and current brought me to your shores.

"There I tried to land, but could not, for it was a bad place and the waves dashed me against the rocks, so I again took to the sea and swam on till I came to a river that seemed the most likely landing place, for there were no rocks and it was sheltered from the wind. Here, then, I got out of the water and gathered my senses together again. Night was coming on, so I left the river and went into a thicket, where I covered myself all over with leaves, and presently heaven sent me off into a very deep sleep. Sick and sorry as I was I slept among the leaves all night, and through the next day till afternoon, when I woke as the sun was westering, and saw your daughter's maidservants playing upon the beach, and your daughter among them looking like a goddess. I besought her aid, and she proved to be of an excellent disposition, much more so than could be expected from so young a person—for young people are apt to be thoughtless. She gave me plenty of bread and wine, and when she had me washed in the river she also gave me the clothes in which you see me. Now, therefore, though it has pained me to do so, I have told you the whole truth."

Then Alcinous said, "Stranger, it was very wrong of my daughter not to bring you on at once to my house along with the maids, seeing that she was the first person whose aid you asked."

"Pray do not scold her," replied Odysseus; "she is not to blame. She did tell me to follow along with the maids, but I was ashamed and afraid, for I thought you might perhaps be displeased if you saw me. Every human being is sometimes a little suspicious and irritable."

"Stranger," replied Alcinous, "I am not the kind of man to get angry about nothing; it is always better to be reasonable. But by Father Zeus, Athene, and Apollo, now that I see what kind of person you are, and how much you think as I do, I wish you would stay here, marry my daughter, and become my son-in-law. If you will stay I will give you a house and an estate; but no one (heaven forbid) shall keep you here against your own wish, and that you may be sure of this, I will attend tomorrow to the matter of your escort. You can sleep during the whole voyage if you like, and the men shall sail you over smooth waters either to your own home, or wherever you please, even though it be a long way further off than Euboea, which those of my people who saw it, when they took yellow-haired Rhadamanthus to see Tityus the son of Gaia, tell me is the furthest of any place. And yet they did the whole voyage in a single day without distressing themselves, and came back again afterwards. You will thus see how much my ships excel all others, and what magnificent oarsmen my sailors are."

Then was Odysseus glad and prayed aloud, saying, "Father Zeus, grant that Alcinous may do all as he has said, for so he will win an imperishable name among mankind, and at the same time I shall return to my own country."

Thus did they converse. Then Arete told her maids to set a bed in the room that was in the gatehouse, and make it with good red rugs, and to spread coverlets on the top of them with woolen cloaks for Odysseus to wear. The maids thereon went out with torches in their hands, and when they had made the bed they came up to Odysseus and said, "Rise, sir stranger, and come with us for your bed is ready," and glad indeed was he to go to his rest.

So Odysseus slept in a bed placed in a room over the echoing gateway; but Alcinous lay in the inner part of the house, with the queen his wife by his side.

BOOK VIII

The next day King Alcinous orders a ship made ready for Odysseus and gives a magnificent banquet to the Phaeacians. The blind bard Demodocus sings, and afterward there are games of prowess. Odysseus, challenged to take part, excels in disc-throwing. The Phaeacians dance, and the chiefs bestow gifts on Odysseus. Demodocus sings of the Trojan War, Odysseus weeps, and the king begs him to declare who he is.

NOW WHEN THE CHILD OF MORNING, ROSY-fingered Dawn, appeared, Alcinous and Odysseus both rose, and Alcinous led the way to the Phaeacian place of assembly, which was near the ships. When they got there they sat down side by side on a seat of polished stone, while Athene took the form of one of Alcinous' servants, and went round the town in order to help Odysseus to get home. She went up to the citizens, man by man, and said: "Aldermen and town councilors of the Phaeacians, come to the assembly all of you and listen to the stranger who has just come off a long voyage to the house of King Alcinous. He looks like an immortal god."

With these words she made them all want to come, and they flocked to the assembly till seats and standing room were alike crowded. Everyone was struck with the appearance of Odysseus, for Athene had beautified him about the head and shoulders, making him look taller and stouter than he really was, that he might impress the Phaeacians favorably as being a very remarkable man, and might come off well in the many trials of skill to which they would challenge him. Then, when they were got together, Alcinous spoke:

"Hear me," said he, "aldermen and town councilors of the Phaeacians, that I may speak even as I am minded. This stranger, whoever he may be, has found his way to my house from somewhere or other either east or west. He wants an escort and wishes to have the matter settled. Let us then get one ready for him, as we have done for others before him. Indeed, no one who ever yet came to my house has been able to complain of me for not speeding him on his way soon enough. Let us draw a ship into the sea—one that has never yet made a voyage—and man her with two and fifty of our smartest young sailors. Then when you have made fast your oars each by his own seat, leave the ship and come to my house to prepare a feast.[1] I will supply you with everything. I am giving these instructions to the young men who will form the crew. As regards you aldermen and town councilors, you will join me in entertaining our guest in the cloisters. I can take no excuses, and we will have Demodocus to sing to us; for there is no bard like him, whatever he may choose to sing about."

Alcinous then led the way, and the others followed after, while a servant went to fetch Demodocus. The fifty-two picked oarsmen went to the seashore as they had been told, and when they got there they drew the ship into the water, got her mast and sails inside her, bound the oars to the thole-pins with twisted thongs of leather, all in due course, and spread the white sails aloft. They moored the vessel a little way out from land, and then came on shore and went to the house of King Alcinous. The outhouses, yards, and all the precincts were filled with crowds of men in great multitudes both

---

[1] There were two classes—the lower who were given provisions which they had to cook for themselves in the yards and outer precincts, where they would also eat— and the upper who would eat in the cloisters of the inner court, and have their cooking done for them. (B.)

old and young, and Alcinous killed them a dozen sheep, eight full-grown pigs, and two oxen. These were skinned and dressed so as to provide a magnificent banquet.

A servant presently led in the famous bard Demodocus, whom the muse had dearly loved, but to whom she had given both good and evil, for though she had endowed him with a divine gift of song, she had robbed him of his eyesight. Pontonous set a seat for him among the guests, leaning it up against a bearing-post. He hung the lyre for him on a peg over his head, and showed him where he was to feel for it with his hands. He also set a fair table with a basket of victuals by his side, and a cup of wine from which he might drink whenever he was so disposed.

The company then laid their hands upon the good things that were before them, but as soon as they had had enough to eat and drink, the muse inspired Demodocus to sing the feats of heroes, and more especially a matter that was then in the mouths of all men, to wit, the quarrel between Odysseus and Achilles, and the fierce words that they heaped on one another as they sat together at a banquet.[2] But Agamemnon was glad when he heard his chieftains quarreling with one another, for Apollo had foretold him this at Pytho when he crossed the stone floor to consult the oracle. Here was the beginning of the evil that by the will of Zeus fell both upon Danaans and Trojans.

Thus sang the bard, but Odysseus drew his purple mantle over his head and covered his face, for he was ashamed to let the Phaeacians see that he was weeping. When the bard left off singing, he wiped the tears from his eyes, uncovered his face, and, taking his cup, made a drink offering to the gods; but when the Phaeacians pressed Demodocus to sing further, for they delighted in his lays, then Odysseus again drew his mantle over his head and wept bitterly. No one noticed his distress except Alcinous, who was sitting near him, and heard the heavy sighs that he was heaving. So he at once said, "Aldermen and town councilors of the Phaeacians, we have had enough now, both of the feast and of the minstrelsy that

[2] No account of this quarrel by any Greek poet has come down to us.

is its due accompaniment. Let us proceed therefore to the athletic sports, so that our guest on his return home may be able to tell his friends how much we surpass all other nations as boxers, wrestlers, jumpers, and runners."

With these words he led the way, and the others followed after. A servant hung Demodocus' lyre on its peg for him, led him out of the cloister, and set him on the same way as that along which all the chief men of the Phaeacians were going to see the sports; a crowd of several thousands of people followed them, and there were many excellent competitors for all the prizes. Acroneos, Ocyalus, Elatreus, Nauteus, Prymneus, Anchialus, Eretmeus, Ponteus, Proreus, Thoon, Anabesineus, and Amphialus son of Polyneus son of Tecton. There was also Euryalus son of Naubolus, who was like Ares himself, and was the best looking man among the Phaeacians except Laodamas. Three sons of Alcinous—Laodamas, Halios, and Clytoneus—competed also.

The foot races came first. The course was set out for them from the starting post, and they raised a dust upon the plain as they all flew forward at the same moment. Clytoneus came in first by a long way; he left everyone else behind him by the length of the furrow that a couple of mules can plow in a fallow field. They then turned to the painful art of wrestling, and here Euryalus proved to be the best man. Amphialus excelled all the others in jumping, while at throwing the disc there was no one who could approach Elatreus. Alcinous' son Laodamas was the best boxer, and he it was who presently said, when they had all been diverted with the games, "Let us ask the stranger whether he excels in any of these sports. He seems very powerfully built; his thighs, calves, hands, and neck are of prodigious strength, nor is he at all old, but he has suffered much lately, and there is nothing like the sea for making havoc with a man, no matter how strong he is."

"You are quite right, Laodamas," replied Euryalus, "go up to your guest and speak to him about it yourself."

When Laodamas heard this he made his way into the middle of the crowd and said to Odysseus, "I hope, sir, that you will enter yourself for some one or other of our competitions if you are skilled in any of them—and you must have gone in for many a one before now. There is nothing that does anyone so much credit all his life long as the showing himself a proper man with his hands and feet. Have a try therefore at something, and banish all sorrow from your mind. Your return home will not be long delayed, for the ship is already drawn into the water, and the crew is found."

Odysseus answered, "Laodamas, why do you taunt me in this way? My mind is set rather on cares than contests; I have been through infinite trouble, and am come among you now as a suppliant, praying your king and people to further me on my return home."

Then Euryalus reviled him outright and said: "I gather, then, that you are unskilled in any of the many sports that men generally delight in. I suppose you are one of those grasping traders that go about in ships as captains or merchants, and who think of nothing but of their outward freights and homeward cargoes. There does not seem to be much of the athlete about you."

"For shame, sir!" answered Odysseus, fiercely. "You are an insolent fellow—so true is it that the gods do not grace all men alike in speech, person, and understanding. One man may be of weak presence, but heaven has adorned him with such a good conversation that he charms everyone who sees him; his honeyed moderation carries his hearers with him so that he is leader in all assemblies of his fellows, and wherever he goes he is looked up to. Another may be as handsome as a god, but his good looks are not crowned with discretion. This is your case. No god could make a finer looking fellow than you are, but you are a fool. Your ill-judged remarks have made me exceedingly angry, and you are quite mistaken, for I excel in a great many athletic exercises. Indeed, so long as I had youth and strength, I was among the first athletes of the age. Now, however, I am worn out by labor and sorrow, for I have gone through much both on the field of battle and by the waves of the weary sea. Still, in spite of all this I will compete, for your taunts have stung me to the quick."

So he hurried up without even taking his cloak off, and seized a disc, larger, more massive and much heavier than those used by the Phaeacians when disc-throwing among themselves. Then, swinging it back, he threw it from his brawny hand, and it made a humming sound in the air as he did so. The Phaeacians quailed beneath the rushing of its flight as it sped gracefully from his hand, and flew beyond any mark that had been made yet. Athene, in the form of a man, came and marked the place where it had fallen. "A blind man, sir," said she, "could easily tell your mark by groping for it—it is so far ahead of any other. You may make your mind easy about this contest, for no Phaeacian can come near to such a throw as yours."

Odysseus was glad when he found he had a friend among the lookers-on, so he began to speak more pleasantly. "Young men," said he, "come up to that throw if you can, and I will throw another disc as heavy or even heavier. If anyone wants to have a bout with me let him come on, for I am exceedingly angry. I will box, wrestle, or run, I do not care what it is, with any man of you all except Laodamas, but not with him because I am his guest, and one cannot compete with one's own personal friend. At least I do not think it a prudent or a sensible thing for a guest to challenge his host's family at any game, especially when he is in a foreign country. He will cut the ground from under his own feet if he does. But I make no exception as regards anyone else, for I want to have the matter out and know which is the best man.

"I am a good hand at every kind of athletic sport known among mankind. I am an excellent archer. In battle I am always the first to bring a man down with my arrow, no matter how many more are taking aim at him alongside of me. Philoctetes was the only man who could shoot better than I could when the Achaeans were before Troy and in practice. I far excel everyone else in the whole world of those who still eat bread upon the face of the earth, but I should not like to shoot against the mighty dead, such as Heracles, or Eurytus the Oechalian—men who could shoot against the gods themselves. This in fact was how Eurytus came prematurely by his end, for Apollo was angry with him and killed him because he challenged him as an archer. I can throw a dart farther than anyone else can shoot an arrow. Running is the only point in respect of which I am afraid some of the Phaeacians might beat me, for I have been brought down very low at sea; my provisions ran short, and therefore I am still weak."

They all held their peace except King Alcinous, who began: "Sir, we have had much pleasure in hearing all that you have told us, from which I understand that you are willing to show your prowess, as having been displeased with some insolent remarks that have been made to you by one of our athletes, and which could never have been uttered by anyone who knows how to talk with propriety. I hope you will apprehend my meaning, and will explain to anyone of your chief men who may be dining with yourself and your family when you get home, that we have an hereditary aptitude for accomplishments of all kinds. We are not particularly remarkable for our boxing, nor yet as wrestlers, but we are singularly fleet of foot and are excellent sailors. We are extremely fond of good dinners, music, and dancing; we also like frequent changes of linen, warm baths, and good beds. So now, please, some of you who are the best dancers set about dancing, that our guest on his return home may be able to tell his friends how much we surpass all other nations as sailors, runners, dancers, and minstrels. Demodocus has left his lyre at my house, so run some one or other of you and fetch it for him."

On this a servant hurried off to bring the lyre from the king's house, and the nine men who had been chosen as stewards stood forward. It was their business to manage everything connected with the sports, so they made the ground smooth and marked a wide space for the dancers. Presently the servant came back with Demodocus' lyre, and he took his place in the midst of them, whereon the best young dancers in the town began to foot and trip it so nimbly that Odysseus was delighted with the merry twinkling of their feet.

Meanwhile the bard began to sing the loves of Ares and Aphrodite, and how they first began their intrigue in the house of Hephaestus. Ares made Aphrodite many presents, and defiled King

Hephaestus' marriage bed, so the sun, who saw what they were about, told Hephaestus. Hephaestus was very angry when he heard such dreadful news, so he went to his smithy brooding mischief, got his great anvil into its place, and began to forge some chains which none could either unloose or break, so that they might stay there in that place. When he had finished his snare he went into his bedroom and festooned the bed-posts all over with chains like cobwebs; he also let many hang down from the great beam of the ceiling. Not even a god could see them, so fine and subtle were they. As soon as he had spread the chains all over the bed, he made as though he were setting out for the fair state of Lemnos, which of all places in the world was the one he was most fond of. But Ares kept no blind lookout, and as soon as he saw him start, hurried off to his house, burning with love for Aphrodite.

Now Aphrodite was just come in from a visit to her father Zeus, and was about sitting down when Ares came inside the house, and said as he took her hand in his own, "Let us go to the couch of Hephaestus: he is not at home, but is gone off to Lemnos among the Sintians, whose speech is barbarous."

She was nothing loath, so they went to the couch to take their rest, whereon they were caught in the toils which cunning Hephaestus had spread for them, and could neither get up nor stir hand or foot, but found too late that they were in a trap. Then Hephaestus came up to them, for he had turned back before reaching Lemnos, when his scout the sun told him what was going on. He was in a furious passion, and stood in the vestibule making a dreadful noise as he shouted to all the gods.

"Father Zeus," he cried, "and all you other blessed gods who live forever, come here and see the ridiculous and disgraceful sight that I will show you. Zeus' daughter Aphrodite is always dishonoring me because I am lame. She is in love with Ares, who is handsome and clean built, whereas I am a cripple—but my parents are to blame for that, not I; they ought never to have begotten me. Come and see the pair together asleep on my bed. It makes me furious to look at them. They are very fond of one another, but I do not think they will lie there longer than they can help, nor do I think that they will sleep much. There, however, they shall stay till her father has repaid me the sum I gave him for his baggage of a daughter, who is fair but not honest."

On this the gods gathered to the house of Hephaestus. Earthencircling Poseidon came, and Hermes, the bringer of luck, and King Apollo, but the goddesses stayed at home all of them for shame. Then the givers of all good things stood in the doorway, and the blessed gods roared with inextinguishable laughter, as they saw how cunning Hephaestus had been, whereon one would turn towards his neighbor saying:

"Ill deeds do not prosper, and the weak confound the strong. See how limping Hephaestus, lame as he is, has caught Ares, who is the fleetest god in heaven; and now Ares will be cast in heavy damages."

Thus did they converse, but King Apollo said to Hermes, "Messenger Hermes, giver of good things, you would not care how strong the chains were, would you, if you could sleep with Aphrodite?"

"King Apollo," answered Hermes, "I only wish I might get the chance, though there were three times as many chains—and you might look on, all of you, gods and goddesses, but I would sleep with her if I could."

The immortal gods burst out laughing as they heard him, but Poseidon took it all seriously, and kept on imploring Hephaestus to set Ares free again. "Let him go," he cried, "and I will undertake, as you require, that he shall pay you all the damages that are held reasonable among the immortal gods."

"Do not," replied Hephaestus, "ask me to do this; a bad man's bond is bad security. What remedy could I enforce against you if Ares should go away and leave his debts behind him along with his chains?"

"Hephaestus," said Poseidon, "if Ares goes away without paying his damages, I will pay you myself." So Hephaestus answered, "In this case I cannot and must not refuse you."

Thereon he loosed the bonds that bound them, and as soon as they were free they scampered off, Ares to Thrace and laughter-loving Aphrodite to Cyprus and to Paphos, where is her grove and her altar fragrant with burnt offerings. Here the Graces bathed her, and anointed her with oil of ambrosia such as the immortal gods make use of, and they clothed her in raiment of the most enchanting beauty.

Thus sang the bard, and both Odysseus and the seafaring Phaeacians were charmed as they heard him.

Then Alcinous told Laodamas and Halius to dance alone, for there was no one to compete with them. So they took a red ball which Polybus had made for them, and one of them bent himself backwards and threw it up towards the clouds, while the other jumped from off the ground and caught it with ease before it came down again. When they had done throwing the ball straight up into the air they began to dance, and at the same time kept on throwing it backwards and forwards to one another, while all the young men in the ring applauded and made a great stamping with their feet. Then Odysseus said:

"King Alcinous, you said your people were the nimblest dancers in the world, and indeed they have proved themselves to be so. I was astonished as I saw them."

The king was delighted at this, and exclaimed to the Phaeacians: "Aldermen and town councilors, our guest seems to be a person of singular judgment. Let us give him such proof of our hospitality as he may reasonably expect. There are twelve chief men among you, and counting myself there are thirteen; contribute, each of you, a clean cloak, a shirt, and a talent of fine gold; let us give him all this in a lump down at once, so that when he gets his supper he may do so with a light heart. As for Euryalus, he will have to make a formal apology and a present too, for he has been rude."

Thus did he speak. The others all of them applauded his saying, and sent their servants to fetch the presents. Then Euryalus said: "King Alcinous, I will give the stranger all the satisfaction you require. He shall have my sword, which is of bronze, all but the hilt, which is of silver. I will also give him the scabbard of newly sawn ivory into which it fits. It will be worth a great deal to him."

As he spoke he placed the sword in the hands of Odysseus and said: "Good luck to you, father stranger. If anything has been said amiss, may the winds blow it away with them, and may heaven grant you a safe return, for I understand you have been long away from home and have gone through much hardship."

To which Odysseus answered: "Good luck to you too, my friend, and may the gods grant you every happiness. I hope you will not miss the sword you have given me along with your apology."

With these words he girded the sword about his shoulders and towards sundown the presents began to make their appearance, as the servants of the donors kept bringing them to the house of King Alcinous; here his sons received them, and placed them under their mother's charge. Then Alcinous led the way to the house and bade his guests take their seats.

"Wife," said he, turning to Queen Arete, "go, fetch the best chest we have, and put a clean cloak and shirt in it. Also, set a copper on the fire and heat some water; our guest will take a warm bath. See also to the careful packing of the presents that the noble Phaeacians have made him; he will thus better enjoy both his supper and the singing that will follow. I shall myself give him this golden goblet, which is of exquisite workmanship, that he may be reminded of me for the rest of his life whenever he makes a drink offering to Zeus, or to any of the gods."

Then Arete told her maids to set a large tripod upon the fire as fast as they could, whereon they set a tripod full of bath water on to a clear fire. They threw on sticks to make it blaze, and the water became hot as the flame played about the belly of the tripod. Meanwhile Arete brought a magnificent chest from her own room, and inside it she packed all the beautiful presents of gold and raiment which the Phaeacians had brought. Lastly she added a cloak and a good shirt from Alcinous, and said to Odysseus:

"See to the lid yourself, and have the whole bound round at once, for fear anyone should rob you by the way when you are asleep in your ship."

When Odysseus heard this he put the lid on the chest and made it fast with a bond that Circe had taught him. He had hardly done so before an upper servant told him to come to the bath and wash himself. He was very glad of a warm bath, for he had had no one to wait upon him ever since he left the house of Calypso, who as long as he remained with her had taken as good care of him as though he had been a god. When the servants had done washing and anointing him with oil and had given him a clean cloak and shirt, he left the bathroom and joined the guests who were sitting over their wine. Lovely Nausicaa stood by one of the bearing-posts supporting the roof of the cloister, and admired him as she saw him pass. "Farewell stranger," said she, "do not forget me when you are safe at home again, for it is to me first that you owe a ransom for having saved your life."

And Odysseus said, "Nausicaa, daughter of great Alcinous, may Zeus the mighty husband of Hera grant that I may reach my home; so shall I bless you as my guardian angel all my days, for it was you who saved me."

When he had said this, he seated himself beside Alcinous. Supper was then served, and the wine was mixed for drinking. A servant led in the favorite bard Demodocus, and set him in the midst of the company, near one of the bearing-posts supporting the cloister, that he might lean against it. Then Odysseus cut off a piece of roast pork with plenty of fat (for there was abundance left on the joint) and said to a servant, "Take this piece of pork over to Demodocus and tell him to eat it; for all the pain his lays may cause me I will salute him none the less; bards are honored and respected throughout the world, for the muse teaches them their songs and loves them."

The servant carried the pork in his fingers over to Demodocus, who took it and was very much pleased. They then laid their hands on the good things that were before them, and as soon as they had had enough to eat and drink, Odysseus said to Demodocus: "Demodocus, there is no one in the world whom I admire more than I do you. You must have studied under the Muse, Zeus' daughter, and under Apollo, so accurately do you sing the return of the

Achaeans with all their sufferings and adventures. If you were not there yourself, you must have heard it all from someone who was. Now, however, change your song and tell us of the wooden horse which Epeus made with the assistance of Athene, and which Odysseus got by stratagem into the fort of Troy after freighting it with the men who afterwards sacked the city. If you will sing this tale aright, I will tell all the world how magnificently heaven has endowed you."

The bard inspired of heaven took up the story at the point where some of the Argives set fire to their tents and sailed away while others, hidden within the horse, were waiting with Odysseus in the Trojan place of assembly. For the Trojans themselves had drawn the horse into their fortress, and it stood there while they sat in council round it, and were in three minds as to what they should do. Some were for breaking it up then and there; others would have it dragged to the top of the rock on which the fortress stood, and then thrown down the precipice; while yet others were for letting it remain as an offering and propitiation for the gods. And this was how they settled it in the end, for the city was doomed when it took in that horse, within which were all the bravest of the Argives waiting to bring death and destruction on the Trojans. Anon he sang how the sons of the Achaeans issued from the horse, and sacked the town, breaking out from their ambuscade. He sang how they overran the city hither and thither and ravaged it, and how Odysseus went raging like Ares along with Menelaus to the house of Deiphobus. It was there that the fight raged most furiously, nevertheless by Athene's help he was victorious.

All this he told, but Odysseus was overcome as he heard him, and his cheeks were wet with tears. He wept as a woman weeps when she throws herself on the body of her husband who has fallen before his own city and people, fighting bravely in defense of his home and children. She screams aloud and flings her arms about him as he lies gasping for breath and dying, but her enemies beat her from behind about the back and shoulders, and carry her off into slavery, to a life of labor and sorrow, and the beauty fades from her cheeks.

Even so piteously did Odysseus weep, but none of those present perceived his tears except Alcinous, who was sitting near him, and could hear the sobs and sighs that he was heaving. The king, therefore, at once rose and said:

"Aldermen and town councilors of the Phaeacians, let Demodocus cease his song, for there are those present who do not seem to like it. From the moment that we had done supper and Demodocus began to sing, our guest has been all the time groaning and lamenting. He is evidently in great trouble, so let the bard leave off, that we may all enjoy ourselves, hosts and guests alike. This will be much more as it should be, for all these festivities, with the escort and the presents that we are making with so much good will, are wholly in his honor, and anyone with even a moderate amount of right feeling knows that he ought to treat a guest and a suppliant as though he were his own brother.

"Therefore, sir, do you on your part affect no more concealment or reserve in the matter about which I shall ask you; it will be more polite in you to give me a plain answer. Tell me the name by which your father and mother over yonder used to call you, and by which you were known among your neighbors and fellow citizens. There is no one, either rich or poor, who is absolutely without any name whatever, for people's fathers and mothers give them names as soon as they are born. Tell me also your country, nation, and city, that our ships may shape their purpose accordingly and take you there. For the Phaeacians have no pilots; their vessels have no rudders as those of other nations have, but the ships themselves understand what it is that we are thinking about and want; they know all the cities and countries in the whole world, and can traverse the sea just as well even when it is covered with mist and clouds, so that there is no danger of being wrecked or coming to any harm. Still I do remember hearing my father say that Poseidon was angry with us for being too easygoing in the matter of giving people escorts. He said that one of these days he should wreck a ship of ours as it was returning from having escorted someone,[3] and bury our city under

---

[3] The reader will find this threat fulfilled in Book XIII.

a high mountain. This is what my father used to say, but whether the god will carry out his threat or no is a matter which he will decide for himself.

"And now, tell me and tell me true. Where have you been wandering, and in what countries have you traveled? Tell us of the peoples themselves, and of their cities—who were hostile, savage, and uncivilized, and who, on the other hand, hospitable and humane. Tell us also why you are made so unhappy on hearing about the return of the Argive Danaans from Troy. The gods arranged all this, and sent them their misfortunes in order that future generations might have something to sing about. Did you lose some brave kinsman of your wife's when you were before Troy—a son-in-law or father-in-law, which are the nearest relations a man has outside his own flesh and blood? Or was it some brave and kindly-natured comrade—for a good friend is as dear to a man as his own brother?"

BOOK IX

*Odysseus now tells his name and begins the long chronicle
of his adventures since leaving Troy. With twelve ships he
sailed first to Ismarus, where he sacked a city. Thence he
was driven by tempests to the far-off land of the Lotus-eaters.
Setting sail again, he reached the land of the Cyclopes.
Trapped in the cave of the monster Polyphemus, Odysseus
and six of his men escaped through a clever stratagem, but
six others were killed.*

AND ODYSSEUS ANSWERED, "KING ALCINOUS, IT
is a good thing to hear a bard with such a divine voice as
this man has. There is nothing better or more delightful
than when a whole people make merry together, with the guests
sitting orderly to listen, while the table is loaded with bread and
meats, and the cup-bearer draws wine and fills his cup for every
man. This is indeed as fair a sight as a man can see. Now, however,
since you are inclined to ask the story of my sorrows, and rekindle
my own sad memories in respect of them, I do not know how to
begin, nor yet how to continue and conclude my tale, for the hand
of heaven has been laid heavily upon me.

"Firstly, then, I will tell you my name that you too may know it, and one day, if I outlive this time of sorrow, may become my guests though I live so far away from all of you. I am Odysseus son of Laertes, renowned among mankind for all manner of subtlety, so that my fame ascends to heaven. I live in Ithaca, where there is a high mountain called Neritum, covered with forests; and not far from it there is a group of islands very near to one another—Dulichium, Same, and the wooded island of Zacynthus. It lies squat on the horizon, all highest up in the sea towards the sunset, while the others lie away from it towards dawn. It is a rugged island, but it breeds brave men, and my eyes know none that they better love to look upon. The goddess Calypso kept me with her in her cave, and wanted me to marry her, as did also the cunning Aeaean goddess Circe; but they could neither of them persuade me, for there is nothing dearer to a man than his own country and his parents, and however splendid a home he may have in a foreign country, if it be far from father or mother, he does not care about it. Now, however, I will tell you of the many hazardous adventures which by Zeus' will I met with on my return from Troy.

"When I had set sail thence the wind took me first to Ismarus, which is the city of the Cicones. There I sacked the town and put the people to the sword. We took their wives and also much booty, which we divided equitably amongst us, so that none might have reason to complain. I then said that we had better make off at once, but my men very foolishly would not obey me, so they stayed there drinking much wine and killing great numbers of sheep and oxen on the seashore. Meanwhile the Cicones cried out for help to other Cicones who lived inland. These were more in number, and stronger, and they were more skilled in the art of war, for they could fight, either from chariots or on foot as the occasion served. In the morning, therefore, they came as thick as leaves and bloom in summer, and the hand of heaven was against us, so that we were hard pressed. They set the battle in array near the ships, and the hosts aimed their bronze-shod spears at one another. So long as the day waxed and it was still morning, we held our own against them, though they were more in number than we; but as the sun went down, towards the time when men loose their oxen, the Cicones got the better of us, and we lost half a dozen men from every ship we had; so we got away with those that were left.

"Thence we sailed onward with sorrow in our hearts, but glad to have escaped death though we had lost our comrades, nor did we leave till we had thrice invoked each one of the poor fellows who had perished by the hands of the Cicones. Then Zeus raised the north wind against us till it blew a hurricane, so that land and sky were hidden in thick clouds, and night sprang forth out of the heavens. We let the ships run before the gale, but the force of the wind tore our sails to tatters, so we took them down for fear of ship-wreck, and rowed our hardest towards the land. There we lay two days and two nights suffering much alike from toil and distress of mind, but on the morning of the third day we again raised our masts, set sail, and took our places, letting the wind and steersmen direct our ship. I should have got home at that time unharmed had not the north wind and the currents been against me as I was doubling Cape Malea, and set me off my course hard by the island of Cythera.

"I was driven thence by foul winds for a space of nine days upon the sea, but on the tenth day we reached the land of the Lotus-eaters, who live on a food that comes from a kind of flower. Here we landed to take in fresh water, and our crews got their midday meal on the shore near the ships. When they had eaten and drunk, I sent two of my company to see what manner of men the people of the place might be, and they had a third man under them. They started at once and went about among the Lotus-eaters, who did them no hurt, but gave them to eat of the lotus, which was so delicious that those who ate of it left off caring about home, and did not even want to go back and say what had happened to them, but were for staying and munching lotus with the Lotus-eaters without thinking further of their return. Nevertheless, though they wept bitterly I forced them back to the ships and made them fast under the benches. Then I told the rest to go on board at once, lest any of them should taste of the lotus and leave off wanting to get home, so they took their places and smote the gray sea with their oars.

"We sailed hence, always in much distress, till we came to the land of the lawless and inhuman Cyclopes. Now the Cyclopes neither plant nor plow, but trust in providence, and live on such wheat, barley, and grapes as grow wild without any kind of tillage, and their wild grapes yield them wine as the sun and the rain may grow them. They have no laws or assemblies of the people, but live in caves on the tops of high mountains; each is lord and master in his family, and they take no account of their neighbors.

"Now off their harbor there lies a wooded and fertile island not quite close to the land of the Cyclopes, but still not far. It is overrun with wild goats, that breed there in great numbers and are never disturbed by foot of man. For sportsmen—who as a rule will suffer so much hardship in forest or among mountain precipices—do not go there, nor yet again is it ever plowed or fed down, but it lies a wilderness untilled and unsown from year to year, and has no living thing upon it but only goats. For the Cyclopes have no ships, nor yet shipwrights who could make ships for them. They cannot therefore go from city to city, or sail over the sea to one another's country as people who have ships can do. If they had had these they would have colonized the island, for it is a very good one, and would yield everything in due season. There are meadows that in some places come right down to the seashore, well watered and full of luscious grass; grapes would do there excellently; there is level land for plowing, and it would always yield heavily at harvest time, for the soil is deep. There is a good harbor where no cables are wanted, nor yet anchors, nor need a ship be moored, but all one has to do is to beach one's vessel and stay there till the wind becomes fair for putting out to sea again. At the head of the harbor there is a spring of clear water coming out of a cave, and there are poplars growing all round it.

"Here we entered, but so dark was the night that some god must have brought us in, for there was nothing whatever to be seen. A thick mist hung all round our ships; the moon was hidden behind a mass of clouds so that no one could have seen the island if he had looked for it, nor were there any breakers to tell us we were close in shore before we found ourselves upon the land itself. When, however, we had beached the ships, we took down the sails, went ashore and camped upon the beach till daybreak.

"When the child of morning, rosy-fingered Dawn, appeared, we admired the island and wandered all over it, while the nymphs, Zeus' daughters, roused the wild goats that we might get some meat for our dinner. On this we fetched our spears and bows and arrows from the ships, and dividing ourselves into three bands began to shoot the goats. Heaven sent us excellent sport; I had twelve ships with me, and each ship got nine goats, while my own ship had ten; thus through the livelong day to the going down of the sun we ate and drank our fill, and we had plenty of wine left, for each one of us had taken many jars full when we sacked the city of the Cicones, and this had not yet run out. While we were feasting we kept turning our eyes towards the land of the Cyclopes, which was hard by, and saw the smoke of their stubble fires. We could almost fancy we heard their voices and the bleating of their sheep and goats, but when the sun went down and it came on dark, we camped down upon the beach, and next morning I called a council.

" 'Stay here, my brave fellows,' said I, 'all the rest of you, while I go with my ship and explore these people myself. I want to see if they are uncivilized savages, or a hospitable and humane race.'

"I went on board, bidding my men to do so also and loose the hawsers; so they took their places and smote the gray sea with their oars. When we got to the land, which was not far, there, on the face of a cliff near the sea, we saw a great cave overhung with laurels. It was a station for a great many sheep and goats, and outside there was a large yard, with a high wall round it made of stones built into the ground and of trees both pine and oak. This was the abode of a huge monster who was then away from home shepherding his flocks. He would have nothing to do with other people, but led the life of an outlaw. He was a horrid creature, not like a human being at all, but resembling rather some crag that stands out boldly against the sky on the top of a high mountain.

"I told my men to draw the ship ashore, and stay where they were, all but the twelve best among them, who were to go along with myself. I also took a goatskin of sweet black wine which had been given me by Maron son of Euanthes, who was priest of Apollo the patron god of Ismarus, and lived within the wooded precincts of the temple. When we were sacking the city we respected him, and spared his life, as also his wife and child; so he made me some presents of great value—seven talents of fine gold, and a bowl of silver, with twelve jars of sweet wine, unblended, and of the most exquisite flavor. Not a man or maid in the house knew about it, but only himself, his wife, and one housekeeper. When he drank it he mixed twenty parts of water to one of wine, and yet the fragrance from the mixing-bowl was so exquisite that it was impossible to refrain from drinking. I filled a large skin with this wine, and took a wallet full of provisions with me, for my mind misgave me that I might have to deal with some savage who would be of great strength, and would respect neither right nor law.

"We soon reached his cave, but he was out shepherding, so we went inside and took stock of all that we could see. His cheese-racks were loaded with cheeses, and he had more lambs and kids than his pens could hold. They were kept in separate flocks; first there were the hoggets, then the oldest of the younger lambs, and lastly the very young ones, all kept apart from one another. As for his dairy, all the vessels, bowls, and milk pails into which he milked, were swimming with whey. When they saw all this, my men begged me to let them first steal some cheeses, and make off with them to the ship; they would then return, drive down the lambs and kids, put them on board and sail away with them. It would have been indeed better if we had done so, but I would not listen to them, for I wanted to see the owner himself, in the hope that he might give me a present. When, however, we saw him my poor men found him ill to deal with.

"We lit a fire, offered some of the cheeses in sacrifice, ate others of them, and then sat waiting till the Cyclops should come in with his sheep. When he came, he brought in with him a huge load of dry firewood to light the fire for his supper, and this he flung with such a noise on to the floor of his cave that we hid ourselves for fear at the far end of the cavern. Meanwhile he drove all the ewes inside, as well as the she-goats that he was going to milk, leaving the males, both rams and he-goats, outside in the yards. Then he rolled a huge stone to the mouth of the cave—so huge that two and twenty strong four-wheeled wagons would not be enough to draw it from its place against the doorway. When he had so done he sat down and milked his ewes and goats, all in due course, and then let each of them have her own young. He curdled half the milk and set it aside in wicker strainers, but the other half he poured into bowls that he might drink it for his supper. When he had got through with all his work, he lit the fire, and then caught sight of us, whereon he said:

" 'Strangers, who are you? Where do you sail from? Are you traders, or do you sail the sea as rovers, with your hands against every man, and every man's hand against you?'

"We were frightened of our senses by his loud voice and monstrous form, but I managed to say: 'We are Achaeans on our way home from Troy, but by the will of Zeus and stress of weather we have been driven far out of our course. We are the people of Agamemnon son of Atreus, who has won infinite renown throughout the whole world by sacking so great a city and killing so many people. We therefore humbly pray you to show us some hospitality, and otherwise make us such presents as visitors may reasonably expect. May your excellency fear the wrath of heaven, for we are your suppliants, and Zeus takes all respectable travelers under his protection, for he is the avenger of all suppliants and foreigners in distress.'

"To this he gave me but a pitiless answer, 'Stranger,' said he, 'you are a fool, or else you know nothing of this country. Talk to me, indeed, about fearing the gods or shunning their anger? We Cyclopes do not care about Zeus or any of your blessed gods, for we are ever so much stronger than they. I shall not spare either yourself or your companions out of any regard for Zeus, unless I am in the humor for doing so. And now tell me where you made your ship fast when you came on shore. Was it round the point, or is she lying straight off the land?'

"He said this to draw me out, but I was too cunning to be caught in that way, so I answered with a lie. 'Poseidon,' said I, 'sent my ship on the rocks at the far end of your country, and wrecked it. We were driven onto them from the open sea, but I and those who are with me escaped the jaws of death.'

"The cruel wretch vouchsafed me not one word of answer, but with a sudden clutch he gripped up two of my men at once and dashed them down upon the ground as though they had been puppies. Their brains were shed upon the ground, and the earth was wet with their blood. Then he tore them limb from limb and supped upon them. He gobbled them up like a lion in the wilderness, flesh, bones, marrow, and entrails, without leaving anything uneaten. As for us, we wept and lifted up our hands to heaven on seeing such a horrid sight, for we did not know what else to do; but when the Cyclops had filled his huge paunch, and had washed down his meal of human flesh with a drink of neat milk, he stretched himself full length upon the ground among his sheep, and went to sleep. I was at first inclined to seize my sword, draw it, and drive it into his vitals, but I reflected that if I did we should all certainly be lost, for we should never be able to shift the stone which the monster had put in front of the door. So we stayed sobbing and sighing where we were till morning came.

"When the child of morning, rosy-fingered Dawn, appeared, he again lit his fire, milked his goats and ewes, all quite rightly, and then let each have her own young one; as soon as he had got through with all his work, he clutched up two more of my men, and began eating them for his morning's meal. Presently, with the utmost ease, he rolled the stone away from the door and drove out his sheep, but he at once put it back again—as easily as though he were merely clapping the lid on to a quiver full of arrows. As soon as he had done so he shouted and cried, 'Shoo, shoo,' after his sheep to drive them on to the mountain; so I was left to scheme some way of taking my revenge and covering myself with glory.

"In the end I deemed it would be the best plan to do as follows. The Cyclops had a great club which was lying near one of the sheep pens; it was of green olive wood, and he had cut it intending to use it for a staff as soon as it should be dry. It was so huge that we could only compare it to the mast of a twenty-oared merchant vessel of large burden, and able to venture out into open sea. I went up to this club and cut off about six feet of it; I then gave this piece to the men and told them to fine it evenly off at one end, which they proceeded to do, and lastly I brought it to a point myself, charring the end in the fire to make it harder. When I had done this I hid it under the dung, which was lying about all over the cave, and told the men to cast lots which of them should venture along with myself to lift it and bore it into the monster's eye while he was asleep. The lot fell upon the very four whom I should have chosen, and I myself made five. In the evening the wretch came back from shepherding, and drove his flocks into the cave—this time driving them all inside, and not leaving any in the yards; I suppose some fancy must have taken him, or a god must have prompted him to do so. As soon as he had put the stone back to its place against the door, he sat down, milked his ewes and his goats all quite rightly, and then let each have her own young one; when he had got through with all this work, he gripped up two more of my men, and made his supper off them. So I went up to him with an ivy-wood bowl of black wine in my hands:

" 'Look here, Cyclops,' said I, 'you have been eating a great deal of man's flesh, so take this and drink some wine, that you may see what kind of liquor we had on board my ship. I was bringing it to you as a drink offering, in the hope that you would take compassion upon me and further me on my way home, whereas all you do is to go on ranting and raving most intolerably. You ought to be ashamed of yourself. How can you expect people to come and see you any more if you treat them in this way?'

"He then took the cup and drank. He was so delighted with the taste of the wine that he begged me for another bowl full. 'Be so kind,' he said, 'as to give me some more, and tell me your name at once. I want to make you a present that you will be glad to have. We have wine even in this country, for our soil grows grapes and the sun ripens them, but this drink is like nectar and ambrosia all in one.'

"I then gave him some more; three times did I fill the bowl for him and three times did he drain it without thought or heed. Then, when I saw that the wine had got into his head, I said to him as plausibly as I could: 'Cyclops, you ask my name and I will tell it you; give me, therefore, the present you promised me. My name is Noman; this is what my father and mother and my friends have always called me.'

"But the cruel wretch said, 'Then I will eat all Noman's comrades before Noman himself, and will keep Noman for the last. This is the present that I will make him.'

"As he spoke, he reeled and fell sprawling face upwards on the ground. His great neck hung heavily backwards and a deep sleep took hold upon him. Presently he turned sick, and threw up both wine and the gobbets of human flesh on which he had been gorging, for he was very drunk. Then I thrust the beam of wood far into the embers to heat it, and encouraged my men lest any of them should turn faint-hearted. When the wood, green though it was, was about to blaze, I drew it out of the fire glowing with heat, and my men gathered round me, for heaven had filled their hearts with courage. We drove the sharp end of the beam into the monster's eye, and bearing upon it with all my weight I kept turning it round and round as though I were boring a hole in a ship's plank with an auger, which two men with a wheel and strap can keep on turning as long as they choose. Even thus did we bore the red-hot beam into his eye, till the boiling blood bubbled all over it as we worked it round and round, so that the steam from the burning eyeball scalded his eyelids and eyebrows, and the roots of the eye sputtered in the fire. As a blacksmith plunges an axe or hatchet into cold water to temper it—for it is this that gives strength to the iron—and it makes a great hiss as he does so, even thus did the Cyclops' eye hiss round

the beam of olive wood, and his hideous yells made the cave ring
again. We ran away in a fright, but he plucked the beam all be-
smirched with gore from his eye, and hurled it from him in a frenzy
of rage and pain, shouting as he did so to the other Cyclopes who
lived on the bleak headlands near him. So they gathered from all
quarters round his cave when they heard him crying, and asked
what was the matter with him.

" 'What ails you, Polyphemus,' said they, 'that you make such a
noise, breaking the stillness of the night, and preventing us from
being able to sleep? Surely no man is carrying off your sheep?
Surely no man is trying to kill you either by fraud or by force?'

"But Polyphemus shouted to them from inside the cave, 'Noman
is killing me by fraud! Noman is killing me by force!'

" 'Then,' said they, 'if no man is attacking you, you must be ill;
when Zeus makes people ill, there is no help for it, and you had
better pray to your father Poseidon.'

No Man

"Then they went away, and I laughed inwardly at the success of
my clever stratagem, but the Cyclops, groaning and in an agony of
pain, felt about with his hands till he found the stone and took it
from the door; then he sat in the doorway and stretched his hands
in front of it to catch anyone going out with the sheep, for he
thought I might be foolish enough to attempt this.

"As for myself I kept on puzzling to think how I could best save
my own life and those of my companions. I schemed and schemed,
as one who knows that his life depends upon it, for the danger was
very great. In the end I deemed that this plan would be the best.
The male sheep were well grown, and carried a heavy black fleece,
so I bound them noiselessly in threes together, with some of the
withies on which the wicked monster used to sleep. There was to be
a man under the middle sheep, and the two on either side were to
cover him, so that there were three sheep to each man. As for myself
there was a ram finer than any of the others, so I caught hold of him
by the back, esconced myself in the thick wool under his belly, and
hung on patiently to his fleece, face upwards, keeping a firm hold
on it all the time.

"Thus, then, did we wait in great fear of mind till morning came, but when the child of morning, rosy-fingered Dawn, appeared, the male sheep hurried out to feed, while the ewes remained bleating about the pens waiting to be milked, for their udders were full to bursting; but their master, in spite of all his pain, felt the backs of all the sheep as they stood upright, without being sharp enough to find out that the men were underneath their bellies. As the ram was going out, last of all, heavy with its fleece and with the weight of my crafty self, Polyphemus laid hold of it and said:

" 'My good ram, what is it that makes you the last to leave my cave this morning? You are not wont to let the ewes go before you, but lead the mob with a run whether to flowery mead or bubbling fountain, and are the first to come home again at night; but now you lag last of all. Is it because you know your master has lost his eye, and are sorry because that wicked Noman and his horrid crew have got him down in his drink and blinded him? But I will have his life yet. If you could understand and talk, you would tell me where the wretch is hiding, and I would dash his brains upon the ground till they flew all over the cave. I should thus have some satisfaction for the harm this no-good Noman has done me.'

"As he spoke he drove the ram outside, but when we were a little way out from the cave and yards, I first got from under the ram's belly, and then freed my comrades; as for the sheep, which were very fat, by constantly heading them in the right direction we managed to drive them down to the ship. The crew rejoiced greatly at seeing those of us who had escaped death, but wept for the others whom the Cyclops had killed. However, I made signs to them by nodding and frowning that they were to hush their crying, and told them to get all the sheep on board at once and put out to sea. So they went aboard, took their places, and smote the gray sea with their oars. Then, when I had got as far out as my voice would reach, I began to jeer at the Cyclops.

" 'Cyclops,' said I, 'you should have taken better measure of your man before eating up his comrades in your cave. You wretch, eat up your visitors in your own house? You might have known that your

sin would find you out, and now Zeus and the other gods have
punished you.'

"He got more and more furious as he heard me, so he tore the
top off from a high mountain, and flung it just in front of my ship
so that it was within a little of hitting the end of the rudder. The
sea quaked as the rock fell into it, and the wash of the wave it raised
carried us back towards the mainland, and forced us towards the
shore. But I snatched up a long pole and kept the ship off, making
signs to my men by nodding my head, that they must row for their
lives, whereon they laid out with a will. When we had got twice as
far as we were before, I was for jeering at the Cyclops again, but the
men begged and prayed of me to hold my tongue.

" 'Do not,' they exclaimed, 'be mad enough to provoke this savage
creature further. He has thrown one rock at us already which drove
us back again to the mainland, and we made sure it had been the
death of us. If he had then heard any further sound of voices he
would have pounded our heads and our ship's timbers into a jelly
with the rugged rocks he would have heaved at us, for he can throw
them a long way."

"But I would not listen to them, and shouted out to him in my
rage, 'Cyclops, if anyone asks you who it was that put your eye out
and spoiled your beauty, say it was the valiant warrior Odysseus son
of Laertes, who lives in Ithaca.'

"On this he groaned, and cried out, 'Alas, alas, then the old
prophecy about me is coming true. There was a prophet here, at one
time, a man both brave and of great stature, Telemus son of Eury-
mus, who was an excellent seer, and did all the prophesying for the
Cyclopes till he grew old. He told me that all this would happen to
me some day, and said I should lose my sight by the hand of Odysseus. I have been all along expecting someone of imposing presence
and superhuman strength, whereas he turns out to be a little insig-
nificant weakling, who has managed to blind my eye by taking advantage of me in my drink. Come here, then, Odysseus, that I may
make you presents to show my hospitality, and urge Poseidon to
help you forward on your journey—for Poseidon and I are father

and son. He, if he so will, shall heal me, which no one else neither god nor man can do.'

"Then I said, 'I wish I could be as sure of killing you outright and sending you down to the house of Hades, as I am that it will take more than Poseidon to cure that eye of yours.'

"On this he lifted up his hands to the firmament of heaven and prayed, saying: 'Hear me, great Poseidon! If I am indeed your own true-begotten son, grant that Odysseus may never reach his home alive; or if he must get back to his friends at last, let him do so late and in sore plight after losing all his men. Let him reach his home in another man's ship and find trouble in his house.'

"Thus did he pray, and Poseidon heard his prayer. Then he picked up a rock much larger than the first, swung it aloft and hurled it with prodigious force. It fell just short of the ship, but was within a little of hitting the end of the rudder. The sea quaked as the rock fell into it, and the wash of the wave it raised drove us onwards on our way towards the shore of the island.

"When at last we got to the island where we had left the rest of our ships, we found our comrades lamenting us and anxiously awaiting our return. We ran our vessel upon the sands and got out of her on to the seashore. We also landed the Cyclops' sheep, and divided them equitably amongst us so that none might have reason to complain. As for the ram, my companions agreed that I should have it as an extra share; so I sacrificed it on the seashore, and burned its thighbones to Zeus, who is the lord of all. But he heeded not my sacrifice, and only thought how he might destroy both my ships and my comrades.

"Thus through the livelong day to the going down of the sun we feasted our fill on meat and drink, but when the sun went down and it came on dark, we camped upon the beach. When the child of morning, rosy-fingered Dawn, appeared, I bade my men go on board and loose the hawsers. Then they took their places and smote the gray sea with their oars; so we sailed on with sorrow in our hearts, but glad to have escaped death though we had lost our comrades."

BOOK X

Odysseus and his fleet came next to the isle of Aeolus. When they departed, Odysseus was given a bag of the winds, to hold tight until he reached home. But while he slept, his men wickedly opened the bag, allowing the winds to escape. The ships were blown back to Aeolus' isle, and thence to the land of the savage Laestrygonians, who sunk eleven of them and devoured their crews. Odysseus and the one crew remaining to him sought shelter on Circe's isle. Here half of his men drank Circe's magic potion and were changed into pigs. Odysseus compelled Circe to restore them to human shape, and they stayed feasting with her for a year.

THENCE WE WENT ON TO THE AEOLIAN ISLAND where lives Aeolus son of Hippotas, dear to the immortal gods. It is an island that floats (as it were) upon the sea, iron bound with a wall that girds it. Now Aeolus has six daughters and six lusty sons, so he made the sons marry the daughters, and they all live with their dear father and mother, feasting and enjoying every conceivable kind of luxury. All day long the atmosphere of the house is loaded with the savor of roasting meats till it groans again, yard and all; but by night they sleep on their well-made bedsteads, each with his own wife between the blankets. These were the people among whom we had now come.

"Aeolus entertained me for a whole month asking me questions all the time about Troy, the Argive fleet, and the return of the Achaeans. I told him exactly how everything had happened, and when I said I must go, and asked him to further me on my way, he made no sort of difficulty, but set about doing so at once. Moreover, he flayed me a prime oxhide to hold the ways of the roaring winds, which he shut up in the hide as in a sack—for Zeus had made him captain over the winds, and he could stir or still each one of them according to his own pleasure. He put the sack in the ship, and bound the mouth so tightly with a silver thread that not even a breath of a side-wind could blow from any quarter. The west wind which was fair for us did he alone let blow as it chose; but it all came to nothing, for we were lost through our own folly.

"Nine days and nine nights did we sail, and on the tenth day our native land showed on the horizon. We got so close in that we could see the stubble fires burning, and I, being then dead beat, fell into a light sleep, for I had never let the rudder out of my own hands, that we might get home the faster. On this the men fell to talking among themselves, and said I was bringing back gold and silver in the sack that Aeolus had given me. 'Bless my heart,' would one turn to his neighbor, saying, 'how this man gets honored and makes friends to whatever city or country he may go. See what fine prizes he is taking home from Troy, while we, who have traveled just as far as he has, come back with hands as empty as we set out with—and now Aeolus has given him ever so much more. Quick, let us see what it all is, and how much gold and silver there is in the sack he gave him.'

"Thus they talked and evil counsels prevailed. They loosed the sack, whereupon the winds flew howling forth and raised a storm that carried us weeping out to sea and away from our own country. Then I awoke, and knew not whether to throw myself into the sea or to live on and make the best of it; but I bore it, covered myself up, and lay down in the ship, while the men lamented bitterly as the fierce winds bore our fleet back to the Aeolian island.

"When we reached it we went ashore to take in water, and dined hard by the ships. Immediately after dinner I took a herald and one of my men and I went straight to the house of Aeolus, where I found him feasting with his wife and family; so we sat down as suppliants on the threshold. They were astounded when they saw us and said, 'Odysseus, what brings you here? What god has been ill-treating you? We took great pains to further you on your way home to Ithaca, or wherever it was that you wanted to go to.

"Thus did they speak, but I answered sorrowfully, 'My men have undone me; they, and cruel sleep, have ruined me. My friends, mend me this mischief, for you can if you will.'

"I spoke as movingly as I could, but they said nothing, till their father answered, 'Vilest of mankind, get you gone at once out of the island; him whom heaven hates will I in no wise help. Be off, for you come here as one abhorred of heaven.' And with these words he sent me sorrowing from his door.

"Thence we sailed sadly on till the men were worn out with long and fruitless rowing, for there was no longer any wind to help them. Six days, night and day, did we toil, and on the seventh day we reached the rocky stronghold of Lamus—Telepylus, the city of the Laestrygonians, where the shepherd who is driving in his sheep and goats to be milked salutes him who is driving out his flock to feed and this last answers the salute. In that country a man who could do without sleep might earn double wages, one as a herdsman of cattle, and another as a shepherd, for they work much the same by night as they do by day.

"When we reached the harbor we found it landlocked under steep cliffs, with a narrow entrance between two headlands. My captains took all their ships inside, and made them fast close to one another, for there was never so much as a breath of wind inside, but it was always dead calm. I kept my own ship outside, and moored it to a rock at the very end of the point; then I climbed a high rock to reconnoiter, but could see no sign either of man or cattle, only some smoke rising from the ground. So I sent two of my company with an attendant to find out what sort of people the inhabitants were.

"The men when they got on shore followed a level road by which the people draw their firewood from the mountains into the town, till presently they met a young woman who had come outside to fetch water, and who was daughter to a Laestrygonian named Antiphates. She was going to the fountain Artacia from which the people bring in their water, and when my men had come close up to her, they asked her who the king of that country might be, and over what kind of people he ruled. So she directed them to her father's house, but when they got there they found his wife to be a giantess as huge as a mountain, and they were horrified at the sight of her.

"She at once called her husband Antiphates from the place of assembly, and forthwith he set about killing my men. He snatched up one of them, and began to make his dinner off him then and there, whereon the other two ran back to the ships as fast as ever they could. But Antiphates raised a hue and cry after them, and thousands of sturdy Laestrygonians sprang up from every quarter— ogres, not men. They threw vast rocks at us from the cliffs as though they had been mere stones, and I heard the horrid sound of the ships crunching up against one another, and the death cries of my men, as the Laestrygonians speared them like fishes and took them home to eat them. While they were thus killing my men within the harbor I drew my sword, cut the cable of my own ship, and told my men to row with all their might if they too would not fare like the rest; so they laid out for their lives, and we were thankful enough when we got into open water out of reach of the rocks they hurled at us. As for the others, there was not one of them left.

"Thence we sailed sadly on, glad to have escaped death, though we had lost our comrades, and came to the Aeaean island, where Circe lives, a great and cunning goddess, who is own sister to the magician Aeetes, for they are both children of the sun by Perse, who is daughter to Oceanus. We brought our ship into a safe harbor without a word, for some god guided us thither, and having landed we lay there for two days and two nights, worn out in body and mind. When the morning of the third day came I took my spear and my sword, and went away from the ship to reconnoiter, and see if I could discover signs of human handiwork, or hear the sound of voices. Climbing to the top of a high lookout I espied the smoke of Circe's house rising upwards amid a dense forest of trees, and when I saw this I doubted whether, having seen the smoke, I should not go on at once and find out more. But in the end I deemed it best to go back to the ship, give the men their dinners, and send some of them instead of going myself.

"When I had nearly got back to the ship, some god took pity upon my solitude and sent a fine antlered stag right into the very middle of my path. He was coming down from his pasture in the forest to drink of the river, for the heat of the sun drove him, and as he passed I struck him in the middle of the back; the bronze point of the spear went clean through him, and he lay groaning in the dust until the life went out of him. Then I set my foot upon him, drew my spear from the wound, and laid it down. I also gathered rough grass and rushes and twisted them into a fathom or so of good stout rope with which I bound the four feet of the noble creature together. Having so done I hung him round my neck and walked back to the ship leaning upon my spear, for the stag was much too big for me to be able to carry him on my shoulder, steadying him with one hand. As I threw him down in front of the ship, I called the men and spoke cheeringly man by man to each of them. 'Look here, my friends,' said I, 'we are not going to die so much before our time after all, and at any rate we will not starve so long as we have got something to eat and drink on board.' On this they uncovered their heads upon the seashore and admired the stag, for he was indeed a splendid fellow. Then, when they had feasted their eyes upon him sufficiently, they washed their hands and began to cook him for dinner.

"Thus through the livelong day to the going down of the sun we stayed there eating and drinking our fill, but when the sun went down and it came on dark, we camped upon the seashore. When the child of morning, rosy-fingered Dawn, appeared, I called a council and said, 'My friends, we are in very great difficulties; listen therefore to me. We have no idea where the sun either sets or rises, so that we do not even know east from west. I see no way out of it; nevertheless, we must try and find one. We are certainly on an island, for I went as high as I could this morning, and saw the sea reaching all round it to the horizon; it lies low, but towards the middle I saw smoke rising from out of a thick forest of trees.'

"Their hearts sank as they heard me, for they remembered how they had been treated by the Laestrygonian Antiphates and by the savage ogre Polyphemus. They wept bitterly in their dismay, but there was nothing to be got by crying, so I divided them into two companies and set a captain over each; I gave one company to Eurylochus, while I took command of the other myself. Then we cast lots in a helmet, and the lot fell upon Eurylochus; so he set out with his twenty-two men, and they wept, as also did we who were left behind.

"When they reached Circe's house they found it built of cut stones, on a site that could be seen from far, in the middle of the forest. There were wild mountain wolves and lions prowling all round it—poor bewitched creatures whom she had tamed by her enchantments and drugged into subjection. They did not attack my men, but wagged their great tails, fawned upon them, and rubbed their noses lovingly against them. As hounds crowd round their master when they see him coming from dinner—for they know he will bring them something—even so did these wolves and lions with their great claws fawn upon my men, but the men were terribly frightened at seeing such strange creatures. Presently they reached the gates of the goddess's house, and as they stood there they could hear Circe within, singing most beautifully as she worked at her loom, making a web so fine, so soft, and of such dazzling colors as no one but a goddess could weave. On this Polites, whom I valued and trusted more than any other of my men, said, 'There is someone inside working at a loom and singing most beautifully; the whole place resounds with it, let us call her and see whether she is woman or goddess.'

"They called her and she came down, unfastened the door, and

bade them enter. They, thinking no evil, followed her, all except
Eurylochus, who suspected mischief and stayed outside. When she
had got them into her house, she set them upon benches and seats
and mixed them a mess with cheese, honey, meal, and Pramnian
wine, but she drugged it with wicked poisons to make them forget
their homes, and when they had drunk she turned them into pigs
by a stroke of her wand, and shut them up in her pigsties. They
were like pigs—head, hair, and all, and they grunted just as pigs
do; but their senses were the same as before, and they remembered
everything.

"Thus then were they shut up squealing, and Circe threw them
some acorns and beech mast such as pigs eat, but Eurylochus hurried back to tell me about the sad fate of our comrades. He was so
overcome with dismay that though he tried to speak he could find
no words to do so; his eyes filled with tears and he could only sob
and sigh, till at last we forced his story out of him, and he told us
what had happened to the others.

" 'We went,' said he, 'as you told us, through the forest, and in
the middle of it there was a fine house built with cut stones in a
place that could be seen from far. There we found a woman, or else
she was a goddess, working at her loom and singing sweetly; so the
men shouted to her and called her, whereon she at once came down,
opened the door, and invited us in. The others did not suspect any
mischief so they followed her into the house, but I stayed where
I was, for I thought there might be some treachery. From that moment I saw them no more, for not one of them ever came out,
though I sat a long time watching for them.'

"Then I took my sword of bronze and slung it over my shoulders;
I also took my bow, and told Eurylochus to come back with me and
show me the way. But he laid hold of me with both his hands and
spoke piteously, saying, 'Sir, do not force me to go with you, but let
me stay here, for I know you will not bring one of them back with
you, nor even return alive yourself. Let us rather see if we cannot
escape at any rate with the few that are left us, for we may still save
our lives.'

" 'Stay where you are, then,' answered I, 'eating and drinking at the ship, but I must go, for I am most urgently bound to do so.'

"With this I left the ship and went up inland. When I got through the charmed grove, and was near the great house of the enchantress Circe, I met Hermes with his golden wand, disguised as a young man in the heyday of his youth and beauty with the down just coming upon his face. He came up to me and took my hand within his own, saying: 'My poor unhappy man, whither are you going over this mountain top, alone and without knowing the way? Your men are shut up in Circe's pigsties, like so many wild boars in their lairs. You surely do not fancy that you can set them free? I can tell you that you will never get back and will have to stay there with the rest of them. But never mind, I will protect you and get you out of your difficulty. Take this herb, which is one of great virtue, and keep it about you when you go to Circe's house. It will be a talisman to you against every kind of mischief.

" 'And I will tell you of all the wicked witchcraft that Circe will try to practice upon you. She will mix a mess for you to drink, and she will drug the meal with which she makes it, but she will not be able to charm you, for the virtue of the herb that I shall give you will prevent her spells from working. I will tell you all about it. When Circe strikes you with her wand, draw your sword and spring upon her as though you were going to kill her. She will then be frightened and will desire you to go to bed with her. On this you must not point-blank refuse her, for you want her to set your companions free, and to take good care also of yourself, but you must make her swear solemnly by all the blessed gods that she will plot no further mischief against you, or else when she has got you naked she will unman you and make you fit for nothing.'

"As he spoke he pulled the herb out of the ground and showed me what it was like. The root was black, while the flower was as white as milk; the gods call it Moly, and mortal men cannot uproot it, but the gods can do whatever they like.

"Then Hermes went back to high Olympus, passing over the wooded island; but I fared onward to the house of Circe, and my heart was clouded with care as I walked along. When I got to the gates I stood there and called the goddess, and as soon as she heard me she came down, opened the door, and asked me to come in; so I followed her—much troubled in my mind. She set me on a richly decorated seat inlaid with silver, there was a footstool also under my feet, and she mixed a mess in a golden goblet for me to drink; but she drugged it, for she meant me mischief. When she had given it me, and I had drunk it without its charming me, she struck me with her wand. 'There now,' she cried, 'be off to the pigsty, and make your lair with the rest of them.'

"But I rushed at her with my sword drawn as though I would kill her, whereon she fell with a loud scream, clasped my knees, and spoke piteously, saying: 'Who and whence are you? From what place and people have you come? How can it be that my drugs have no power to charm you? Never yet was any man able to stand so much as a taste of the herb I gave you; you must be spell-proof. Surely you can be none other than the bold hero Odysseus, who Hermes always said would come here some day with his ship while on his way home from Troy. So be it then; sheathe your sword and let us go to bed, that we may make friends and learn to trust each other.'

"And I answered: 'Circe, how can you expect me to be friendly with you when you have just been turning all my men into pigs? And now that you have got me here myself, you mean me mischief when you ask me to go to bed with you, and will unman me and make me fit for nothing. I shall certainly not consent to go to bed with you unless you will first take your solemn oath to plot no further harm against me.'

"So she swore at once as I had told her, and when she had completed her oath, then I went to bed with her.

"Meanwhile her four servants, who are her housemaids, set about their work. They are the children of the groves and fountains, and of the holy waters that run down into the sea. One of them spread a fair purple cloth over a seat, and laid a carpet underneath it. Another brought tables of silver up to the seats, and set them with baskets of gold. A third mixed some sweet wine with water in a silver bowl and put golden cups upon the tables, while the fourth brought in water and set it to boil in a large cauldron over a good fire which she had lighted. When the water in the cauldron was boiling, she poured cold into it till it was just as I liked it, and then she set me in a bath and began washing me from the cauldron about the head and shoulders, to take the tire and stiffness out of my limbs. As soon as she had done washing me and anointing me with oil, she arrayed me in a good cloak and shirt and led me to a richly decorated seat inlaid with silver; there was a footstool also under my feet. A maidservant then brought me water in a beautiful golden ewer and poured it into a silver basin for me to wash my hands, and she drew a clean table beside me. An upper servant brought me bread and offered me many good things of what there was in the house, and then Circe bade me eat, but I would not, and sat without heeding what was before me, still moody and suspicious.

"When Circe saw me sitting there without eating, and in great grief, she came to me and said, 'Odysseus, why do you sit like that as though you were dumb, gnawing at your own heart, and refusing both meat and drink? Is it that you are still suspicious? You ought not to be, for I have already sworn solemnly that I will not hurt you.'

"And I said, 'Circe, no man with any sense of what is right can think of either eating or drinking in your house until you have set his friends free and let him see them. If you want me to eat and drink, you must free my men and bring them to me that I may see them with my own eyes.'

"When I had said this, she went straight through the court with her wand in her hand and opened the pigsty doors. My men came out like so many prime hogs and stood looking at her, but she went about among them and anointed each with a second drug, whereon the bristles that the bad drug had given them fell off, and they became men again, younger than they were before, and much taller and better looking. They knew me at once, seized me each of them by the hand, and wept for joy till the whole house was filled with the sound of their hullabalooing, and Circe herself was so sorry for them that she came up to me and said, 'Odysseus, noble son of Laertes, go back at once to the sea where you have left your ship, and first draw it on to the land. Then hide all your ship's gear and property in some cave, and come back here with your men.'

"I agreed to this, so I went back to the seashore, and found the men at the ship weeping and wailing most piteously. When they saw me, the silly blubbering fellows began frisking round me as calves break out and gambol round their mothers when they see them coming home to be milked after they have been feeding all day, and the homestead resounds with their lowing. They seemed as glad to see me as though they had got back to their own rugged Ithaca, where they had been born and bred. 'Sir,' said the affectionate creatures, 'we are as glad to see you back as though we had got safe home to Ithaca; but tell us all about the fate of our comrades.'

"I spoke comfortingly to them and said, 'We must draw our ship onto the land, and hide the ship's gear with all our property in some cave; then come with me, all of you, as fast as you can to Circe's house, where you will find your comrades eating and drinking in the midst of great abundance.'

"On this the men would have come with me at once, but Eurylochus tried to hold them back and said: 'Alas, poor wretches that we are, what will become of us? Rush not on your ruin by going to the house of Circe, who will turn us all into pigs or wolves or lions, and we shall have to keep guard over her house. Remember how the Cyclops treated us when our comrades went inside his cave, and Odysseus with them. It was all through his sheer folly that those men lost their lives.'

"When I heard him, I was in two minds whether or no to draw the keen blade that hung by my sturdy thigh and cut his head off in spite of his being a near relation of my own; but the men interceded for him and said, 'Sir, if it may so be, let this fellow stay here and mind the ship, but take the rest of us with you to Circe's house.'

"On this we all went inland, and Eurylochus was not left behind after all, but came on too, for he was frightened by the severe reprimand that I had given him.

"Meanwhile Circe had been seeing that the men who had been left behind were washed and anointed with olive oil; she had also given them woolen cloaks and shirts, and when we came we found them all comfortably at dinner in her house. As soon as the men saw each other face to face and knew one another, they wept for joy and cried aloud till the whole palace rang again. Thereon Circe came up to me and said: 'Odysseus, noble son of Laertes, tell your men to leave off crying. I know how much you have all of you suffered at sea, and how ill you have fared among cruel savages on the mainland, but that is over now. So stay here, and eat and drink till you are once more as strong and hearty as you were when you left Ithaca; for at present you are weakened both in body and mind. You keep all the time thinking of the hardships you have suffered during your travels, so that you have no more cheerfulness left in you.'

"Thus did she speak and we assented. We stayed with Circe for a whole twelvemonth feasting upon an untold quantity both of meat and wine. But when the year had passed in the waning of moons and the long days had come round, my men called me apart and said, 'Sir, it is time you began to think about going home, if so be you are to be spared to see your house and native country at all.'

"Thus did they speak and I assented. Thereon through the live-long day to the going down of the sun we feasted our fill on meat and wine, but when the sun went down and it came on dark the men laid themselves down to sleep in the covered cloisters. I, however, after I had got into bed with Circe, besought her by her knees, and the goddess listened to what I had got to say. 'Circe,' said I, 'please to keep the promise you made me about furthering me on my homeward voyage. I want to get back and so do my men. They are always pestering me with their complaints as soon as ever your back is turned.'

"And the goddess answered, 'Odysseus, noble son of Laertes, you shall none of you stay here any longer if you do not want to, but there is another journey which you have got to take before you can sail homewards. You must go to the house of Hades and of dread Persephone to consult the ghost of the blind Theban prophet Teiresias, whose reason is still unshaken. To him alone has Persephone left his understanding even in death, but the other ghosts flit about aimlessly.'

"I was dismayed when I heard this. I sat up in bed and wept, and would gladly have lived no longer to see the light of the sun. But presently when I was tired of weeping and tossing myself about, I said, 'And who shall guide me upon this voyage—for the house of Hades is a port that no ship can reach.'

" 'You will want no guide,' she answered; 'raise your mast, set your white sails, sit quite still, and the north wind will blow you there of itself. When your ship has traveled the waters of Oceanus, you will reach the fertile shore of Persephone's country with its groves of tall poplars and willows that shed their fruit untimely; here beach your ship upon the shore of Oceanus, and go straight on to the dark abode of Hades. You will find it near the place where the rivers Pyriphlegethon and Cocytus (which is a branch of the river Styx) flow into Acheron, and you will see a rock near it, just where the two roaring rivers run into one another.

" 'When you have reached this spot, as I now tell you, dig a trench a cubit or so in length, breadth, and depth, and pour into it as a drink offering to all the dead, first, honey mixed with milk, then wine, and in the third place water—sprinkling white barley meal over the whole. Moreover, you must offer many prayers to the poor feeble ghosts, and promise them that when you get back to Ithaca you will sacrifice a barren heifer to them, the best you have, and will load the pyre with good things. More particularly you must promise that Teiresias shall have a black sheep all to himself, the finest in all your flocks.

" 'When you shall have thus besought the ghosts with your prayers, offer them a ram and a black ewe, bending their heads towards Erebus; but yourself turn away from them as though you would make towards the river. On this, many dead men's ghosts will come to you, and you must tell your men to skin the two sheep that you have just killed, and offer them as a burnt sacrifice with prayers to Hades and to Persephone. Then draw your sword and sit there, so as to prevent any other poor ghost from coming near the spilt blood before Teiresias shall have answered your questions. The seer will presently come to you, and will tell you about your voyage— what stages you are to make, and how you are to sail the sea so as to reach your home.'

"It was daybreak by the time she had done speaking, so she dressed me in my shirt and cloak. As for herself, she threw a beautiful light gossamer fabric over her shoulders, fastening it with a golden girdle round her waist, and she covered her head with a mantle. Then I went about among the men everywhere all over the house, and spoke kindly to each of them man by man: 'You must not lie sleeping here any longer,' said I to them, 'we must be going, for Circe has told me all about it.' And on this they did as I bade them.

"Even so, however, I did not get them away without misadventure. We had with us a certain youth named Elpenor, not very remarkable for sense or courage, who had got drunk and was lying on the house-top away from the rest of the men, to sleep off his liquor in the cool. When he heard the noise of the men bustling about, he jumped up on a sudden and forgot all about coming down by the main staircase, so he tumbled right off the roof and broke his neck, and his soul went down to the house of Hades.

"When I had got the men together I said to them, 'You think you are about to start home again, but Circe has explained to me that instead of this, we have got to go to the house of Hades and Persephone to consult the ghost of the Theban prophet Teiresias.'

"The men were brokenhearted as they heard me, and threw themselves on the ground groaning and tearing their hair, but they did not mend matters by crying. When we reached the seashore, weeping and lamenting our fate, Circe brought the ram and the ewe, and we made them fast hard by the ship. She passed through the midst of us without our knowing it, for who can see the comings and goings of a god, if the god does not wish to be seen?

BOOK XI

*Having been told by Circe that he must consult the blind
prophet Teiresias in the house of Hades, Odysseus sailed next
to the dark underworld, home of the dead. Here he met and
conversed with the ghosts of Teiresias, who foretold for him
his future; of his mother, of his old comrades in arms, Agamemnon, Achilles, and Ajax, and of Heracles, and saw many
dread and fearful things.*

THEN, WHEN WE HAD GOT DOWN TO THE SEA-
shore we drew our ship into the water and got her mast and sails
into her. We also put the sheep on board and took our places,
weeping and in great distress of mind. Circe, that great and cunning goddess, sent us a fair wind that blew dead aft and stayed
steadily with us keeping our sails all the time well filled; so we did
whatever wanted doing to the ship's gear and let her go as the wind
and helmsman headed her. All day long her sails were full as she
held her course over the sea, but when the sun went down and
darkness was over all the earth, we got into the deep waters of the
river Oceanus, where lie the land and city of the Cimmerians who
live enshrouded in mist and darkness, which the rays of the sun
never pierce either at his rising or as he goes down again out of the

heavens, but the poor wretches live in one long melancholy night. When we got there we beached the ship, took the sheep out of her, and went along by the waters of Oceanus till we came to the place of which Circe had told us.

"Here Perimedes and Eurylochus held the victims, while I drew my sword and dug the trench a cubit each way. I made a drink offering to all the dead, first with honey and milk, then with wine, and thirdly with water, and I sprinkled white barley meal over the whole, praying earnestly to the poor feckless ghosts, and promising them that when I got back to Ithaca I would sacrifice a barren heifer for them, the best I had, and would load the pyre with good things. I also particularly promised that Teiresias should have a black sheep to himself, the best in all my flocks. When I had prayed sufficiently to the dead, I cut the throats of the two sheep and let the blood run into the trench, whereon the ghosts came trooping up from Erebus—brides, young bachelors, old men worn out with toil, maids who had been crossed in love, and brave men who had been killed in battle, with their armor still smirched with blood; they came from every quarter and flitted round the trench with a strange kind of screaming sound that made me turn pale with fear. When I saw them coming I told the men to be quick and flay the carcasses of the two dead sheep and make burnt offerings of them, and at the same time to repeat prayers to Hades and to Persephone; but I sat where I was with my sword drawn and would not let the poor feckless ghosts come near the blood till Teiresias should have answered my questions.

"The first ghost that came was that of my comrade Elpenor, for he had not yet been laid beneath the earth. We had left his body unwaked and unburied in Circe's house, for we had had too much else to do. I was very sorry for him, and cried when I saw him, 'Elpenor,' said I, 'how did you come down here into this gloom and darkness? You have got here on foot quicker than I have with my ship.'

" 'Sir,' he answered with a groan, 'it was all bad luck, and my own unspeakable drunkenness. I was lying asleep on the top of Circe's house, and never thought of coming down again by the great staircase but fell right off the roof and broke my neck, so my soul came down to the house of Hades. And now I beseech you by all those whom you have left behind you, though they are not here, by your wife, by the father who brought you up when you were a child, and by Telemachus who is the one hope of your house, do what I shall now ask you. I know that when you leave this limbo you will again hold your ship for the Aeaean island. Do not go thence leaving me unwaked and unburied behind you, or I may bring heaven's anger upon you; but burn me with whatever armor I have, build a barrow for me on the seashore, that may tell people in days to come what a poor unlucky fellow I was, and plant over my grave the oar I used to row with when I was yet alive and with my messmates.' And I said, 'My poor fellow, I will do all that you have asked of me.'

"Thus, then, did we sit and hold sad talk with one another, I on the one side of the trench with my sword held over the blood, and the ghost of my comrade saying all this to me from the other side. Then came the ghost of my dead mother Anticlea, daughter to Autolycus. I had left her alive when I set out for Troy and was moved to tears when I saw her, but even so, for all my sorrow I would not let her come near the blood till I had asked my questions of Teiresias.

"Then came also the ghost of Theban Teiresias, with his golden scepter in his hand. He knew me and said, 'Odysseus, noble son of Laertes, why, poor man, have you left the light of day and come down to visit the dead in this sad place? Stand back from the trench and withdraw your sword that I may drink of the blood and answer your questions truly.'

"So I drew back and sheathed my sword, whereon when he had drank of the blood he began with his prophecy.

" 'You want to know,' said he, 'about your return home, but heaven will make this hard for you. I do not think that you will escape the eye of Poseidon, who still nurses his bitter grudge against you for having blinded his son. Still, after much suffering you may get home if you can restrain yourself and your companions when your ship reaches the Thrinacian island,[1] where you will find the sheep and cattle belonging to the sun, who sees and gives ear to everything. If you leave these flocks unharmed and think of nothing but of getting home, you may yet after much hardship reach Ithaca; but if you harm them, then I forewarn you of the destruction both of your ship and of your men. Even though you may yourself escape, you will return in bad plight after losing all your men, in another man's ship, and you will find trouble in your house, which will be overrun by high-handed people, who are devouring your substance under the pretext of paying court and making presents to your wife.

" 'When you get home you will take your revenge on these suitors; and after you have killed them by force or fraud in your own house, you must take a well-made oar and carry it on and on, till you come to a country where the people have never heard of the sea and do not even mix salt with their food, nor do they know anything about ships, and oars that are as the wings of a ship. I will give you this certain token which cannot escape your notice. A wayfarer will meet you and will say it must be a winnowing shovel that you have got upon your shoulder; on this you must fix the oar in the ground and sacrifice a ram, a bull, and a boar to Poseidon.[2] Then go home and offer hecatombs to all the gods in heaven one after the other. As for yourself, death shall come to you from the sea, and your life shall ebb away very gently when you are full of years and peace of mind, and your people shall bless you. All that I have said will come true.'

" 'This,' I answered, 'must be as it may please heaven, but tell me and tell me true, I see my poor mother's ghost close by us; she is sitting by the blood without saying a word, and though I am her own son she does not remember me and speak to me. Tell me, sir, how I can make her know me.'

" 'That,' said he, 'I can soon do. Any ghost that you let taste of

[1] Trinacria was the ancient name of the island of Sicily.
[2] Odysseus was to become a missionary and preach Poseidon to people who knew not his name. I was fortunate enough to meet in Sicily a woman carrying one of these winnowing shovels; it was not much shorter than an oar, and I was able at once to see what the writer of the Odyssey intended. (B.)

the blood will talk with you like a reasonable being, but if you do not let them have any blood they will go away again.' '

"On this the ghost of Teiresias went back to the house of Hades, for his prophesyings had now been spoken, but I sat still where I was until my mother came up and tasted the blood. Then she knew me at once and spoke fondly to me, saying, 'My son, how did you come down to this abode of darkness while you are still alive? It is a hard thing for the living to see these places, for between us and them there are great and terrible waters, and there is Oceanus, which no man can cross on foot, but he must have a good ship to take him. Are you all this time trying to find your way home from Troy, and have you never yet got back to Ithaca, nor seen your wife in your own house?'

" 'Mother,' said I, 'I was forced to come here to consult the ghost of the Theban prophet Teiresias. I have never yet been near the Achaean land nor set foot on my native country, and I have had nothing but one long series of misfortunes from the very first day that I set out with Agamemnon for Ilium, the land of noble steeds, to fight the Trojans. But tell me, and tell me true, in what way did you die? Did you have a long illness, or did heaven vouchsafe you a gentle easy passage to eternity? Tell me also about my father, and the son whom I left behind me. Is my property still in their hands, or has someone else got hold of it, who thinks that I shall not return to claim it? Tell me again what my wife intends doing, and in what mind she is. Does she live with my son and guard my estate securely, or has she made the best match she could and married again?'

"My mother answered: 'Your wife still remains in your house, but she is in great distress of mind and spends her whole time in tears both night and day. No one as yet has got possession of your fine property, and Telemachus still holds your lands undisturbed. He has to entertain largely, as of course he must, considering his position as a magistrate, and how everyone invites him. Your father remains at his old place in the country and never goes near the town. He has no comfortable bed nor bedding; in the winter he sleeps on the floor in front of the fire with the men and goes about all in rags, but in summer, when the warm weather comes on again, he lies out in the vineyard on a bed of vine leaves thrown anyhow upon the ground. He grieves continually about your never having come home, and suffers more and more as he grows older. As for my own end it was in this wise: heaven did not take me swiftly and painlessly in my own house, nor was I attacked by any illness such as those that generally wear people out and kill them, but my longing to know what you were doing and the force of my affection—this it was that was the death of me.' [3]

"Then I tried to find some way of embracing my poor mother's ghost. Thrice I sprung towards her and tried to clasp her in my arms, but each time she flitted from my embrace as it were a dream or phantom, and being touched to the quick I said to her, 'Mother, why do you not stay still when I would embrace you? If we could throw our arms around one another we might find sad comfort in the sharing of our sorrows even in the house of Hades. Does Persephone want to lay a still further load of grief upon me by mocking me with a phantom only?'

" 'My son,' she answered, 'most ill-fated of all mankind, it is not Persephone that is beguiling you, but all people are like this when they are dead. The sinews no longer hold the flesh and bones together; these perish in the fierceness of consuming fire as soon as life has left the body, and the soul flits away as though it were a dream. Now, however, go back to the light of day as soon as you can, and note all these things that you may tell them to your wife hereafter.'

"Thus did we converse, and anon Persephone sent up the ghosts of the wives and daughters of all the most famous men. They gathered in crowds about the blood, and I considered how I might question them severally. In the end I deemed that it would be best to draw the keen blade that hung by my sturdy thigh, and keep them from all drinking the blood at once. So they came up one after the other, and each one as I questioned her told me her race and lineage.

"The first I saw was Tyro. She was daughter of Salmoneus and

[3] Tradition says that she had hanged herself. See also Book XV, p. 191.

wife of Cretheus the son of Aeolus.[4] She fell in love with the river
Enipeus, who is much the most beautiful river in the whole world.
Once when she was taking a walk by his side as usual, Poseidon,
disguised as her lover, lay with her at the mouth of the river, and
a huge blue wave arched itself like a mountain over them to hide
both woman and god, whereon he loosed her virgin girdle and laid
her in a deep slumber. When the god had accomplished the deed of
love, he took her hand in his own and said, 'Tyro, rejoice in all good
will; the embraces of the gods are not fruitless, and you will have
fine twins about this time twelve months. Take great care of them.
I am Poseidon, so now go home, but hold your tongue and do not
tell anyone.'

"Then he dived under the sea, and she in due course bore Pelias
and Neleus,[5] who both of them served Zeus with all their might.
Pelias was a great breeder of sheep and lived in Iolcus, but the other
lived in Pylos. The rest of her children were by Cretheus, namely,
Aeson, Pheres, and Amythaon, who was a mighty warrior and char-
ioteer.

"Next to her I saw Antiope daughter of Asopus, who could boast
of having slept in the arms of even Zeus himself, and who bore him
two sons, Amphion and Zethus. These founded Thebes with its
seven gates, and built a wall all round it; for strong though they
were they could not hold Thebes till they had walled it.

"Then I saw Alcmena, the wife of Amphitryon, who also bore to
Zeus indomitable Heracles; and Megara, who was daughter to great
King Creon, and married the redoubtable son of Amphitryon.

"I also saw fair Epicaste,[6] mother of King Oedipus, whose awful
lot it was to marry her own son without suspecting it. He married
her after having killed his father, but the gods proclaimed the whole
story to the world; whereon he remained king of Thebes, in great
grief for the spite the gods had borne him; but Epicaste went to the

[4] Not to be confounded with Aeolus, king of the winds. (B.)
[5] Father of Nestor.
[6] We know her better as Jocasta, under which name she appears in Sophocles' great
tragedy of *Oedipus Tyrannus*.

house of the mighty jailor Hades, having hanged himself for grief, and the avenging spirits haunted him as for an outraged mother—to his ruing bitterly thereafter.

"Then I saw Chloris, whom Neleus married for her beauty, having given priceless presents for her. She was youngest daughter to Amphion, son of Iasus and king of Minyan Orchomenus, and was queen in Pylos. She bore Nestor, Chromius, and Periclymenus, and she also bore that marvelously lovely woman Pero, who was wooed by all the country round; but Neleus would only give her to him who should raid the cattle of Iphicles from the grazing grounds of Phylace, and this was a hard task. The only man who would undertake to raid them was a certain excellent seer,[7] but the will of heaven was against him, for the rangers of the cattle caught him and put him in prison. Nevertheless, when a full year had passed and the same season came round again, Iphicles set him at liberty, after he had expounded all the oracles of heaven. Thus, then, was the will of Zeus accomplished.

"And I saw Leda the wife of Tyndarus, who bore him two famous sons, Castor, breaker of horses, and Pollux, the mighty boxer. Both these heroes are lying under the earth, though they are still alive, for by a special dispensation of Zeus, they die and come to life again, each one of them every other day throughout all time, and they have the rank of gods.

"After her I saw Iphimedeia wife of Aloeus, who boasted the embrace of Poseidon. She bore two sons, Otus and Ephialtes, but both were short lived. They were the finest children that were ever born in this world, and the best looking, Orion only excepted; for at nine years old they were nine fathoms high, and measured nine cubits round the chest. They threatened to make war with the gods in Olympus, and tried to set Mount Ossa on the top of Mount Olympus, and Mount Pelion on the top of Ossa, that they might scale heaven itself, and they would have done it too if they had been grown up. But Apollo son of Leto killed both of them, before they had got so much as a sign of hair upon cheeks or chin.

[7] Melampus, see Book XV, p. 188.

"Then I saw Phaedra, and Procris, and fair Ariadne, daughter of the magician Minos, whom Theseus was carrying off from Crete to Athens,[8] but he did not enjoy her, for before he could do so Artemis killed her in the island of Dia on account of what Dionysus had said against her.

"I also saw Maera and Clymene and hateful Eriphyle, who sold her own husband for gold. But it would take me all night if I were to name every single one of the wives and daughters of heroes whom I saw, and it is time for me to go to bed, either on board ship with my crew, or here. As for my escort, heaven and yourselves will see to it."

Here he ended, and the guests sat all of them enthralled and speechless throughout the covered cloister. Then Arete said to them:

"What do you think of this man, O Phaeacians? Is he not tall and good looking, and is he not clever? True, he is my own guest, but you all of you share in the distinction. Do not be in a hurry to send him away, nor niggardly in the presents you make to one who is in such great need, for heaven has blessed all of you with great abundance."

Then spoke the aged hero Echeneus, who was one of the oldest men among them. "My friends," said he, "what our august queen has just said to us is both reasonable and to the purpose, therefore be persuaded by it; but the decision whether in word or deed rests ultimately with King Alcinous."

"The thing shall be done," exclaimed Alcinous, "as surely as I still live and reign over the Phaeacians. Our guest is indeed very anxious to get home; still we must persuade him to remain with us until tomorrow, by which time I shall be able to get together the whole sum that I mean to give him. As regards his escort, it will be a matter for you all, and mine above all others as the chief person among you."

And Odysseus answered: "King Alcinous, if you were to bid me to stay here for a whole twelve months, and then speed me on my

[8] Ariadne, it may be remembered, had helped Theseus to escape from the Minotaur.

way, loaded with your noble gifts, I should obey you gladly and it would redound greatly to my advantage, for I should return fuller-handed to my own people, and should thus be more respected and beloved by all who see me when I get back to Ithaca."

"Odysseus," replied Alcinous, "not one of us who sees you has any idea that you are a charlatan or a swindler. I know there are many people going about who tell such plausible stories that it is very hard to see through them, but there is a style about your language which assures me of your good disposition. Moreover you have told the story of your own misfortunes, and those of the Argives, as though you were a practiced bard; but tell me, and tell me true, whether you saw any of the mighty heroes who went to Troy at the same time with yourself, and perished there. The evenings are still at their longest, and it is not yet bedtime. Go on, therefore, with your divine story, for I could stay here listening till tomorrow morning, so long as you will continue to tell us of your adventures."

"Alcinous," answered Odysseus, "there is a time for making speeches, and a time for going to bed; nevertheless, since you so desire, I will not refrain from telling you the still sadder tale of those of my comrades who did not fall fighting with the Trojans, but perished on their return, through the treachery of a wicked woman.

"When Persephone had dismissed the female ghosts in all directions, the ghost of Agamemnon son of Atreus came sadly up to me, surrounded by those who had perished with him in the house of Aegisthus. As soon as he had tasted the blood he knew me, and weeping bitterly stretched out his arms towards me to embrace me; but he had no strength or substance any more, and I too wept and pitied him as I beheld him. 'How did you come by your death,' said I, 'King Agamemnon? Did Poseidon raise his winds and waves against you when you were at sea, or did your enemies make an end of you on the mainland when you were cattle-lifting or sheep-stealing, or while they were fighting in defense of their wives and city?'

" 'Odysseus,' he answered, 'noble son of Laertes, I was not lost at sea in any storm of Poseidon's raising, nor did my foes despatch me upon the mainland, but Aegisthus and my wicked wife were the death of me between them. He asked me to his house, feasted me, and then butchered me most miserably, as though I were a fat beast in a slaughter house, while all around me my comrades were slain like sheep or pigs for the wedding breakfast, or picnic, or gorgeous banquet of some great nobleman. You must have seen numbers of men killed, either in a general engagement or in single combat, but you never saw anything so truly pitiable as the way in which we fell in that cloister, with the mixing-bowl and the loaded tables lying all about, and the ground reeking with our blood. I heard Priam's daughter Cassandra[9] scream as Clytemnestra killed her close beside me. I lay dying upon the earth with the sword in my body, and raised my hands to kill the slut of a murderess, but she slipped away from me. She would not even close my lips or my eyes when I was dying, for there is nothing in this world so cruel and so shameless as a woman when she has fallen into such guilt as hers was. Fancy murdering her own husband! I thought I was going to be welcomed home by my children and my servants, but her abominable crime has brought disgrace on herself and all women who shall come after —even on the good ones.'

"And I said, 'In truth Zeus has hated the house of Atreus from first to last in the matter of their women's counsels. See how many of us fell for Helen's sake, and now it seems that Clytemnestra hatched mischief against you too during your absence.' [10]

" 'Be sure, therefore,' continued Agamemnon, 'and not be too friendly even with your own wife. Do not tell her all that you know perfectly well yourself. Tell her a part only, and keep your own counsel about the rest. Not that your wife, Odysseus, is likely to murder you, for Penelope is a very admirable woman, and has an excellent nature. We left her a young bride with an infant at her breast when we set out for Troy. This child no doubt is now grown up happily to man's estate, and he and his father will have a joyful

---

[9] Cassandra had been allotted to Agamemnon as a part of his booty from the sack of Troy.
[10] Menelaus, husband of Helen, whose sin was the cause of the Trojan War, was, it is to be remembered, a son of Atreus and brother of Agamemnon.

meeting and embrace one another as it is right they should do, whereas my wicked wife did not even allow me the happiness of looking upon my son, but killed me ere I could do so. Furthermore I say—and lay my saying to your heart—do not tell people when you are bringing your ship to Ithaca, but steal a march upon them, for after all this there is no trusting women. But now tell me, and tell me true, can you give me any news of my son Orestes? Is he in Orchomenus, or at Pylos, or is he at Sparta with Menelaus? For I presume that he is still living.'

"And I said, 'Agamemnon, why do you ask me? I do not know whether your son is alive or dead, and it is not right to talk when one does not know.'

"As we two sat weeping and talking thus sadly with one another, the ghost of Achilles came up to us with Patroclus, Antilochus, and Ajax, who was the finest and goodliest man of all the Danaans after the son of Peleus. The fleet descendant of Aeacus knew me and spoke piteously, saying, 'Odysseus, noble son of Laertes, what deed of daring will you undertake next, that you venture down to the house of Hades among us silly dead, who are but the ghosts of them that can labor no more?'

"And I said, 'Achilles, son of Peleus, foremost champion of the Achaeans, I came to consult Teiresias, and see if he could advise me about my return home to Ithaca, for I have never yet been able to get near the Achaean land, or to set foot in my own country, but have been in trouble all the time. As for you, Achilles, no one was ever yet so fortunate as you have been, nor ever will be, for you were adored by all us Argives as long as you were alive, and now that you are here you are a great prince among the dead. Do not, therefore, take it so much to heart even if you are dead.'

" 'Say not a word,' he answered, 'in death's favor; I would rather be a paid servant in a poor man's house and be above ground than king of kings among the dead. But give me news about my son; is he gone to the wars and will he be a great soldier, or is this not so? Tell me also if you have heard anything about my father Peleus— does he still rule among the Myrmidons, or do they show him no respect throughout Hellas and Phthia now that he is old and his limbs fail him? Could I but stand by his side, in the light of day, with the same strength that I had when I killed the bravest of our foes upon the plain of Troy—could I but be as I then was and go even for a short time to my father's house, anyone who tried to do him violence or supersede him would soon rue it.'

" 'I have heard nothing,' I answered, 'of Peleus, but I can tell you all about your son Neoptolemus, for I took him in my own ship from Scyros with the Achaeans. In our councils of war before Troy he was always first to speak, and his judgment was unerring. Nestor and I were the only two who could surpass him; and when it came to fighting on the plain of Troy, he would never remain with the body of his men, but would dash on far in front, foremost of them all in valor. Many a man did he kill in battle—I cannot name every single one of those whom he slew while fighting on the side of the Argives, but will only say how he killed that valiant hero Eurypylus son of Telephus, who was the handsomest man I ever saw except Memnon; many others also of the Ceteians fell around him by reason of a woman's bribes. Moreover, when all the bravest of the Argives went inside the horse that Epeus had made, and it was left to me to settle when we should either open the door of our ambuscade, or keep it closed, though all the other leaders and chief men among the Danaans were drying their eyes and quaking in every limb, I never once saw him turn pale or wipe a tear from his cheek. He was all the time urging me to break out from the horse—grasping the handle of his sword and his bronze-shod spear, and breathing fury against the foe. Yet when we had sacked the city of Priam he got his handsome share of the prize money and went on board (such is the fortune of war) without a wound upon him, neither from a thrown spear nor in close combat, for the rage of Ares is a matter of great chance.'

"When I had told him this, the ghost of Achilles strode off across a meadow full of asphodel, exulting over what I had said concerning the prowess of his son.

"The ghosts of other dead men stood near me and told me each

his own melancholy tale; but that of Ajax son of Telamon alone
held aloof—still angry with me for having won the cause in our dispute about the armor of Achilles. Thetis had offered it as a prize,
but the Trojan prisoners and Athene were the judges. Would that I
had never gained the day in such a contest, for it cost the life of
Ajax, who was foremost of all the Danaans after the son of Peleus,
alike in stature and prowess.[11]

"When I saw him I tried to pacify him and said, 'Ajax, will you
not forget and forgive even in death, but must the judgment about
that hateful armor still rankle with you? It cost us Argives dear
enough to lose such a tower of strength as you were to us. We
mourned you as much as we mourned Achilles son of Peleus himself, nor can the blame be laid on anything but on the spite which
Zeus bore against the Danaans, for it was this that made him counsel
your destruction. Come hither, therefore, bring your proud spirit
into subjection, and hear what I can tell you.'

"He would not answer, but turned away to Erebus and to the
other ghosts. Nevertheless, I should have made him talk to me in
spite of his being so angry, or I should have gone on talking to him,
only that there were still others among the dead whom I desired to
see.

"Then I saw Minos son of Zeus with his golden scepter in his
hand, sitting in judgment on the dead, and the ghosts were gathered
sitting and standing round him in the spacious house of Hades, to
learn his sentences upon them.

"After him I saw huge Orion in a meadow full of asphodel, driving the ghosts of the wild beasts that he had killed upon the mountains, and he had a great bronze club in his hand, unbreakable for
ever and ever.

"And I saw Tityus son of Gaia stretched upon the plain and covering some nine acres of ground. Two vultures on either side of
him were digging their beaks into his liver, and he kept on trying
to beat them off with his hands, but could not; for he had violated

[11] After the death of Achilles, his beautiful armor was offered by his mother, the
nymph Thetis, to the man who was judged bravest among the surviving Greeks. It
was awarded to Odysseus, whereupon Ajax killed himself.

Zeus' mistress Leto as she was going through Panopeus on her way to Pytho.

"I saw also the dreadful fate of Tantalus, who stood in a lake that reached his chin. He was dying to quench his thirst, but could never reach the water, for whenever the poor creature stooped to drink, it dried up and vanished, so that there was nothing but dry ground—parched by the spite of heaven. There were tall trees, moreover, that shed their fruit over his head—pears, pomegranates, apples, sweet figs and juicy olives, but whenever the poor creature stretched out his hand to take some, the wind tossed the branches back again to the clouds.

"And I saw Sicyphus at his endless task raising his prodigious stone with both his hands. With hands and feet he tried to roll it up to the top of the hill, but always, just before he could roll it over on to the other side, its weight would be too much for him, and the pitiless stone would come thundering down again on to the plain. Then he would begin trying to push it up hill again, and the sweat ran off him and the steam rose after him.

"After him I saw mighty Heracles, but it was his phantom only, for he is feasting ever with the immortal gods, and has lovely Hebe to wife, who is daughter of Zeus and Hera. The ghosts were screaming round him like scared birds flying all whithers. He looked black as night with his bare bow in his hands and his arrow on the string, glaring around as though ever on the point of taking aim. About his breast there was a wondrous golden belt adorned in the most marvelous fashion with bears, wild boars, and lions with gleaming eyes; there was also war, battle, and death. The man who made that belt, do what he might, would never be able to make another like it. Heracles knew me at once when he saw me, and spoke piteously, saying, 'My poor Odysseus, noble son of Laertes, are you too leading the same sorry kind of life that I did when I was above ground? I was son of Zeus, but I went through an infinity of suffering, for I became bondsman to one who was far beneath me—a low fellow who set me all manner of labors. He once sent me here to fetch the hellhound—for he did not think he could find anything harder for me than this, but I got the hound out of Hades and brought him to him, for Hermes and Athene helped me.'

"On this Heracles went down again into the house of Hades, but I stayed where I was in case some other of the mighty dead should come to me. And I should have seen still other of them that are gone before, whom I would fain have seen—Theseus and Pirithous— glorious children of the gods, but so many thousands of ghosts came round me and uttered such appalling cries, that I was panic-stricken lest Persephone should send up from the house of Hades the head of that awful monster Gorgon. On this I hastened back to my ship and ordered my men to go on board at once and loose the hawsers; so they embarked and took their places, whereon the ship went down the stream of the river Oceanus. We had to row at first, but presently a fair wind sprang up."

BOOK XII

From the house of Hades, Odysseus returned to Circe, who warned him of the dangers ahead and how to meet them. They sailed then, as directed, past the rocks of the Sirens and Scylla and Charybdis. Landing on the island of Sicily, Odysseus' men slaughtered the fine cattle there, the property of the Sun-god. In punishment, Zeus destroyed their ship with his thunderbolts. Odysseus alone escaped drowning and was stranded on Calypso's isle. With this he brings his tale to an end.

AFTER WE WERE CLEAR OF THE RIVER OCEANUS, and had got out into the open sea, we went on till we reached the Aeaean island where there is dawn and sunrise as in other places. We then drew our ship on to the sands and got out of her on to the shore, where we went to sleep and waited till day should break.

"Then, when the child of morning, rosy-fingered Dawn, appeared, I sent some men to Circe's house to fetch the body of Elpenor. We cut firewood from a wood where the headland jutted out into the sea, and after we had wept over him and lamented him we performed his funeral rites. When his body and armor had been burned to ashes, we raised a cairn, set a stone over it, and at the top of the cairn we fixed the oar that he had been used to row with.

"While we were doing all this, Circe, who knew that we had got back from the house of Hades, dressed herself and came to us as fast as she could; and her maidservants came with her bringing us bread, meat, and wine. Then she stood in the midst of us and said, 'You have done a bold thing in going down alive to the house of Hades, and you will have died twice, to other people's once. Now, then, stay here for the rest of the day, feast your fill, and go on with your voyage at daybreak tomorrow morning. In the meantime I will tell Odysseus about your course, and will explain everything to him so as to prevent your suffering from misadventure either by land or sea.'

"We agreed to do as she had said, and feasted through the live-long day to the going down of the sun, but when the sun had set and it came on dark, the men laid themselves down to sleep by the stern cables of the ship. Then Circe took me by the hand and bade me be seated away from the others, while she reclined by my side and asked me all about our adventures.

" 'So far so good,' said she, when I had ended my story, 'and now pay attention to what I am about to tell you—heaven itself, indeed, will recall it to your recollection. First you will come to the Sirens who enchant all who come near them. If anyone unwarily draws in too close and hears the singing of the Sirens, his wife and chil-dren will never welcome him home again, for they sit in a green field and warble him to death with the sweetness of their songs. There is a great heap of dead men's bones lying all around, with the flesh still rotting off them. Therefore pass these Sirens by, and stop your men's ears with wax that none of them may hear; but if you like you can listen yourself, for you may get the men to bind you as you stand upright on a cross-piece halfway up the mast, and they must lash the rope's ends to the mast itself, that you may have the pleasure of listening. If you beg and pray the men to unloose you, then they must bind you faster.

" 'When your crew have taken you past these Sirens, I cannot give you coherent directions as to which of two courses you are to take; I will lay the two alternatives before you, and you must consider them for yourself. On the one hand there are some overhanging rocks against which the deep blue waves of Amphitrite beat with terrific fury; the blessed gods call these rocks the Wanderers. Here not even a bird may pass, no, not even the timid doves that bring ambrosia to Father Zeus, but the sheer rock always carries off one of them, and Father Zeus has to send another to make up their number. No ship that ever yet came to these rocks has got away again, but the waves and whirlwinds of fire are freighted with wreckage and with the bodies of dead men. The only vessel that ever sailed and got through was the famous Argo on her way from the house of Aeetes, and she too would have gone against these great rocks, only that Hera piloted her past them for the love she bore to Jason.

" 'Of these two rocks the one reaches heaven and its peak is lost in a dark cloud. This never leaves it, so that the top is never clear not even in summer and early autumn. No man, though he had twenty hands and twenty feet, could get a foothold on it and climb it, for it runs sheer up, as smooth as though it had been polished. In the middle of it there is a large cavern, looking west and turned towards Erebus; you must take your ship this way, but the cave is so high up that not even the stoutest archer could send an arrow into it. Inside it Scylla sits and yelps with a voice that you might take to be that of a young hound, but in truth she is a dreadful monster and no one—not even a god—could face her without being terror-struck. She has twelve misshapen feet, and six necks of the most prodigious length; and at the end of each neck she has a frightful head with three rows of teeth in each, all set very close together, so that they would crunch anyone to death in a moment. She sits deep within her shady cell thrusting out her heads and peering all round the rock, fishing for dolphins or dogfish or any larger monster that she can catch, of the thousands with which Amphitrite teems.

No ship ever yet got past her without losing some men, for she shoots out all her heads at once, and carries off a man in each mouth.

" 'You will find the other rock lies lower, but they are so close together that there is not more than a bow-shot between them. A large fig tree in full leaf grows upon it, and under it lies the sucking whirlpool of Charybdis. Three times in the day does she vomit forth her waters, and three times she sucks them down again. See that you be not there when she is sucking, for if you are, Poseidon himself could not save you; you must hug the Scylla side and drive your ship by as fast as you can, for you had better lose six men than your whole crew.'

" 'Is there no way,' said I, 'of escaping Charybdis, and at the same time keeping Scylla off when she is trying to harm my men?'

" 'You daredevil,' replied the goddess, 'you are always wanting to fight somebody or something; you will not let yourself be beaten even by the immortals. For Scylla is not mortal; moreover she is savage, extreme, rude, cruel and invincible. There is no help for it; your best chance will be to get by her as fast as ever you can, for if you dwindle about her rock while you are putting on your armor, she may catch you with a second cast of her six heads, and snap up another half dozen of your men. So drive your ship past her at full speed, and roar out lustily to Crataiis who is Scylla's dam, bad luck to her; she will then stop her from making a second raid upon you.

" 'You will now come to the Thrinacian island, and here you will see many herds of cattle and flocks of sheep belonging to the sun-god—seven herds of cattle and seven flocks of sheep, with fifty head in each flock. They do not breed, nor do they become fewer in number, and they are tended by the goddesses Phaethusa and Lampetie, who are children of the sun-god Hyperion by Neaera. Their mother, when she had borne them and had done suckling them, sent them to the Thrinacian island, which was a long way off, to live there and look after their father's flocks and herds. If you leave these flocks unharmed, and think of nothing but getting home, you may yet after much hardship reach Ithaca. But if you harm them, then I forewarn you of the destruction both of your ship and of your comrades; and even though you may yourself escape, you will return late, in bad plight, after losing all your men.'

"Here she ended, and dawn enthroned in gold began to show in heaven, whereon she returned inland. I then went on board and told my men to loose the ship from her moorings; so they at once got into her, took their places, and began to smite the gray sea with their oars. Presently the great and cunning goddess Circe befriended us with a fair wind that blew dead aft, and stayed steadily with us, keeping our sails well filled, so we did whatever wanted doing to the ship's gear, and let her go as wind and helmsman headed her.

"Then, being much troubled in mind, I said to my men, 'My friends, it is not right that one or two of us alone should know the prophecies that Circe has made me, I will therefore tell you about them, so that whether we live or die we may do so with our eyes open. First she said we were to keep clear of the Sirens, who sit and sing most beautifully in a field of flowers; but she said I might hear them myself so long as no one else did. Therefore, take me and bind me to the crosspiece halfway up the mast; bind me as I stand upright, with a bond so fast that I cannot possibly break away, and lash the rope's ends to the mast itself. If I beg and pray you to set me free, then bind me more tightly still.'

"I had hardly finished telling everything to the men before we reached the island of the two Sirens, for the wind had been very favorable. Then all of a sudden it fell dead calm; there was not a breath of wind or ripple upon the water, so the men furled the sails and stowed them; then taking to their oars they whitened the water with the foam they raised in rowing. Meanwhile I took a large wheel of wax and cut it up small with my sword. Then I kneaded the wax in my strong hands till it became soft, which it soon did between the kneading and the rays of the sun-god son of Hyperion. Then I stopped the ears of all my men, and they bound me hands and feet to the mast as I stood upright on the crosspiece; but they went on rowing themselves. When we had got within earshot of the land, and the ship was going at a good rate, the Sirens saw that we were getting in shore and began with their singing.

" 'Come here,' they sang, 'renowned Odysseus, honor to the Achaean name, and listen to our two voices. No one ever sailed past us without staying to hear the enchanting sweetness of our song—and he who listens will go on his way not only charmed, but wiser, for we know all the ills that the gods laid upon the Argives and Trojans before Troy, and can tell you everything that is going to happen over the whole world.'

"They sang these words most musically, and as I longed to hear them further I made signs by frowning to my men that they should set me free; but they quickened their stroke, and Eurylochus and Perimedes bound me with still stronger bonds till we had got out of hearing of the Sirens' voices. Then my men took the wax from their ears and unbound me.

"Immediately after we had got past the island I saw a great wave from which spray was rising, and I heard a loud roaring sound. The men were so frightened that they loosed hold of their oars, for the whole sea resounded with the rushing of the waters, but the ship stayed where it was, for the men had left off rowing. I went round, therefore, and exhorted them man by man not to lose heart.

" 'My friends,' said I, 'this is not the first time that we have been in danger, and we are in nothing like so bad a case as when the Cyclops shut us up in his cave; nevertheless, my courage and wise counsel saved us then, and we shall live to look back on all this as well. Now, therefore, let us all do as I say, trust in Zeus and row on with might and main. As for you, coxswain, these are your orders —attend to them, for the ship is in your hands: turn her head away from these steaming rapids and hug the rock, or she will give you the slip and be over yonder before you know where you are, and you will be the death of us.'

"So they did as I told them; but I said nothing about the awful monster Scylla, for I knew the men would not go on rowing if I did, but would huddle together in the hold. In one thing only did

I disobey Circe's strict instructions—I put on my armor. Then seizing two strong spears I took my stand on the ship's bows, for it was there that I expected first to see the monster of the rock, who was to do my men so much harm; but I could not make her out anywhere, though I strained my eyes looking the gloomy rock all over and over.

"Then we entered the Straits[1] in great fear of mind, for on the one hand was Scylla, and on the other dread Charybdis kept sucking up the salt water. As she vomited it up, it was like the water in a cauldron when it is boiling over upon a great fire, and the spray reached the top of the rocks on either side. When she began to suck again, we could see the water all inside whirling round and round, and it made a deafening sound as it broke against the rocks. We could see the bottom of the whirlpool all black with sand and mud, and the men were at their wits ends for fear. While we were taken up with this, and were expecting each moment to be our last, Scylla pounced down suddenly upon us and snatched up my six best men. I was looking at once after both ship and men, and in a moment I saw their hands and feet ever so high above me, struggling in the air as Scylla was carrying them off, and I heard them call out my name in one last despairing cry. As a fisherman, seated, spear in hand, upon some jutting rock,[2] throws bait into the water to deceive the poor little fishes, and spears them with the ox's horn with which his spear is shod, throwing them gasping on to the land as he catches them one by one—even so did Scylla land these panting creatures on her rock and munch them up at the mouth of her den, while they screamed and stretched out their hands to me in their mortal agony. This was the most sickening sight that I saw throughout all my voyages.

"When we had passed the [Wandering] rocks, with Scylla and terrible Charybdis, we reached the noble island of the sun-god, where were the goodly cattle and sheep belonging to the sun Hy-

---

[1] These straits are generally understood to be the Straits of Messina.
[2] In the islands of Favognana and Marettimo off Sicily I have seen men fish exactly as here described. They chew bread into a paste and throw it into the sea to attract the fish, which they then spear. No line is used. (B.)

perion. While still at sea in my ship I could hear the cattle lowing
as they came home to the yards, and the sheep bleating. Then I remembered what the blind Theban prophet Teiresias had told me,
and how carefully Aeaean Circe had warned me to shun the island
of the blessed sun-god. So being much troubled, I said to the men,
'My men, I know you are hard pressed, but listen while I tell you
the prophecy that Teiresias made me, and how carefully Aeaean
Circe warned me to shun the island of the blessed sun-god, for it
was here, she said, that our worst danger would lie. Head the ship,
therefore, away from the island.'

"The men were in despair at this, and Eurylochus at once gave
me an insolent answer. 'Odysseus,' said he, 'you are cruel. You are
very strong yourself and never get worn out; you seem to be made
of iron, and now, though your men are exhausted with toil and
want to sleep, you will not let them land and cook themselves a good
supper upon this island, but bid them put out to sea and go faring
fruitlessly on through the watches of the flying night. It is by night
that the winds blow hardest and do so much damage. How can we
escape should one of those sudden squalls spring up from southwest
or west, which so often wreck a vessel when our lords the gods are
unpropitious? Now, therefore, let us obey the behests of night and
prepare our supper here hard by the ship; tomorrow morning we
will go on board again and put out to sea.'

"Thus spoke Eurylochus, and the men approved his words. I saw
that heaven meant us a mischief and said, 'You force me to yield, for
you are many against one, but at any rate each one of you must take
his solemn oath that if he meet with a herd of cattle or a large flock
of sheep, he will not be so mad as to kill a single head of either, but
will be satisfied with the food that Circe has given us.'

"They all swore as I bade them, and when they had completed
their oath we made the ship fast in a harbor that was near a stream
of fresh water, and the men went ashore and cooked their suppers.
As soon as they had had enough to eat and drink, they began talking
about their poor comrades whom Scylla had snatched up and eaten;

this set them weeping, and they went on crying till they fell off into a sound sleep.

"In the third watch of the night when the stars had shifted their places, Zeus raised a great gale of wind that blew a hurricane so that land and sea were covered with thick clouds, and night sprang forth out of the heavens. When the child of morning, rosy-fingered Dawn, appeared, we brought the ship to land and drew her into a cave wherein the sea-nymphs hold their courts and dances, and I called the men together in council.

" 'My friends,' said I, 'we have meat and drink in the ship, let us mind, therefore, and not touch the cattle, or we shall suffer for it; for these cattle and sheep belong to the mighty sun, who sees and gives ear to everything.' And again they promised that they would obey.

"For a whole month the wind blew steadily from the south, and there was no other wind, but only south and east.[3] As long as corn and wine held out the men did not touch the cattle when they were hungry. When, however, they had eaten all there was in the ship, they were forced to go further afield, fishing with hook and line, catching birds, and taking whatever they could lay their hands on, for they were starving. One day, therefore, I went up inland that I might pray heaven to show me some means of getting away. When I had gone far enough to be clear of all my men, and had found a place that was well sheltered from the wind, I washed my hands and prayed to all the gods in Olympus till by and by they sent me off into a sweet sleep.

"Meanwhile Eurylochus had been giving evil counsel to the men. 'Listen to me,' said he, 'my poor comrades. All deaths are bad enough, but there is none so bad as famine. Why should not we drive in the best of these cows and offer them in sacrifice to the immortal gods? If we ever get back to Ithaca, we can build a fine temple to the sun-god and enrich it with every kind of ornament. If,

[3] The writer evidently regards Odysseus as on a coast that looked east at no great distance south of the Straits of Messina somewhere, say, near Tauromenium, now Taormina. (B.)

however, he is determined to sink our ship out of revenge for these horned cattle, and the other gods are of the same mind, I for one would rather drink salt water once for all and have done with it than be starved to death by inches in such a desert island as this is.'

"Thus spoke Eurylochus, and the men approved his words. Now the cattle, so fair and goodly, were feeding not far from the ship; the men, therefore, drove in the best of them, and they all stood round them saying their prayers, and using young oak-shoots instead of barley meal, for there was no barley left. When they had done praying they killed the cows and dressed their carcasses; they cut out the thighbones, wrapped them round in two layers of fat, and set some pieces of raw meat on the top of them. They had no wine with which to make drink offerings over the sacrifice while it was cooking, so they kept pouring on a little water from time to time while the inward meats were being grilled. Then, when the thigh-bones were burned and they had tasted the inward meats, they cut the rest up small and put the pieces upon the spits.

"By this time my deep sleep had left me, and I turned back to the ship and to the seashore. As I drew near I began to smell hot roast meat, so I groaned out a prayer to the immortal gods. 'Father Zeus,' I exclaimed, 'and all you other gods who live in everlasting bliss, you have done me a cruel mischief by the sleep into which you have sent me. See what fine work these men of mine have been making in my absence.'

"Meanwhile Lampetie went straight off to the sun and told him we had been killing his cows, whereon he flew into a great rage, and said to the immortals, 'Father Zeus, and all you other gods who live in everlasting bliss, I must have vengeance on the crew of Odysseus' ship. They have had the insolence to kill my cows, which were the one thing I loved to look upon, whether I was going up heaven or down again. If they do not square accounts with me about my cows, I will go down to Hades and shine there among the dead.'

" 'Sun,' said Zeus, 'go on shining upon us gods and upon mankind over the fruitful earth. I will shiver their ship into little pieces with a bolt of white lightning as soon as they get out to sea.'

"I was told all this by Calypso, who said she had heard it from the mouth of Hermes.

"As soon as I got down to my ship and to the seashore, I rebuked each one of the men separately, but we could see no way out of it, for the cows were dead already. And indeed the gods began at once to show signs and wonders among us, for the hides of the cattle crawled about, and the joints upon the spits began to low like cows, and the meat, whether cooked or raw, kept on making a noise just as cows do.

"For six days my men kept driving in the best cows and feasting upon them, but when Zeus the son of Cronus had added a seventh day, the fury of the gale abated; we therefore went on board, raised our masts, spread sail, and put out to sea. As soon as we were well away from the island, and could see nothing but sky and sea, the son of Cronus raised a black cloud over our ship, and the sea grew dark beneath it. We did not get on much further, for in another moment we were caught by a terrific squall from the west that snapped the forestays of the mast so that it fell aft, while all the ship's gear tumbled about at the bottom of the vessel. The mast fell upon the head of the helmsman in the ship's stern, so that the bones of his head were crushed to pieces, and he fell overboard as though he were diving, with no more life left in him.

"Then Zeus let fly his thunderbolts, and the ship went round and round, and was filled with fire and brimstone as the lightning struck it. The men all fell into the sea; they were carried about in the water round the ship, looking like so many sea gulls, but the god presently deprived them of all chance of getting home again.

"I stuck to the ship till the sea knocked her sides from her keel (which drifted about by itself) and struck the mast out of her in the direction of the keel; but there was a backstay of stout ox-thong still hanging about it, and with this I lashed the mast and keel together, and getting astride of them was carried wherever the winds chose to take me.

"The gale from the west had now spent its force, and the wind got into the south again, which frightened me lest I should be taken back to the terrible whirlpool of Charybdis. This indeed was what actually happened, for I was borne along by the waves all night, and by sunrise had reached the rock of Scylla, and the whirlpool. She was then sucking down the salt sea water, but I was carried aloft toward the fig tree, which I caught hold of and clung on to like a bat. I could not plant my feet anywhere so as to stand securely, for the roots were a long way off and the boughs that overshadowed the whole pool were too high, too vast, and too far apart for me to reach them; so I hung patiently on, waiting till the pool should discharge my mast and raft again—and a very long while it seemed. A juryman is not more glad to get home to supper, after having been long detained in court by troublesome cases, than I was to see my raft beginning to work its way out of the whirlpool again. At last I let go with my hands and feet, and fell heavily into the sea, hard by my raft on to which I then got, and began to row with my hands. As for Scylla, the father of gods and men would not let her get further sight of me—otherwise I should have certainly been lost.

"Hence I was carried along for nine days till on the tenth night the gods stranded me on the Ogygian island, where dwells the great and powerful goddess Calypso. She took me in and was kind to me, but I need say no more about this, for I told you and your noble wife all about it yesterday, and I hate saying the same thing over and over again."

BOOK XIII

Odysseus is given more rich gifts by Alcinous and his nobles and sent away at night in a ship to Ithaca. On arrival he is carried, sleeping, ashore and set gently down with his treasure on his native soil. The ship on its return is changed by angry Poseidon into a rock. When Odysseus wakes, Athene appears to tell him where he is and counsel him to caution. She helps him conceal his treasure and then transforms him into an ugly old beggar.

THUS DID HE SPEAK, AND THEY ALL HELD THEIR peace throughout the covered cloister, enthralled by the charm of his story, till presently Alcinous began to speak.

"Odysseus," said he, "now that you have reached my house I doubt not you will get home without further misadventure no matter how much you have suffered in the past. To you others, however, who come here night after night to drink my choicest wine and listen to my bard, I would insist as follows. Our guest has already packed up the clothes, wrought gold, and other valuables which you have brought for his acceptance; let us now, therefore, present him further, each one of us, with a large tripod and a cauldron. We will recoup ourselves by the levy of a general rate; for private individuals cannot be expected to bear the burden of such a handsome present."

Everyone approved of this, and then they went home to bed each in his own abode. When the child of morning, rosy-fingered Dawn, appeared, they hurried down to the ship and brought their cauldrons with them. Alcinous went on board and saw everything so securely stowed under the ship's benches that nothing could break adrift and injure the rowers. Then they went to the house of Alcinous to get dinner, and he sacrificed a bull for them in honor of Zeus, who is the lord of all. They set the steaks to grill and made an excellent dinner, after which the inspired bard, Demodocus, who was a favorite with everyone, sang to them; but Odysseus kept on turning his eyes towards the sun, as though to hasten his setting, for he was longing to be on his way. As one who has been all day plowing a fallow field with a couple of oxen keeps thinking about his supper and is glad when night comes that he may go and get it, for it is all his legs can do to carry him, even so did Odysseus rejoice when the sun went down, and he at once said to the Phaeacians, addressing himself more particularly to King Alcinous:

"Sir, and all of you, farewell. Make your drink offerings and send me on my way rejoicing, for you have fulfilled my heart's desire by giving me an escort, and making me presents, which heaven grant that I may turn to good account. May I find my admirable wife living in peace among friends, and may you whom I leave behind me give satisfaction to your wives and children. May heaven vouchsafe you every good grace, and may no evil thing come among your people."

Thus did he speak. His hearers all of them approved his saying and agreed that he should have his escort, inasmuch as he had spoken reasonably. Alcinous therefore said to his servant, "Pontonous, mix some wine and hand it round to everybody, that we may offer a prayer to father Zeus and speed our guest upon his way."

Pontonous mixed the wine and handed it to everyone in turn. The others each from his own seat made a drink offering to the blessed gods that live in heaven, but Odysseus rose and placed the double cup in the hands of Queen Arete.

"Farewell, Queen," said he, "henceforth and forever, till age and death, the common lot of mankind, lay their hands upon you. I now take my leave; be happy in this house with your children, your people, and with King Alcinous."

As he spoke he crossed the threshold, and Alcinous sent a man to conduct him to his ship and to the seashore. Arete also sent some maidservants with him—one with a clean shirt and cloak, another to carry his strong-box, and a third with corn and wine. When they got to the water side the crew took these things and put them on board, with all the meat and drink; but for Odysseus they spread a rug and a linen sheet on deck that he might sleep soundly in the stern of the ship. Then he too went on board and lay down without a word, but the crew took every man his place and loosed the hawser from the pierced stone to which it had been bound. Thereon, when they began rowing out to sea, Odysseus fell into a deep, sweet, and almost deathlike slumber.

The ship bounded forward on her way as a four-in-hand chariot flies over the course when the horses feel the whip. Her prow curveted as it were the neck of a stallion, and a great wave of dark blue water seethed in her wake. She held steadily on her course, and even a falcon, swiftest of all birds, could not have kept pace with her. Thus, then, she cut her way through the water, carrying one who was as cunning as the gods, but who was now sleeping peacefully, forgetful of all that he had suffered both on the field of battle and by the waves of the weary sea.

When the bright star that heralds the approach of dawn began to show, the ship drew near to land. Now there is in Ithaca a haven of the old merman Phorcys, which lies between two points that break the line of the sea and shut the harbor in. These shelter it from the storms of wind and sea that rage outside, so that, when once within it, a ship may lie without being even moored. At the head of this harbor there is a large olive tree, and at no great distance a fine overarching cavern sacred to the nymphs who are called Naiads. There are mixing-bowls within it and wine-jars of stone, and the bees hive there. Moreover, there are great looms of stone on which the nymphs weave their robes of sea purple—very curious to see—and at all times there is water within it. It has two entrances, one facing north by which mortals can go down into the cave, while the other comes from the south and is more mysterious. Mortals cannot possibly get in by it, it is the way taken by the gods.

Into this harbor, then, they took their ship, for they knew the place. She had so much way upon her that she ran half her own length on to the shore. When, however, they had landed, the first thing they did was to lift Odysseus with his rug and linen sheet out of the ship, and lay him down upon the sand still fast asleep. Then they took out the presents which Athene had persuaded the Phaeacians to give him when he was setting out on his voyage homewards. They put these all together by the root of the olive tree, away from the road, for fear some passer-by might come and steal them before Odysseus awoke; and then they made the best of their way home again.

But Poseidon did not forget the threats with which he had already threatened Odysseus, so he took counsel with Zeus. "Father Zeus," said he, "I shall no longer be held in any sort of respect among you gods, if mortals like the Phaeacians, who are my own flesh and blood, show such small regard for me. I said I would let Odysseus get home when he had suffered sufficiently. I did not say that he should never get home at all, for I knew you had already nodded your head about it, and promised that he should do so. But now they have brought him in a ship fast asleep and have landed him in Ithaca, after loading him with magnificent presents of bronze, gold, and raiment that he would ever have brought back from Troy, if he had had his share of the spoil and got home without misadventure."

And Zeus answered: "What, O Lord of the Earthquake, are you talking about? The gods are by no means wanting in respect for you. It would be monstrous were they to insult one so old and honored as you are. As regards mortals, however, if any of them is indulging in insolence and treating you disrespectfully, it will always rest with yourself to deal with him as you may think proper, so do just as you please.

"I should have done so at once," replied Poseidon, "if I were not anxious to avoid anything that might displease you; now, therefore, I should like to wreck the Phaeacian ship as it is returning from its escort. This will stop them from escorting people in future; and I should also like to bury their city under a huge mountain."

"My good friend," answered Zeus, "I should recommend you at the very moment when the people from the city are watching the ship on her way, to turn it into a rock near the land and looking like a ship. This will astonish everybody, and you can then bury their city under the mountain."

When earth-encircling Poseidon heard this, he went to Scheria where the Phaeacians live and stayed there till the ship, which was making rapid way, had got close in. Then he went up to it, turned it into stone, and drove it down with the flat of his hand so as to root it in the ground. After this he went away.

The Phaeacians then began talking among themselves, and one would turn towards his neighbor, saying, "Bless my heart, who is it that can have rooted the ship in the sea just as she was getting into port? We could see the whole of her only a moment ago."

This was how they talked, but they knew nothing about it; and Alcinous said: "I remember now the old prophecy of my father. He said that Poseidon would be angry with us for taking everyone so safely over the sea, and would one day wreck a Phaeacian ship as it was returning from an escort, and bury our city under a high mountain. This was what my old father used to say, and now it is all coming true. Now therefore let us all do as I say. In the first place we must leave off giving people escorts when they come here, and in the next let us sacrifice twelve picked bulls to Poseidon that he may have mercy upon us, and not bury our city under the high mountain." When the people heard this they were afraid and got ready the bulls.

Thus did the chiefs and rulers of the Phaeacians pray to King Poseidon, standing round his altar; and at the same time Odysseus woke up once more upon his own soil. He had been so long away that he did not know it again. Moreover, Zeus' daughter Athene had made it a foggy day, so that people might not know of his having come, and that she might tell him everything without either his wife or his fellow citizens and friends recognizing him until he had taken his revenge upon the wicked suitors. Everything, therefore, seemed quite different to him—the long straight tracks, the harbors, the precipices, and the goodly trees, appeared all changed as he started up and looked upon his native land. So he smote his thighs with the flat of his hands and cried aloud despairingly.

"Alas," he exclaimed, "among what manner of people am I fallen? Are they savage and uncivilized or hospitable and humane? Where shall I put all this treasure, and which way shall I go? I wish I had stayed over there with the Phaeacians; or I could have gone to some other great chief who would have been good to me and given me an escort. As it is I do not know where to put my treasure, and I cannot leave it here for fear somebody else should get hold of it. In good truth the chiefs and rulers of the Phaeacians have not been dealing fairly by me, and have left me in the wrong country; they said they would take me back to Ithaca and they have not done so. May Zeus, the protector of suppliants, chastise them, for he watches over everybody and punishes those who do wrong. Still, I suppose I must count my goods and see if the crew have gone off with any of them."

He counted his goodly coppers and cauldrons, his gold and all his clothes, but there was nothing missing. Still he kept grieving about not being in his own country, and wandered up and down by the shore of the sounding sea bewailing his hard fate. Then Athene came up to him disguised as a young shepherd of delicate and princely mien, with a good cloak folded double about her shoulders; she had sandals on her comely feet and held a javelin in her hand. Odysseus was glad when he saw her, and went straight up to her.

"My friend," said he, "you are the first person whom I have met with in this country. I salute you, therefore, and beg you to be well disposed towards me. Protect these my goods, and myself too, for I embrace your knees and pray to you as though you were a god. Tell me, then, and tell me truly, what land and country is this?

Who are its inhabitants? Am I on an island, or is this the seaboard of some continent?"

Athene answered: "Stranger, you must be very simple, or must have come from somewhere a long way off, not to know what country this is. It is a very celebrated place, and everybody knows it both east and west. It is rugged and not a good driving country, but it is by no means a bad island for what there is of it. It grows any quantity of corn and also wine, for it is watered both by rain and dew; it breeds cattle also and goats. All kinds of timber grow here, and there are watering places where the water never runs dry. So, sir, the name of Ithaca is known even as far as Troy, which I understand to be a long way off from this Achaean country."

Odysseus was glad at finding himself, as Athene told him, in his own country, and he began to answer, but he did not speak the truth, and made up a lying story in the instinctive wiliness of his heart.

"I heard of Ithaca," said he, "when I was in Crete beyond the seas, and now it seems I have reached it with all these treasures. I have left as much more behind me for my children, but am flying because I killed Orsilochus son of Idomeneus, the fleetest runner in Crete. I killed him because he wanted to rob me of the spoils I had got from Troy with so much trouble and danger both on the field of battle and by the waves of the weary sea. He said I had not served his father loyally at Troy as vassal, but had set myself up as an independent ruler, so I lay in wait for him with one of my followers by the roadside, and speared him as he was coming into town from the country. It was a very dark night and nobody saw us. It was not known, therefore, that I had killed him, but as soon as I had done so I went to a ship and besought the owners, who were Phoenicians, to take me on board and set me in Pylos or in Elis where the Epeans rule, giving them as much spoil as satisfied them. They meant no guile, but the wind drove them off their course, and we sailed on till we came hither by night. It was all we could do to get inside the harbor, and none of us said a word about supper though we wanted it badly, but we all went on shore and lay down just as we were. I was very tired and fell asleep directly, so they took my goods out of the ship and placed them beside me where I was lying upon the sand. Then they sailed away to Sidonia, and I was left here in great distress of mind."

Such was his story, but Athene smiled and caressed him with her hand. Then she took the form of a woman, fair, stately, and wise. "He must be indeed a shifty lying fellow," said she, "who could surpass you in all manner of craft even though you had a god for your antagonist. Daredevil that you are, full of guile, unwearying in deceit, can you not drop your tricks and your instinctive false-hood, even now that you are in your own country again? We will say no more, however, about this, for we can both of us deceive upon occasion. You are the most accomplished counselor and orator among all mankind, while I for diplomacy and subtlety have no equal among the gods. Did you not know Zeus' daughter Athene—me, who have been ever with you, who kept watch over you in all your troubles, and who made the Phaeacians take so great a liking to you? And now, again, I am come here to talk things over with you, and help you to hide the treasure I made the Phaeacians give you. I want to tell you about the troubles that await you in your own house; you have got to face them, but tell no one, neither man nor woman, that you have come home again. Bear everything and put up with every man's insolence without a word."

And Odysseus, answered: "A man, goddess, may know a great deal, but you are so constantly changing your appearance that when he meets you it is a hard matter for him to know whether it is you or not. This much, however, I know exceedingly well; you were very kind to me as long as we Achaeans were fighting before Troy, but from the day on which we went on board ship after having sacked the city of Priam, and heaven dispersed us—from that day, Athene, I saw no more of you, and cannot ever remember your com-ing to my ship to help me in a difficulty. I had to wander on sick and sorry till the gods delivered me from evil and I reached the city of the Phaeacians, where you encouraged me and took me into the town. And now, I beseech you in your father's name, tell me the truth, for I do not believe I am really back in Ithaca. I am in some other country and you are mocking me and deceiving me in all you have been saying. Tell me then truly, have I really got back to my own country?"

"You are always taking something of that sort into your head," replied Athene, "and that is why I cannot desert you in your afflictions; you are so plausible, shrewd, and shifty. Anyone but yourself on returning from so long a voyage would at once have gone home to see his wife and children, but you do not seem to care about asking after them or hearing any news about them till you have made sure of your wife, who remains at home vainly grieving for you, and having no peace night or day for the tears she sheds on your behalf. As for my not coming near you, I was never uneasy about you, for I was certain you would get back safely, though you would lose all your men. I did not wish to quarrel with my uncle Poseidon, who never forgave you for having blinded his son.[1] I will now, however, point out to you the lie of the land, and you will then perhaps believe me. This is the haven of the old merman Phorcys, and here is the olive tree that grows at the head of it; near it is the cave sacred to the Naiads; here too is the overarching cavern in which you have offered many an acceptable hecatomb to the nymphs, and this is the wooded mountain Neritum."

As she spoke, the goddess dispersed the mist and the land appeared. Then Odysseus rejoiced at finding himself again in his own land, and kissed the bounteous soil. He lifted up his hands and prayed to the nymphs, saying, "Naiad nymphs, daughters of Zeus, I made sure that I was never again to see you, now therefore I greet you with all loving salutations, and I will bring you offerings as in the old days, if Zeus' redoubtable daughter will grant me life, and bring my son to manhood."

"Take heart, and do not trouble yourself about that," rejoined Athene, "let us rather set about stowing your things at once in the cave, where they will be quite safe. Let us see how we can best manage it all."

[1] That is, the Cyclops Polyphemus.

Therewith she went down into the cave to look for the safest hiding places, while Odysseus brought up all the treasure of gold, bronze, and good clothing which the Phaeacians had given him. They stowed everything carefully away, and Athene set a stone against the door of the cave. Then the two sat down by the root of the great olive, and consulted how to compass the destruction of the wicked suitors.

"Odyessus," said Athene, "noble son of Laertes, think how you can lay hands on these disreputable people who have been lording it in your house these three years, courting your wife and making wedding presents to her, while she does nothing but lament your absence, giving hope and sending encouraging messages to every one of them, but meaning the very opposite of all she says."

And Odysseus answered: "In good truth, goddess, it seems I should have come to much the same bad end in my own house as Agamemnon did, if you had not given me such timely information. Advise me how I shall best avenge myself. Stand by my side and put your courage into my heart as on the day when we loosed Troy's fair diadem from her brow. Help me now as you did then, and I will fight three hundred men, if you, goddess, will be with me."

"Trust me for that," said she, "I will not lose sight of you when once we set about it, and I imagine that some of those who are devouring your substance will then bespatter the pavement with their blood and brains. I will begin by disguising you so that no human being shall know you. I will cover your body with wrinkles; you shall lose all your yellow hair. I will clothe you in a garment that shall fill all who see it with loathing; I will blear your fine eyes for you, and make you an unseemly object in the sight of the suitors, of your wife, and of the son whom you left behind you. Then go at once to the swineherd who is in charge of your pigs; he has been always well affected towards you, and is devoted to Penelope and your son. You will find him feeding his pigs near the rock that is called Raven by the fountain Arethusa, where they are fattening on beech mast and spring water after their manner. Stay with him and find out how things are going, while I proceed to Sparta and see your son, who is with Menelaus at Sparta, where he has gone to try and find out whether you are still alive."

"But why," said Odysseus, "did you not tell him, for you know all about it? Did you want him too to go sailing about amid all kinds of hardship while others are eating up his estate?"

Athene answered: "Never mind about him, I sent him that he might be well spoken of for having gone. He is in no sort of difficulty, but is staying quite comfortably with Menelaus, and is surrounded with abundance of every kind. The suitors have put out to sea and are lying in wait for him, for they mean to kill him before he can get home. I do not much think they will succeed, but rather that some of those who are now eating up your estate will first find a grave themselves."

As she spoke Athene touched him with her wand and covered him with wrinkles, took away all his yellow hair, and withered the flesh over his whole body. She bleared his eyes, which were naturally very fine ones; she changed his clothes and threw an old rag of a wrap about him, and a tunic, tattered, filthy, and begrimed with smoke. She also gave him an undressed deerskin as an outer garment, and furnished him with a staff and a wallet all in holes, with a twisted thong for him to sling it over his shoulder.

When the pair had thus laid their plans they parted, and the goddess went straight to Sparta to fetch Telemachus.

BOOK XIV

Odysseus finds the hut of his swineherd Eumaeus. He is made welcome and learns the news of home. He does not reveal himself to Eumaeus, but tells him a long lying story with a feigned report in it of Odysseus' probable return. They make sacrifices and eat together. Odysseus spends the night comfortably in Eumaeus' hut.

ODYSSEUS NOW LEFT THE HAVEN, AND TOOK the rough track up through the wooded country and over the crest of the mountain till he reached the place where Athene had said that he would find the swineherd, who was the most thrifty servant he had. He found him sitting in front of his hut, which was by the yards that he had built on a site which could be seen from far. He had made them spacious and fair to see, with a free run for the pigs all round them; he had built them during his master's absence, of stones which he had gathered out of the ground, without saying anything to Penelope or Laertes, and he had fenced them on top with thorn bushes. Outside the yard he had run a strong fence of oaken posts, split, and set pretty close together, while inside he had built twelve sties near one another for the sows to lie in. There were fifty pigs wallowing in each sty, all of them breeding sows; but the boars slept outside and were much fewer

in number, for the suitors kept on eating them, and the swineherd
had to send them the best he had continually. There were three
hundred and sixty boar pigs, and the herdsman's four hounds, which
were as fierce as wolves, slept always with them. The swineherd
was at that moment cutting out a pair of sandals from a good stout
oxhide. Three of his men were out herding the pigs in one place
or another, and he had sent the fourth to town with a boar that he
had been forced to send the suitors that they might sacrifice it and
have their fill of meat.

When the hounds saw Odysseus they set up a furious barking
and flew at him, but Odysseus was cunning enough to sit down and
loose his hold of the stick that he had in his hand. Still, he would
have been torn by them in his own homestead had not the swineherd dropped his oxhide, rushed full speed through the gate of the
yard and driven the dogs off by shouting and throwing stones at
them. Then he said to Odysseus: "Old man, the dogs were likely
to have made short work of you, and then you would have got me
into trouble. The gods have given me quite enough worries without
that, for I have lost the best of masters, and am in continual grief
on his account. I have to attend swine for other people to eat, while
he, if he yet lives to see the light of day, is starving in some distant
land. But come inside, and when you have had your fill of bread
and wine, tell me where you come from, and all about your misfortunes."

On this the swineherd led the way into the hut and bade him sit
down. He strewed a good thick bed of rushes upon the floor, and on
the top of this he threw the shaggy chamois skin—a great thick one
—on which he used to sleep by night. Odysseus was pleased at being
made thus welcome, and said, "May Zeus, sir, and the rest of the
gods grant you your heart's desire in return for the kind way in
which you have received me."

To this you answered, O swineherd Eumaeus: "Stranger, though
a still poorer man should come here, it would not be right for me
to insult him, for all strangers and beggars are from Zeus. You must
take what you can get and be thankful, for servants live in fear

when they have young lords for their masters. And this is my misfortune now, for heaven has hindered the return of him who would have been always good to me and given me something of my own—a house, a piece of land, a good-looking wife, and all else that a liberal master allows a servant who has worked hard for him, and whose labor the gods have prospered as they have mine in the situation which I hold. If my master had grown old here he would have done great things by me, but he is gone, and I wish that Helen's whole race were utterly destroyed, for she has been the death of many a good man. It was this matter that took my master to Ilium, the land of noble steeds, to fight the Trojans in the cause of King Agamemnon."

As he spoke he bound his girdle round him and went to the sties where the young sucking pigs were penned. He picked out two which he brought back with him and sacrificed. He singed them, cut them up, and spitted them; when the meat was cooked he brought it all in and set it before Odysseus, hot and still on the spit, whereon Odysseus sprinkled it over with white barley meal. The swineherd then mixed wine in a bowl of ivy-wood, and taking a seat opposite Odysseus told him to begin.

"Fall to, stranger," said he, "on a dish of servant's pork. The fat pigs have to go to the suitors, who eat them up without shame or scruple; but the blessed gods love not such shameful doings, and respect those who do what is lawful and right. Even the fierce freebooters who go raiding on other people's land, and Zeus gives them their spoil—even they, when they have filled their ships and got home again, live conscience-stricken, and look fearfully for judgment. But some god seems to have told these people that Odysseus is dead and gone. They will not, therefore, go back to their own homes and make their offers of marriage in the usual way, but waste his estate by force, without fear or stint. Not a day or night comes out of heaven, but they sacrifice not one victim or two only, and they take the run of his wine, for he was exceedingly rich. No other great man either in Ithaca or on the mainland is as rich as he was; he had as much as twenty men put together. I will tell you what he had. There are twelve herds of cattle upon the mainland, and as many flocks of sheep, there are also twelve droves of pigs, while his own men and hired strangers feed him twelve widely spreading herds of goats. Here in Ithaca he runs eleven large flocks of goats on the far end of the island, and they are in the charge of excellent goatherds. Each one of these sends the suitors the best goat in the flock every day. As for myself, I am in charge of the pigs that you see here, and I have to keep picking out the best I have and sending it to them."

This was his story, but Odysseus went on eating and drinking ravenously without a word, brooding his revenge. When he had eaten enough and was satisfied, the swineherd took the bowl from which he usually drank, filled it with wine, and gave it to Odysseus, who was pleased, and said as he took it in his hands, "My friend, who was this master of yours that bought you and paid for you, so rich and so powerful as you tell me? You say he perished in the cause of King Agamemnon; tell me who he was, in case I may have met with such a person. Zeus and the other gods know, but I may be able to give you news of him, for I have traveled much."

Eumaeus answered: "Old man, no traveler who comes here with news will get Odysseus' wife and son to believe his story. Nevertheless, tramps in want of a lodging keep coming with their mouths full of lies, and not a word of truth. Everyone who finds his way to Ithaca goes to my mistress and tells her falsehoods, whereon she takes them in, makes much of them, and asks them all manner of questions, crying all the time as women will when they have lost their husbands. And you too, old man, for a shirt and cloak would doubtless make up a very pretty story. But the wolves and birds of prey have long since torn Odysseus to pieces, or the fishes of the sea have eaten him, and his bones are lying buried deep in sand upon some foreign shore. He is dead and gone, and a bad business it is for all his friends—for me especially. Go where I may I shall never find so good a master, not even if I were to go home to my father and mother where I was bred and born. I do not so much care, however, about my parents now, though I should dearly like to see them again in my own country. It is the loss of Odysseus that grieves me most; I cannot speak of him without reverence though he is here no longer, for he was very fond of me, and took such care of me that wherever he may be I shall always honor his memory."

"My friend," replied Odysseus, "you are very positive, and very hard of belief about your master's coming home again; nevertheless, I will not merely say, but will swear, that he is coming. Do not give me anything for my news till he has actually come, you may then give me a shirt and cloak of good wear if you will. I am in great want, but I will not take anything at all till then, for I hate a man, even as I hate hell fire, who lets his poverty tempt him into lying. I swear by King Zeus, by the rites of hospitality, and by that hearth of Odysseus to which I have now come, that all will surely happen as I have said it will. Odysseus will return in this selfsame year; with the end of this moon and the beginning of the next he will be here to do vengeance on all those who are ill-treating his wife and son."

To this you answered, O swineherd Eumaeus: "Old man, you will neither get paid for bringing good news, nor will Odysseus ever come home. Drink your wine in peace, and let us talk about something else. Do not keep on reminding me of all this; it always pains me when anyone speaks about my honored master. As for your oath, we will let it alone, but I only wish he may come, as do Penelope, his old father Laertes, and his son Telemachus. I am terribly unhappy too about this same boy of his. He was running up fast into manhood, and bade fare to be no worse man, face and figure, than his father, but someone, either god or man, has been unsettling his mind, so he has gone off to Pylos to try and get news of his father, and the suitors are lying in wait for him as he is coming home, in the hope of leaving the house of Arceisius without a name in Ithaca. But let us say no more about him, and leave him to be taken, or else to escape, if the son of Cronus holds his hand over him to protect him. And now, old man, tell me your own story; tell me also, for I want to know, who you are and where you come from. Tell me of your town and parents, what manner of ship you came in, how your crew brought you to Ithaca, and from what country they professed to come—for you cannot have come by land."

And Odysseus answered: "I will tell you all about it. If there were meat and wine enough, and we could stay here in the hut with nothing to do but to eat and drink while the others go to their work, I could easily talk on for a whole twelve months without ever finishing the story of the sorrows with which it has pleased heaven to visit me.

"I am by birth a Cretan; my father was a well-to-do man, who had many sons born in marriage, whereas I was the son of a slave whom he had purchased for a concubine. Nevertheless, my father Castor son of Hylax (whose lineage I claim, and who was held in the highest honor among the Cretans for his wealth, prosperity, and the valor of his sons) put me on the same level with my brothers who had been born in wedlock. When, however, death took him to the house of Hades, his sons divided his estate and cast lots for their shares, but to me they gave a holding and little else. Nevertheless, my valor enabled me to marry into a rich family, for I was not given to bragging, or shirking on the field of battle. It is all over now; still, if you look at the straw you can see what the ear was, for I have had trouble enough and to spare. Ares and Athene made me doughty in war. When I had picked my men to surprise the enemy with an ambuscade, I never gave death so much as a thought, but was the first to leap forward and spear all whom I could overtake. Such was I in battle, but I did not care about farm work, nor the frugal home life of those who would bring up children. My delight was in ships, fighting, javelins, and arrows—things that most men shudder to think of. But one man likes one thing and another another, and this was what I was most naturally inclined to. Before the Achaeans went to Troy, nine times was I in command of men and ships on foreign service, and I amassed much wealth. I had my pick of the spoil in the first instance, and much more was allotted to me later on.

"My house grew apace and I became a great man among the Cretans, but when Zeus counseled that terrible expedition in which

so many perished, the people required me and Idomeneus to lead
their ships to Troy, and there was no way out of it, for they insisted
on our doing so. There we fought for nine whole years, but in the
tenth we sacked the city of Priam and sailed home again as heaven
dispersed us. Then it was that Zeus devised evil against me. I spent
but one month happily with my children, wife, and property, and
then I conceived the idea of making a descent on Egypt, so I fitted
out a fine fleet and manned it. I had nine ships, and the people
flocked to fill them. For six days I and my men made feast, and I
found them many victims both for sacrifice to the gods and for themselves, but on the seventh day we went on board and set sail from
Crete with a fair north wind behind us as though we were going
down a river. Nothing went ill with any of our ships, and we had no
sickness on board, but sat where we were and let the ships go as the
wind and steersmen took them. On the fifth day we reached the
river Aegyptus; there I stationed my ships in the river, bidding my
men stay by them and keep guard over them while I sent out scouts
to reconnoiter from every point of vantage.

"But the men disobeyed my orders, took to their own devices, and
ravaged the land of the Egyptians, killing the men, and taking their
wives and children captive. The alarm was soon carried to the city,
and when they heard the war cry, the people came out at daybreak
till the plain was filled with horsemen and foot soldiers and with the
gleam of armor. Then Zeus spread panic among my men, and they
would no longer face the enemy, for they found themselves surrounded. The Egyptians killed many of us, and took the rest alive to
do forced labor for them. Zeus, however, put it in my mind to do
thus—and I wish I had died then and there in Egypt instead, for
there was much sorrow in store for me. I took off my helmet and
shield and dropped my spear from my hand; then I went straight up
to the king's chariot, clasped his knees and kissed them, whereon he
spared my life, bade me get into his chariot, and took me weeping
to his own home. Many made at me with their ashen spears and tried
to kill me in their fury, but the king protected me, for he feared the

wrath of Zeus, the protector of strangers, who punishes those who do evil.

"I stayed there for seven years and got together much money among the Egyptians, for they all gave me something. But when it was now going on for eight years there came a certain Phoenician, a cunning rascal, who had already committed all sorts of villainy, and this man talked me over into going with him to Phoenicia, where his house and his possessions lay. I stayed there for a whole twelve months, but at the end of that time when months and days had gone by till the same season had come round again, he set me on board a ship bound for Libya, on a pretense that I was to take a cargo along with him to that place, but really that he might sell me as a slave and take the money I fetched. I suspected his intention, but went on board with him, for I could not help it.

"The ship ran before a fresh north wind till we had reached the sea that lies between Crete and Libya. There, however, Zeus counseled their destruction, for as soon as we were well out from Crete and could see nothing but sea and sky, he raised a black cloud over our ship and the sea grew dark beneath it. Then Zeus let fly with his thunderbolts and the ship went round and round and was filled with fire and brimstone as the lightning struck it. The men fell all into the sea; they were carried about in the water round the ship looking like so many sea gulls, but the gods presently deprived them of all chance of getting home again. I was all dismayed; Zeus, however, sent the ship's mast within my reach, which saved my life, for I clung to it, and drifted before the fury of the gale. Nine days did I drift but in the darkness of the tenth night a great wave bore me on to the Thesprotian coast. There Pheidon, king of the Thesprotians, entertained me hospitably without charging me anything at all—for his son found me when I was nearly dead with cold and fatigue, whereon he raised me by the hand, took me to his father's house and gave me clothes to wear.

"There it was that I heard news of Odysseus, for the king told me he had entertained him, and shown him much hospitality while he was on his homeward journey. He showed me also the treasure of gold, bronze, and wrought iron that Odysseus had got together. There was enough to keep his family for ten generations, so much had he left in the house of King Pheidon. But the king said Odysseus had gone to Dodona that he might learn Zeus' mind from the god's high oak tree, and know whether after so long an absence he should return to Ithaca openly, or in secret. Moreover, the king swore in my presence, making drink offerings in his own house as he did so, that the ship was by the water side, and the crew found, that should take him to his own country. He sent me off, however, before Odysseus returned, for there happened to be a Thesprotian ship sailing for the wheat-growing island of Dulichium, and he told those in charge of her to be sure and take me safely to King Acastus.

"These men hatched a plot against me that would have reduced me to the very extreme of misery, for when the ship had got some way out from land they resolved on selling me as a slave. They stripped me of the shirt and cloak that I was wearing, and gave me instead the tattered old clouts in which you now see me. Then, towards nightfall, they reached the tilled lands of Ithaca, and there they bound me with a strong rope fast in the ship, while they went on shore to get supper by the seaside. But the gods soon undid my bonds for me, and having drawn my rags over my head I slid down the rudder into the sea, where I struck out and swam till I was well clear of them, and came ashore near a thick wood in which I lay concealed. They were very angry at my having escaped and went searching about for me, till at last they thought it was no further use and went back to their ship. The gods, having hidden me thus easily, then took me to a good man's door—for it seems that I am not to die yet awhile."

To this you answered, O swineherd Eumaeus: "Poor unhappy stranger, I have found the story of your misfortunes extremely interesting, but that part about Odysseus is not right; and you will never get me to believe it. Why should a man like you go about telling lies in this way? I know all about the return of my master. The gods, one and all of them, detest him, or they would have taken him before

Troy, or let him die with friends around him when the days of his fighting were done; for then the Achaeans would have built a mound over his ashes and his son would have been heir to his renown, but now the storm winds have spirited him away we know not whither.

"As for me, I live out of the way here with the pigs, and never go to this town unless when Penelope sends for me on the arrival of some news about Odysseus. Then they all sit round and ask questions, both those who grieve over the king's absence, and those who rejoice at it because they can eat up his property without paying for it. For my own part, I have never cared about asking anyone else since the time when I was taken in by an Aetolian, who had killed a man and come a long way till at last he reached my station, and I was very kind to him. He said he had seen Odysseus with Idomeneus among the Cretans, refitting his ships which had been damaged in the gale. He said Odysseus would return in the following summer or autumn with his men, and that he would bring back much wealth. And now you, you unfortunate old man, since fate has brought you to my door, do not try to flatter me in this way with vain hopes. It is not for any such reason that I shall treat you kindly, but only out of respect for Zeus the god of hospitality, as fearing him and pitying you."

Odysseus answered: "I see that you are of an unbelieving mind; I have given you my oath, and yet you will not credit me. Let us then make a bargain, and call all the gods in heaven to witness it. If your master comes home, give me a cloak and shirt of good wear, and send me to Dulichium where I want to go; but if he does not come as I say he will, set your men on to me, and tell them to throw me from yonder precipice, as a warning to tramps not to go about the country telling lies."

"And a pretty figure I should cut then," replied Eumaeus, "both now and hereafter, if I were to kill you after receiving you into my hut and showing you hospitality. I should have to say my prayers in good earnest if I did. But it is just supper time and I hope my men will come in directly, that we may cook something savory for supper."

Thus did they converse, and presently the swineherds came up with the pigs, which were then shut up for the night in their sties, and a tremendous squealing they made as they were being driven into them. But Eumaeus called to his men and said, "Bring in the best pig you have, that I may sacrifice him for this stranger, and we will take toll of him ourselves. We have had trouble enough this long time feeding pigs, while others reap the fruit of our labor."

On this he began chopping firewood, while the others brought in a fine fat five-year-old boar pig, and set it at the altar. Eumaeus did not forget the gods, for he was a man of good principles, so the first thing he did was to cut bristles from the pig's face and throw them into the fire, praying to all the gods as he did so that Odysseus might return home again. Then he clubbed the pig with a billet of oak which he had kept back when he was chopping the firewood, and stunned it, while the others slaughtered and singed it. Then they cut it up, and Eumaeus began by putting raw pieces from each joint on to some of the fat; these he sprinkled with barley meal, and laid upon the embers; they cut the rest of the meat up small, put the pieces upon the spits and roasted them till they were done; when they had taken them off the spits they threw them on to the dresser in a heap. The swineherd, who was a most equitable man, then stood up to give everyone his share. He made seven portions; one of these he set apart for Hermes the son of Maia and the nymphs, praying to them as he did so; the others he dealt out to the men, man by man. He gave Odysseus some slices cut lengthways down the loin as a mark of especial honor, and Odysseus was much pleased. "I hope, Eumaeus," said he, "that Zeus will be as well disposed towards you as I am, for the respect you are showing to an outcast like myself."

To this you answered, O swineherd Eumaeus, "Eat, my good fellow, and enjoy your supper, such as it is. God grants this and withholds that, just as he thinks right, for he can do whatever he chooses."

As he spoke he cut off the first piece and offered it as a burnt sacrifice to the immortal gods; then he made them a drink offering, put the cup in the hands of Odysseus, and sat down to his own portion. Mesaulius brought them their bread. The swineherd had bought this man on his own account from among the Taphians during his master's absence, and had paid for him with his own money without saying anything either to his mistress or Laertes. They then laid their hands upon the good things that were before them, and when they had had enough to eat and drink, Mesaulius took away what was left of the bread, and they all went to bed after having made a hearty supper.

Now the night came on stormy and very dark, for there was no moon. It poured without ceasing, and the wind blew strong from the west, which is a wet quarter, so Odysseus thought he would see whether Eumaeus, in the excellent care he took of him, would take off his own cloak and give it him, or make one of his men give him one. "Listen to me," said he, "Eumaeus and the rest of you; when I have said a prayer I will tell you something. It is the wine that makes me talk in this way. Wine will make even a wise man fall to singing; it will make him chuckle and dance and say many a word that he had better leave unspoken; still, as I have begun, I will go on. Would that I were still young and strong as when we got up an ambuscade before Troy. Menelaus and Odysseus were the leaders, but I was in command also, for the other two would have it so. When we had come up to the wall of the city we crouched down beneath our armor and lay there under cover of the reeds and thick brushwood that grew about the swamp. It came on to freeze with a north wind blowing; the snow fell small and fine like hoar frost, and our shields were coated thick with rime. The others had all got cloaks and shirts, and slept comfortably enough with their shields about their shoulders, but I had carelessly left my cloak behind me, not thinking that I should be too cold, and had gone off in nothing but my shirt and shield. When the night was two-thirds through and the stars had shifted their places, I nudged Odysseus, who was close to me, with my elbow, and he at once gave me his ear.

" 'Odysseus,' said I, 'this cold will be the death of me, for I have no cloak. Some god fooled me into setting off with nothing on but my shirt, and I do not know what to do.'

"Odysseus, who was as crafty as he was valiant, hit upon the following plan:

" 'Keep still,' said he in a low voice, 'or the others will hear you.' Then he raised his head on his elbow.

" 'My friends,' said he, 'I have had a dream from heaven in my sleep. We are a long way from the ships: I wish someone would go down and tell Agamemnon to send us up more men at once.'

"On this Thoas son of Andraemon threw off his cloak and set out running to the ships, whereon I took the cloak and lay in it comfortably enough till morning. Would that I were still young and strong as I was in those days, for then some one of you swineherds would give me a cloak both out of good will and for the respect due to a brave soldier; but now people look down upon me because my clothes are shabby."

And Eumaeus answered: "Old man, you have told us an excellent story, and have said nothing so far but what is quite satisfactory. For the present, therefore, you shall want neither clothing nor anything else that a stranger in distress may reasonably expect, but tomorrow morning you will have to shake your own old rags about your body again, for we have not many spare cloaks or shirts up here, but every man has only one. When Odysseus' son comes home again he will give you both cloak and shirt, and send you wherever you may want to go."

With this he got up and made a bed for Odysseus by throwing some goatskins and sheepskins on the ground in front of the fire. Here Odysseus lay down, and Eumaeus covered him over with a great heavy cloak that he kept for a change in case of extraordinarily bad weather.

Thus did Odysseus sleep, and the young men slept beside him. But the swineherd did not like sleeping away from his pigs, so he got ready to go outside, and Odysseus was glad to see that he looked after his property during his master's absence. First he slung his sword over his brawny shoulders and put on a thick cloak to keep out the wind. He also took the skin of a large and well-fed goat, and a javelin in case of attack from men or dogs. Thus equipped he went to his rest where the pigs were camping under an overhanging rock that gave them shelter from the north wind.

BOOK XV

*Athene meanwhile appears to Telemachus at Menelaus' house,
bidding him return home. Helen and Menelaus give him
parting gifts. Accompanied by Pisistratus, he drives back to
his boat in Pylos and thence sets sail for Ithaca. Odysseus
stays on with the swineherd Eumaeus, who tells him the story
of his life. Telemachus lands and comes straight to the swineherd's hut.*

BUT ATHENE WENT TO THE FAIR CITY OF SPARTA
to tell Odysseus' son that he was to return at once. She found
him and Pisistratus sleeping in the forecourt of Menelaus'
house. Pisistratus was fast asleep, but Telemachus could get no rest
all night for thinking of his unhappy father, so Athene went close up
to him and said:

"Telemachus, you should not remain so far away from home any
longer, or leave your property with such dangerous people in your
house; they will eat up everything you have among them, and you
will have been on a fool's errand. Ask Menelaus to send you home at
once if you wish to find your excellent mother still there when you
get back. Her father and brothers are already urging her to marry
Eurymachus, who has given her more than any of the others, and
has been greatly increasing his wedding presents. I hope nothing

valuable may have been taken from the house in spite of you, but you know what women are—they always want to do the best they can for the man who marries them, and never give another thought to the children of their first husband, or to their father either when he is dead and done with. Go home, therefore, and put everything in charge of the most respectable womanservant that you have, until it shall please heaven to send you a wife of your own.

"Let me tell you also of another matter which you had better attend to. The chief men among the suitors are lying in wait for you in the Strait between Ithaca and Same, and they mean to kill you before you can reach home. I do not much think they will succeed; it is more likely that some of those who are now eating up your property will find a grave themselves. Sail night and day, and keep your ship well away from the islands. The god who watches over you and protects you will send you a fair wind. As soon as you get to Ithaca, send your ship and men on to the town, but yourself go straight to the swineherd who has charge of your pigs; he is well disposed towards you. Stay with him, therefore, for the night, and then send him to Penelope to tell her that you have got back safe from Pylos."

Then she went back to Olympus; but Telemachus stirred Pisistratus with his heel to rouse him, and said, "Wake up, Pisistratus, and yoke the horses to the chariot, for we must set off home."

But Pisistratus said: "No matter what hurry we are in, we cannot drive in the dark. It will be morning soon; wait till Menelaus has brought his presents and put them in the chariot for us; and let him say good-by to us in the usual way. So long as he lives a guest should never forget a host who has shown him kindness."

As he spoke day began to break, and Menelaus, who had already risen, leaving Helen in bed, came towards them. When Telemachus saw him he put on his shirt as fast as he could, threw a great cloak over his shoulders, and went out to meet him. "Menelaus," said he, "let me go back now to my own country, for I want to get home."

And Menelaus answered: "Telemachus, if you insist on going I will not detain you. I do not like to see a host either too fond of his guest or too rude to him. Moderation is best in all things, and not letting a man go when he wants to do so is as bad as telling him to go if he would like to stay. One should treat a guest well as long as he is in the house and speed him when he wants to leave it. Wait, then, till I can get your beautiful presents into your chariot, and till you have yourself seen them. I will tell the women to prepare a sufficient dinner for you of what there may be in the house; it will be at once more proper and cheaper for you to get your dinner before setting out on such a long journey. If, moreover, you have a fancy for making a tour in Hellas or in the Peloponnese, I will yoke my horses, and will conduct you myself through all our principal cities. No one will send us away empty-handed; everyone will give us something—a bronze tripod, a couple of mules, or a gold cup."

"Menelaus," replied Telemachus, "I want to go home at once, for when I came away I left my property without protection, and fear that while looking for my father I shall come to ruin myself, or find that something valuable has been stolen during my absence."

When Menelaus heard this he immediately told his wife and servants to prepare a sufficient dinner from what there might be in the house. At this moment Eteoneus joined him, for he lived close by and had just got up; so Menelaus told him to light the fire and cook some meat, which he at once did. Then Menelaus went down into his fragrant storeroom, not alone, but Helen went too, with Megapenthes. When he reached the place where the treasures of his house were kept, he selected a double cup, and told his son Megapenthes to bring also a silver mixing-bowl. Meanwhile Helen went to the chest where she kept the lovely dresses which she had made with her own hands, and took out one that was largest and most beautifully enriched with embroidery; it glittered like a star, and lay at the very bottom of the chest. Then they all came back through the house again till they got to Telemachus, and Menelaus said, "Telemachus, may Zeus, the mighty husband of Hera, bring you safely home according to your desire. I will now present you with the finest and most precious piece of plate in all my house. It is a mixing-bowl of pure silver, except the rim, which is inlaid with gold, and it is the work of Hephaestus. Phaedimus, king of the Sidonians, made me a present of it in the course of a visit that I paid him while I was on my return home. I should like to give it to you."

With these words he placed the double cup in the hands of Telemachus, while Megapenthes brought the beautiful mixing-bowl and set it before him. Hard by stood lovely Helen with the robe ready in her hand.

"I too, my son," said she, "have something for you as a keepsake from the hand of Helen; it is for your bride to wear upon her wedding day. Till then, get your dear mother to keep it for you. Thus may you go back rejoicing to your own country and to your home."

So saying she gave the robe over to him and he received it gladly. Then Pisistratus put the presents into the chariot, and admired them all as he did so. Presently Menelaus took Telemachus and Pisistratus into the house, and they both of them sat down to table. A maidservant brought them water in a beautiful golden ewer, and poured it into a silver basin for them to wash their hands, and she drew a clean table beside them; an upper servant brought them bread and offered them many good things of what there was in the house. Eteoneus carved the meat and gave them each their portions, while Megapenthes poured out the wine. Then they laid their hands upon the good things that were before them. But as soon as they had had enough to eat and drink Telemachus and Pisistratus yoked the horses, and took their places in the chariot. They drove out through the inner gateway and under the echoing gatehouse of the outer court, and Menelaus came after them with a golden goblet of wine in his right hand that they might make a drink offering before they set out. He stood in front of the horses and pledged them, saying, "Farewell to both of you; see that you tell Nestor how I have treated you, for he was as kind to me as any father could be while we Achaeans were fighting before Troy."

"We will be sure, sir," answered Telemachus, "to tell him everything as soon as we see him. I wish I were as certain of finding Odysseus returned when I get back to Ithaca, that I might tell him of the very great kindness you have shown me and of the many beautiful presents I am taking with me."

As he was thus speaking a bird flew by on his right hand—an eagle with a great white goose in its talons which it had carried off from the farmyard—and all the men and women were running after it and shouting. It came quite close up to them and flew away on their right hands in front of the horses. When they saw it they were glad, and their hearts took comfort within them, whereon Pisistratus said, "Tell me, Menelaus, has heaven sent this omen for us or for you?"

Menelaus was thinking what would be the most proper answer for him to make, but Helen was too quick for him and said, "I will read this matter as heaven has put it in my heart, and as I doubt not that it will come to pass. The eagle came from the mountain where it was bred and has its nest, and in like manner Odysseus, after having traveled far and suffered much, will return to take his revenge—if indeed he is not back already and hatching mischief for the suitors."

"May Zeus so grant it," replied Telemachus. "If it should prove to be so, I will make vows to you as though you were a god, even when I am at home."

As he spoke he lashed his horses and they started off at full speed through the town towards the open country. They swayed the yoke upon their necks and traveled the whole day long till the sun set and darkness was over all the land. Then they reached Pherae, where Diocles lived who was son of Ortilochus the son of Alpheus. There they passed the night and were treated hospitably. When the child of morning, rosy-fingered Dawn, appeared, they again yoked their horses and took their places in the chariot. They drove out through the inner gateway and under the echoing gatehouse of the outer court. Then Pisistratus lashed his horses on and they flew forward nothing loath; ere long they came to Pylos, and then Telemachus said:

"Pisistratus, I hope you will promise to do what I am going to ask you. You know our fathers were old friends before us; moreover, we are both of an age, and this journey has brought us together still more closely. Do not, therefore, take me past my ship, but leave me there, for if I go to your father's house he will try to keep me in the warmth of his good will towards me, and I must go home at once."

Pisistratus thought how he should do as he was asked, and in the end he deemed it best to turn his horses towards the ship, and put Menelaus' beautiful presents of gold and raiment in the stern of the vessel. Then he said, "Go on board at once and tell your men to do so also before I can reach home to tell my father. I know how obstinate he is, and am sure he will not let you go; he will come down here to fetch you, and he will not go back without you. But he will be very angry."

With this he drove his goodly steeds back to the city of the Pylians and soon reached his home. But Telemachus called the men together and gave his orders. "Now, my men," said he, "get everything in order on board the ship, and let us set out at once."

Thus did he speak, and they went on board even as he had said. But as Telemachus was thus busied, praying also and sacrificing to Athene in the ship's stern, there came to him a man from a distant country, a seer, who was flying from Argos because he had killed a man. He was descended from Melampus, who used to live in Pylos, the land of sheep. He was rich and owned a great house, but he was driven into exile by the great and powerful King Neleus. Neleus seized his goods and held them for a whole year, during which he was a close prisoner in the house of King Phylacus, and in much distress of mind both on account of the daughter of Neleus and because he was haunted by a great sorrow that dread Erinys had laid upon him. In the end, however, he escaped with his life, drove the cattle from Phylace to Pylos, avenged the wrong that had been done him, and gave the daughter of Neleus to his brother. Then he left the country and went to Argos, where it was ordained that he should reign over much people. There he married, established himself, and had two famous sons, Antiphates and Mantius. Antiphates became father of Oicleus, and Oicleus of Amphiaraus, who was dearly beloved both by Zeus and by Apollo, but he did not live to old age, for he was killed in Thebes by reason of a woman's gifts. His sons were Alcmaeon and Amphilochus. Mantius, the other son of Melampus, was father to Polypheides and Cleitus. Aurora, throned in gold, carried off Cleitus for his beauty's sake, that he might dwell among the immortals, but Apollo made Polypheides the greatest seer in the whole world now that Amphiaraus was dead. He quarreled with his father and went to live in Hyperesia, where he remained and prophesied for all men.

His son Theoclymenus it was who now came up to Telemachus as he was making drink offerings and praying in his ship. "Friend," said he, "now that I find you sacrificing in this place, I beseech you by your sacrifices themselves, and by the god to whom you make them, I pray you also by your own head and by those of your followers, tell me the truth and nothing but the truth. Who and whence are you? Tell me also of your town and parents."

Telemachus said, "I will answer you quite truly. I am from Ithaca, and my father is Odysseus, as surely as that he ever lived. But he has come to some miserable end. Therefore I have taken this ship and got my crew together to see if I can hear any news of him, for he has been away a long time."

"I too," answered Theoclymenus, "am an exile, for I have killed a man of my own race. He has many brothers and kinsmen in Argos, and they have great power among the Argives. I am flying to escape death at their hands, and am thus doomed to be a wanderer on the face of the earth. I am your suppliant; take me, therefore, on board your ship that they may not kill me, for I know they are in pursuit."

"I will not refuse you," replied Telemachus, "if you wish to join us. Come, therefore, and in Ithaca we will treat you hospitably according to what we have."

On this he received Theoclymenus' spear and laid it down on the deck of the ship. He went on board and sat in the stern, bidding Theoclymenus sit beside him; then the men let go the hawsers. Telemachus told them to catch hold of the ropes, and they made all haste to do so. They set the mast in its socket in the cross plank, raised it and made it fast with the forestays, and they hoisted their white sails with sheets of twisted oxhide. Athene sent them a fair wind that blew fresh and strong to take the ship on her course as fast as possible. Thus then they passed by Crouni and Chalcis.

Presently the sun set and darkness was over all the land. The vessel made a quick passage to Pheae and thence on to Elis, where the Epeans rule. Telemachus then headed her for the flying islands, wondering within himself whether he should escape death or should be taken prisoner.

Meanwhile Odysseus and the swineherd were eating their meal in the hut, and the men ate with them. As soon as they had had enough to eat and drink, Odysseus began trying to prove the swineherd and see whether he would continue to treat him kindly, and ask him to stay on at the station or pack him off to the city; so he said:

"Eumaeus, and all of you, tomorrow I want to go away and begin begging about the town, so as to be no more trouble to you or to your men. Give me your advice therefore, and let me have a good guide to go with me and show me the way. I will go the round of the city begging as I needs must, to see if anyone will give me a drink and a piece of bread. I should like also to go to the house of Odysseus and bring news of her husband to Queen Penelope. I could then go about among the suitors and see if out of all their abundance they will give me a dinner. I should soon make them an excellent servant in all sorts of ways. Listen and believe when I tell you that by the blessing of Hermes, who gives grace and good name to the works of all men, there is no one living who would make a more handy servant than I should—to put fresh wood on the fire, chop fuel, carve, cook, pour out wine, and do all those services that poor men have to do for their betters."

The swineherd was very much disturbed when he heard this. "Heaven help me," he exclaimed, "what ever can have put such a notion as that into your head? If you go near the suitors you will be undone to a certainty, for their pride and insolence reach the very heavens. They would never think of taking a man like you for a servant. Their servants are all young men, well dressed, wearing good cloaks and shirts, with well looking faces and their hair always tidy. The tables are kept quite clean and are loaded with bread, meat, and wine. Stay where you are, then; you are not in anybody's way. I do not mind your being here, no more do any of the others, and when Telemachus comes home he will give you a shirt and cloak and will send you wherever you want to go."

Odysseus answered: "I hope you may be as dear to the gods as you are to me, for having saved me from going about and getting into trouble; there is nothing worse than being always on the tramp. Still, when men have once got low down in the world they will go through a great deal on behalf of their miserable bellies. Since, however, you press me to stay here and await the return of Telemachus, tell me about Odysseus' mother, and his father whom he left on the threshold of old age when he set out for Troy. Are they still living or are they already dead and in the house of Hades?"

"I will tell you all about them," replied Eumaeus. "Laertes is still living and prays heaven to let him depart peacefully in his own house, for he is terribly distressed about the absence of his son, and also about the death of his wife, which grieved him greatly and aged him more than anything else did. She came to an unhappy end through sorrow for her son. May no friend or neighbor who has dealt kindly by me come to such an end as she did. As long as she was still living, though she was always grieving, I used to like seeing her and asking her how she did, for she brought me up along with her daughter, Ctimene, the youngest of her children. We were boy and girl together, and she made little difference between us. When, however, we both grew up, they sent Ctimene to Same and received a splendid dowry for her. As for me, my mistress gave me a good shirt and cloak with a pair of sandals for my feet, and sent me off into the country, but she was just as fond of me as ever. This is all over now. Still it has pleased heaven to prosper my work in the situation which I now hold. I have enough to eat and drink, and can find something for any respectable stranger who comes here; but there is no getting a kind word or deed out of my mistress, for the house has fallen into the hands of wicked people. Servants want sometimes to see their mistress and have a talk with her; they like to have something to eat and drink at the house, and something too to take back with them into the country. This is what will keep servants in a good humor."

Odysseus answered: "Then you must have been a very little fellow, Eumaeus, when you were taken so far away from your home and parents. Tell me, and tell me true, was the city in which your father and mother lived sacked and pillaged, or did some enemies carry you off when you were alone tending sheep or cattle, ship you off here, and sell you for whatever your master gave them?"

"Stranger," replied Eumaeus, "as regards your question: sit still, make yourself comfortable, drink your wine, and listen to me. The nights are now at their longest; there is plenty of time both for sleeping and sitting up talking together; you ought not to go to bed till bedtime, too much sleep is as bad as too little. If any one of the others wishes to go to bed, let him leave us and do so; he can then take my master's pigs out when he has done breakfast in the morning. We two will sit here eating and drinking in the hut, and telling one another stories about our misfortunes; for when a man has suffered much and been buffeted about in the world, he takes pleasure in recalling the memory of sorrows that have long gone by. As regards your question, then, my tale is as follows:

"You may have heard of an island called Syra that lies over above Ortygia,[1] where the land begins to turn round and look in another direction. It is not very thickly peopled, but the soil is good, with much pasture fit for cattle and sheep, and it abounds with wine and wheat. Dearth never comes there, nor are the people plagued by any sickness, but when they grow old Apollo comes with Artemis and kills them with his painless shafts. It contains two communities, and the whole country is divided between these two. My father Ctesius son of Ormenus, a man comparable to the gods, reigned over both.

"Now to this place there came some cunning traders from Phoenicia (for the Phoenicians are great mariners) in a ship which they had freighted with gewgaws of all kinds. There happened to be a Phoenician woman in my father's house, very tall and comely, and an excellent servant. These scoundrels got hold of her one day when she was washing near their ship, seduced her, and cajoled her in

---

[1] Assuming, as we may safely do, that the Syra and Ortygia of the *Odyssey* refer to the islands on which Syracuse was originally built, it is the fact that not far to the south of these places the land turns sharply round, so that mariners following the coast would find the sun upon the other side of their ship to that on which they had had it hitherto. (B.)

ways that no woman can resist, no matter how good she may be by nature. The man who had seduced her asked her who she was and where she came from, and on this she told him her father's name. 'I come from Sidon,' said she, 'and am daughter to Arybas, a man rolling in wealth. One day as I was coming into the town from the country some Taphian pirates seized me and took me here over the sea, where they sold me to the man who owns this house, and he gave them their price for me.'

"The man who had seduced her then said, 'Would you like to come along with us to see the house of your parents and your parents themselves? They are both alive and are said to be well off.'

" 'I will do so gladly,' answered she, 'if you men will first swear me a solemn oath that you will do me no harm by the way.'

"They all swore as she told them, and when they had completed their oath the woman said, 'Hush; and if any of your men meets me in the street or at the well, do not let him speak to me, for fear someone should go and tell my master, in which case he would suspect something. He would put me in prison, and would have all of you murdered; keep your own counsel therefore. Buy your merchandise as fast as you can, and send me word when you have done loading. I will bring as much gold as I can lay my hands on, and there is something else also that I can do towards paying my fare. I am nurse to the son of the good man of the house, a funny little fellow just able to run about. I will carry him off in your ship, and you will get a great deal of money for him if you take him and sell him in foreign parts.'

"On this she went back to the house. The Phoenicians stayed a whole year till they had loaded their ship with much precious merchandise, and then, when they had got freight enough, they sent to tell the woman. Their messenger, a very cunning fellow, came to my father's house bringing a necklace of gold with amber beads strung among it; and while my mother and the servants had it in their hands admiring it and bargaining about it, he made a sign quietly to the woman and then went back to the ship, whereon she took me by the hand and led me out of the house. In the fore part of the house she saw the tables set with the cups of guests who had been feasting with my father, as being in attendance on him; these were now all gone to a meeting of the public assembly, so she snatched up three cups and carried them off in the bosom of her dress, while I followed her, for I knew no better. The sun was now set, and darkness was over all the land, so we hurried on as fast as we could till we reached the harbor, where the Phoenician ship was lying. When they had got on board they sailed their ways over the sea, taking us with them, and Zeus sent them a fair wind. Six days did we sail both night and day, but on the seventh day Artemis struck the woman and she fell heavily down into the ship's hold as though she were a sea gull alighting on the water; so they threw her overboard to the seals and fishes, and I was left all sorrowful and alone. Presently the winds and waves took the ship to Ithaca, where Laertes gave sundry of his chattels for me, and thus it was that ever I came to set eyes upon this country."

Odysseus answered, "Eumaeus, I have heard the story of your misfortunes with the most lively interest and pity, but Zeus has given you good as well as evil, for in spite of everything you have a good master, who sees that you always have enough to eat and drink; and you lead a good life, whereas I am still going about begging my way from city to city."

Thus did they converse, and they had only a very little time left for sleep, for it was soon daybreak. In the meantime Telemachus and his crew were nearing land, so they loosed the sails, took down the mast, and rowed the ship into the harbor. They cast out their mooring stones and made fast the hawsers; they then got out upon the seashore, mixed their wine, and got dinner ready. As soon as they had had enough to eat and drink Telemachus said, "Take the ship on to the town, but leave me here, for I want to look after the herdsmen on one of my farms. In the evening, when I have seen all I want, I will come down to the city, and tomorrow morning in return for your trouble I will give you all a good dinner with meat and wine."

Then Theoclymenus said, "And what, my dear young friend, is

to become of me? To whose house, among all your chief men, am I to repair? or shall I go straight to your own house and to your mother?"

"At any other time," replied Telemachus, "I should have bidden you go to my own house, for you would find no want of hospitality; at the present moment, however, you would not be comfortable there, for I shall be away, and my mother will not see you. She does not often show herself even to the suitors, but sits at her loom weaving in an upper chamber, out of their way. But I can tell you a man whose house you can go to—I mean Eurymachus the son of Polybus, who is held in the highest estimation by everyone in Ithaca. He is much the best man and the most persistent wooer of all those who are paying court to my mother and trying to take Odysseus' place. Zeus, however, in heaven alone knows whether or no they will come to a bad end before the marriage takes place."

As he was speaking a bird flew by upon his right hand—a hawk, Apollo's messenger. It held a dove in its talons, and the feathers, as it tore them off, fell to the ground midway between Telemachus and the ship. On this Theoclymenus called him apart and caught him by the hand. "Telemachus," said he, "that bird did not fly on your right hand without having been sent there by some god. As soon as I saw it I knew it was an omen. It means that you will remain powerful and that there will be no house in Ithaca more royal than your own."

"I wish it may prove so," answered Telemachus. "If it does, I will show you so much good will and give you so many presents that all who meet you will congratulate you."

Then he said to his friend, Piraeus, "Piraeus son of Clytius, you have throughout shown yourself the most willing to serve me of all those who have accompanied me to Pylos. I wish you would take this stranger to your own house and entertain him hospitably till I can come for him."

And Piraeus answered, "Telemachus, you may stay away as long as you please, but I will look after him for you, and he shall find no lack of hospitality."

As he spoke he went on board, and bade the others do so also and loose the hawsers, so they took their places in the ship. But Telemachus bound on his sandals, and took a long and doughty spear with a head of sharpened bronze from the deck of the ship. Then they loosed the hawsers, thrust the ship off from land, and made on towards the city as they had been told to do, while Telemachus strode on as fast as he could, till he reached the homestead where his countless herds of swine were feeding, and where dwelt the excellent swineherd, who was so devoted a servant to his master.

BOOK XVI

*Telemachus sends Eumaeus into the town to tell Penelope
that her son is safely back. Athene then restores Odysseus
back to his own likeness. He reveals himself to Telemachus, and instructs his son in his plan for the destruction
of the suitors. The suitors confer uneasily together and
Eumaeus returns to his hut.*

MEANWHILE ODYSSEUS AND THE SWINEHERD
had lit a fire in the hut and were getting breakfast ready
at daybreak, for they had sent the men out with the pigs.
When Telemachus came up, the dogs did not bark but fawned upon
him, so Odysseus, hearing the sound of feet and noticing that the
dogs did not bark, said to Eumaeus:

"Eumaeus, I hear footsteps; I suppose one of your men or someone
of your acquaintance is coming here, for the dogs are fawning upon
him and not barking."

The words were hardly out of his mouth before his son stood at
the door. Eumaeus sprang to his feet, and the bowls in which he
was mixing wine fell from his hands, as he made towards his master.
He kissed his head and both his beautiful eyes, and wept for joy. A
father could not be more delighted at the return of an only son, the
child of his old age, after ten years' absence in a foreign country

and after having gone through much hardship. He embraced him, kissed him all over as though he had come back from the dead, and spoke fondly to him, saying:

"So you are come, Telemachus, light of my eyes that you are. When I heard you had gone to Pylos I made sure I was never going to see you any more. Come in, my dear child, and sit down, that I may have a good look at you now you are home again. It is not very often you come into the country to see us herdsmen; you stick pretty close to the town generally. I suppose you think it better to keep an eye on what the suitors are doing."

"So be it, old friend," answered Telemachus, "but I am come now because I want to see you, and to learn whether my mother is still at her old home or whether someone else has married her, so that the bed of Odysseus is without bedding and covered with cobwebs."

"She is still at the house," replied Eumaeus, "grieving and breaking her heart, and doing nothing but weep, both night and day continually."

As he spoke he took Telemachus' spear, whereon he crossed the stone threshold and came inside. Odysseus rose from his seat to give him place as he entered, but Telemachus checked him. "Sit down, stranger," said he, "I can easily find another seat, and there is one here who will lay it for me."

Odysseus went back to his own place, and Eumaeus strewed some green brushwood on the floor and threw a sheepskin on top of it for Telemachus to sit upon. Then the swineherd brought them platters of cold meat, the remains from what they had eaten the day before, and he filled the bread baskets with bread as fast as he could. He mixed wine also in bowls of ivy-wood, and took his seat facing Odysseus. Then they laid their hands on the good things that were before them, and as soon as they had had enough to eat and drink, Telemachus said to Eumaeus, "Old friend, where does this stranger come from? How did his crew bring him to Ithaca, and who were they?—for assuredly he did not come here by land."

To this you answered, O swineherd Eumaeus: "My son, I will tell you the real truth. He says he is a Cretan, and that he has been

a great traveler. At this moment he is running away from a Thesprotian ship, and has taken refuge at my station, so I will put him
into your hands. Do whatever you like with him, only remember
that he is your suppliant."

"I am very much distressed," said Telemachus, "by what you
have just told me. How can I take this stranger into my house? I
am as yet young, and am not strong enough to hold my own if any
man attacks me. My mother cannot make up her mind whether to
stay where she is and look after the house out of respect for public
opinion and the memory of her husband, or whether the time is
now come for her to take the best man of those who are wooing her,
and the one who will make her the most advantageous offer. Still,
as the stranger has come to your station I will find him a cloak and
shirt of good wear, with a sword and sandals, and will send him
wherever he wants to go. Or if you like, you can keep him here at
the station, and I will send him clothes and food that he may be
no burden on you and on your men. But I will not have him go
near the suitors, for they are very insolent, and are sure to ill-treat
him in a way that would greatly grieve me. No matter how valiant
a man may be he can do nothing against numbers, for they will be
too strong for him."

Then Odysseus said: "Sir, it is right that I should say something
myself. I am much shocked by what you have said about the insolent way in which the suitors are behaving in despite of such a
man as you are. Tell me, do you submit to such treatment tamely,
or has some god set your people against you? May you not complain
of your brothers—for it is to these that a man may look for support,
however great his quarrel may be? I wish I were as young as you
are and in my present mind. If I were son to Odysseus, or, indeed,
Odysseus himself, I would rather someone came and cut my head
off, but I would go to the house and be the bane of every one of
these men. If they were too many for me—I being single-handed—I
would rather die fighting in my own house than see such disgraceful
sights day after day, strangers grossly maltreated, and men dragging

the women servants about the house in an unseemly way, wine drawn recklessly, and bread wasted all to no purpose for an end that shall never be accomplished."

And Telemachus answered: "I will tell you truly everything. There is no enmity between me and my people, nor can I complain of brothers, to whom a man may look for support however great his quarrel may be. Zeus has made us a race of only sons. Laertes was the only son of Arceisius, and Odysseus only son of Laertes. I am myself the only son of Odysseus, who left me behind him when he went away, so that I have never been of any use to him. Hence it comes that my house is in the hands of numberless marauders; for the chiefs from all the neighboring islands, Dulichium, Same, Zacynthus, as also all the principal men of Ithaca itself, are eating up my house under the pretext of paying court to my mother, who will neither say point-blank that she will not marry, nor yet bring matters to an end; so they are making havoc of my estate, and before long will do so with myself into the bargain. The issue, however, rests with heaven. But do you, old friend Eumaeus, go at once and tell Penelope that I am safe and have returned from Pylos. Tell it to herself alone, and then come back here without letting anyone else know, for there are many who are plotting mischief against me."

"I understand and heed you," replied Eumaeus; "you need instruct me no further, only as I am going that way say whether I had not better let poor Laertes know that you are returned. He used to superintend the work on his farm in spite of his bitter sorrow about Odysseus, and he would eat and drink at will along with his servants; but they tell me that from the day on which you set out for Pylos he has neither eaten nor drunk as he ought to do, nor does he look after his farm, but sits weeping and wasting the flesh from off his bones."

"More's the pity," answered Telemachus, "I am sorry for him, but we must leave him to himself just now. If people could have everything their own way, the first thing I should choose would be the return of my father. But go, and give your message; then make haste back again, and do not turn out of your way to tell Laertes. Tell my mother to send one of her women secretly with the news at once, and let him hear it from her."

Thus did he urge the swineherd. Eumaeus, therefore, took his sandals, bound them to his feet, and started for the town. Athene watched him well off the station, and then came up to it in the form of a woman—fair, stately, and wise. She stood against the side of the entry, and revealed herself to Odysseus, but Telemachus could not see her, and knew not that she was there, for the gods do not let themselves be seen by everybody. Odysseus saw her, and so did the dogs, for they did not bark, but went scared and whining off to the other side of the yards. She nodded her head and motioned to Odysseus with her eyebrows, whereon he left the hut and stood before her outside the main wall of the yards. Then she said to him:

"Odysseus, noble son of Laertes, it is now time for you to tell your son; do not keep him in the dark any longer, but lay your plans for the destruction of the suitors, and then make for the town. I will not be long in joining you, for I too am eager for the fray."

As she spoke she touched him with her golden wand. First she threw a fair clean shirt and cloak about his shoulders; then she made him younger and of more imposing presence; she gave him back his color, filled out his cheeks, and let his beard become dark again. Then she went away and Odysseus came back inside the hut. His son was astonished when he saw him, and turned his eyes away for fear he might be looking upon a god.

"Stranger," said he, "how suddenly you have changed from what you were a moment or two ago. You are dressed differently and your color is not the same. Are you some one or other of the gods that live in heaven? If so, be propitious to me till I can make you due sacrifice and offerings of wrought gold. Have mercy upon me."

And Odysseus said, "I am no god; why should you take me for one? I am your father, on whose account you grieve and suffer so much at the hands of lawless men."

As he spoke he kissed his son, and a tear fell from his cheek on to the ground, for he had restrained all tears till now. But Telemachus could not yet believe that it was his father, and said:

"You are not my father, but some god is flattering me with vain hopes that I may grieve the more hereafter. No mortal man could of himself contrive to do as you have been doing, and make yourself old and young at a moment's notice, unless a god were with him. A second ago you were old and all in rags, and now you are like some god come down from heaven."

Odysseus answered: "Telemachus, you ought not to be so immeasurably astonished at my being really here. There is no other Odysseus who will come hereafter. Such as I am, it is I, who after long wandering and much hardship have got home in the twentieth year to my own country. What you wonder at is the work of the redoubtable goddess Athene, who does with me whatever she will, for she can do what she pleases. At one moment she makes me like a beggar, and the next I am a young man with good clothes on my back. It is an easy matter for the gods who live in heaven to make any man look either rich or poor."

As he spoke he sat down, and Telemachus threw his arms about his father and wept. They were both so much moved that they cried aloud like eagles or vultures with crooked talons that have been robbed of their half-fledged young by peasants. Thus piteously did they weep, and the sun would have gone down upon their mourning if Telemachus had not suddenly said, "In what ship, my dear father, did your crew bring you to Ithaca? Of what nation did they declare themselves to be—for you cannot have come by land?"

"I will tell you the truth, my son," replied Odysseus. "It was the Phaeacians who brought me here. They are great sailors, and are in the habit of giving escorts to anyone who reaches their coasts. They took me over the sea while I was fast asleep, and landed me in Ithaca, after giving me many presents in bronze, gold, and raiment. These things by heaven's mercy are lying concealed in a cave, and I am now come here on the suggestion of Athene that we may consult about killing our enemies. First, therefore, give me a list of the suitors, with their number, that I may learn who, and how many, they are. I can then turn the matter over in my mind, and see whether we two can fight the whole body of them ourselves, or whether we must find others to help us."

To this Telemachus answered: "Father, I have always heard of your renown both in the field and in council, but the task you talk of is a very great one: I am awed at the mere thought of it; two men cannot stand against many and brave ones. There are not ten suitors only, nor twice ten, but ten many times over; you shall learn their number at once. There are fifty-two chosen youths from Dulichium, and they have six servants; from Same there are twenty-four; twenty young Achaeans from Zacynthus, and twelve from Ithaca itself, all of them well born. They have with them a servant Medon, a bard, and two men who can carve at table. If we face such numbers as this, you may have bitter cause to rue your coming, and your revenge. See whether you cannot think of someone who would be willing to come and help us."

"Listen to me," replied Odysseus, "and think whether Athene and her father Zeus may seem sufficient, or whether I am to try and find someone else as well."

"Those whom you have named," answered Telemachus, "are a couple of good allies, for though they dwell high up among the clouds they have power over both gods and men."

"These two," continued Odysseus, "will not keep long out of the fray, when the suitors and we join fight in my house. Now, therefore, return home early tomorrow morning, and go about among the suitors as before. Later on the swineherd will bring me to the city disguised as a miserable old beggar. If you see them ill-treating me, steel your heart against my sufferings; even though they drag me feet foremost out of the house, or throw things at me, look on and do nothing beyond gently trying to make them behave more reasonably. They will not listen to you, for the day of their reckoning is at hand. Furthermore I say, and lay my saying to your heart, when Athene shall put it in my mind, I will nod my head to you, and on seeing me do this you must collect all the armor that is in the house and hide it in the strong storeroom. Make some excuse when the suitors ask you why you are removing it; say that you have taken it to be out of the way of the smoke, inasmuch as it is no longer what it was when Odysseus went away, but has become soiled and begrimed with soot. Add to this more particularly that you are afraid Zeus may set them on to quarrel over their wine, and that they may do each other some harm which may disgrace both banquet and wooing, for the sight of arms sometimes tempts people to use them. But leave a sword and a spear apiece for yourself and me, and a couple of oxhide shields so that we can snatch them up at any moment; Zeus and Athene will then soon quiet these people. There is also another matter; if you are indeed my son and my blood runs in your veins, let no one know that Odysseus is within the house—neither Laertes, nor yet the swineherd, nor any of the servants, nor even Penelope herself. Let you and me test out the women alone, and let us also make trial of some other of the men-servants, to see who is on our side and whose hand is against us."

"Father," replied Telemachus, "you will come to know me by and by, and when you do you will find that I can keep your counsel. I do not think, however, the plan you propose will turn out well for either of us. Think it over. It will take us a long time to go the round of the farms and find out about the men, and all the time the suitors will be wasting your estate with impunity and without compunction. Prove the women by all means, to see who are disloyal and who guiltless, but I am not in favor of going round and trying the men. We can attend to that later on, if you really have some sign from Zeus that he will support you."

Thus did they converse, and meanwhile the ship which had brought Telemachus and his crew from Pylos had reached the town of Ithaca. When they had come inside the harbor they drew the ship on to the land. Their servants came and took their armor from them, and they left all the presents at the house of Clytius. Then they sent a servant to tell Penelope that Telemachus had gone into the country, but had sent the ship to the town to prevent her from being alarmed and made unhappy. This servant and Eumaeus happened to meet when they were both on the same errand of going to

tell Penelope. When they reached the house, the servant stood up
and said to the queen in the presence of the waiting women, "Your
son, madam, is now returned from Pylos"; but Eumaeus went close
up to Penelope, and said privately all that her son had bidden him
tell her. When he had given his message he left the house with its
outbuildings and went back to his pigs again.

The suitors were surprised and angry at what had happened, so
they went outside the great wall that ran round the outer court,
and held a council near the main entrance. Eurymachus son of
Polybus was the first to speak.

"My friends," said he, "this voyage of Telemachus' is a very serious matter; we had made sure that it would come to nothing. Now,
however, let us draw a ship into the water, and get a crew together
to send after the others and tell them to come back as fast as they
can."

He had hardly done speaking when Amphinomus turned in his
place and saw the ship inside the harbor, with the crew lowering
her sails, and putting by their oars; so he laughed, and said to the
others, "We need not send them any message, for they are here.
Some god must have told them, or else they saw the ship go by, and
could not overtake her."

On this they rose and went to the water side. The crew then
drew the ship on shore; their servants took their armor from them,
and they went up in a body to the place of assembly, but they
would not let anyone, old or young, sit along with them, and Antinous son of Eupeithes spoke first.

"Good heavens," said he, "see how the gods have saved this man
from destruction! We kept a succession of scouts upon the headlands all day long, and when the sun was down we never went on
shore to sleep, but waited in the ship all night till morning in the
hope of capturing and killing him; but some god has conveyed him
home in spite of us. Let us consider how we can make an end of
him. He must not escape us; our affair is never likely to come off
while he is alive, for he is very shrewd, and public feeling is by no
means all on our side. We must make haste before he can call the

Achaeans in assembly. He will lose no time in doing so, for he will be furious with us, and will tell all the world how we plotted to kill him, but failed to take him. The people will not like this when they come to know of it; we must see that they do us no hurt, nor drive us from our own country into exile. Let us try and lay hold of him either on his farm away from the town, or on the road hither. Then we can divide up his property amongst us, and let his mother and the man who marries her have the house. If this does not please you, and you wish Telemachus to live on and hold his father's property, then we must not gather here and eat up his goods in this way, but must make our offers to Penelope each from his own house, and she can marry the man who will give the most for her, and whose lot it is to win her."

They all held their peace until Amphinomus rose to speak. He was the son of Nisus, who was son to King Aretias, and he was foremost among all the suitors from the wheat-growing and well-grassed island of Dulichium. His conversation, moreover, was more agreeable to Penelope than that of any of the other suitors, for he was a man of good natural disposition. "My friends," said he, speaking to them plainly and in all honesty, "I am not in favor of killing Telemachus. It is a heinous thing to kill one who is of noble blood. Let us first take counsel of the gods, and if the oracles of Zeus advise it, I will both help to kill him myself, and will urge everyone else to do so; but if they dissuade us, I would have you hold your hands."

Thus did he speak, and his words pleased them well, so they rose forthwith and went to the house of Odysseus, where they took their accustomed seats.

Then Penelope resolved that she would show herself to the suitors. She knew of the plot against Telemachus, for the servant Medon had overheard their counsels and had told her; she went down therefore to the court attended by her maidens, and when she reached the suitors she stood by one of the bearing-posts supporting the roof of the cloister holding a veil before her face, and rebuked Antinous saying:

"Antinous, insolent and wicked schemer, they say you are the best speaker and counselor of any man your own age in Ithaca, but you are nothing of the kind. Madman, why should you try to compass the death of Telemachus, and take no heed of suppliants, whose witness is Zeus himself? It is not right for you to plot thus against one another. Do you not remember how your father fled to this house in fear of the people, who were enraged against him for having gone with some Taphian pirates and plundered the Thesprotians, who were at peace with us? They wanted to tear him in pieces and eat up everything he had, but Odysseus stayed their hands although they were infuriated, and now you devour his property without paying for it, and break my heart by wooing his wife and trying to kill his son. Leave off doing so, and stop the others also."

To this Eurymachus son of Polybus answered: "Take heart, Queen Penelope daughter of Icarius, and do not trouble yourself about these matters. The man is not yet born, nor never will be, who shall lay hands upon your son Telemachus, while I yet live to look upon the face of the earth. I say—and it shall surely be—that my spear shall be reddened with his blood; for many a time has Odysseus taken me on his knees, held wine up to my lips to drink, and put pieces of meat into my hands. Therefore Telemachus is much the dearest friend I have, and has nothing to fear from the hands of us suitors. Of course, if death comes to him from the gods, he cannot escape it." He said this to quiet her, but in reality he was plotting against Telemachus.

Then Penelope went upstairs again and mourned her husband till Athene shed sleep over her eyes. In the evening Eumaus got back to Odysseus and his son, who had just sacrificed a young pig of a year old and were helping one another to get supper ready. Athene therefore came up to Odysseus, turned him into an old man with a stroke of her wand, and clad him in his old clothes again, for fear that the swineherd might recognize him and not keep the secret, but go and tell Penelope.

Telemachus was the first to speak. "So you have got back, Eumaeus," said he. "What is the news of the town? Have the suitors returned, or are they still waiting over yonder, to take me on my way home?"

"I did not think of asking about that," replied Eumaeus, "when I was in the town. I thought I would give my message and come back as soon as I could. I met a man sent by those who had gone with you to Pylos, and he was the first to tell the news to your mother, but I can say what I saw with my own eyes. I had just got on to the crest of the hill of Hermes above the town when I saw a ship coming into harbor with a number of men in her. They had many shields and spears, and I thought it was the suitors, but I cannot be sure."

On hearing this Telemachus smiled to his father, but so that Eumaeus could not see him.

Then, when they had finished their work and the meal was ready, they ate it, and every man had his full share so that all were satisfied. As soon as they had had enough to eat and drink, they laid down to rest and enjoyed the boon of sleep.

BOOK XVII

Telemachus is welcomed home by his mother Penelope and tells her what he heard from Menelaus about Odysseus. Odysseus, again in the guise of an aged beggar, sets out with Eumaeus for the town. On the threshold of his house, he is recognized by his old dog, Argos, who wags his tail and dies. Odysseus is given food by Telemachus, but a suitor, Antinous, is abusive and strikes him.

WHEN THE CHILD OF MORNING, ROSY-fingered Dawn, appeared, Telemachus bound on his sandals and took a strong spear that suited his hands, for he wanted to go into the city. "Old friend," said he to the swineherd, "I will now go to the town and show myself to my mother, for she will never leave off grieving till she has seen me. As for this unfortunate stranger, take him to the town and let him beg there of anyone who will give him a drink and a piece of bread. I have trouble enough of my own, and cannot be burdened with other people. If this makes him angry, so much the worse for him, but I like to say what I mean."

Then Odysseus said: "Sir, I do not want to stay here. A beggar can always do better in town than country, for anyone who likes can give him something. I am too old to care about remaining here at the beck and call of a master. Therefore let this man do as you have just told him, and take me to the town as soon as I have had a warm by the fire, and the day has got a little heat in it. My clothes are wretchedly thin, and this frosty morning I shall be perished with cold, for you say the city is some way off."

On this Telemachus strode off through the yards, brooding his revenge upon the suitors. When he reached home he stood his spear against a bearing-post of the cloister, crossed the stone floor of the cloister itself, and went inside.

Nurse Euryclea saw him long before anyone else did. She was putting the fleeces on to the seats, and she burst out crying as she ran up to him; all the other maids came up too, and covered his head and shoulders with their kisses. Penelope came out of her room looking like Artemis or Aphrodite, and wept as she flung her arms about her son. She kissed his forehead and both his beautiful eyes, "Light of my eyes," she cried, as she spoke fondly to him, "so you are come home again! I made sure I was never going to see you any more. To think of your having gone off to Pylos without saying anything about it or obtaining my consent. But come, tell me what you saw."

"Do not scold me, mother," answered Telemachus, "nor vex me, seeing what a narrow escape I have had, but wash your face, change your dress, go upstairs with your maids, and promise full and sufficient hecatombs to all the gods if Zeus will only grant us our revenge upon the suitors. I must now go to the place of assembly to invite a stranger who has come back with me from Pylos. I sent him on with my crew, and told Piraeus to take him home and look after him till I could come for him myself."

She heeded her son's words, washed her face, changed her dress, and vowed full and sufficient hecatombs to all the gods if they would only vouchsafe her revenge upon the suitors.

Telemachus went through and out of the cloisters spear in hand —not alone, for his two fleet dogs went with him. Athene endowed him with a presence of such divine comeliness that all marveled at him as he went by, and the suitors gathered round him with fair words in their mouths and malice in their hearts. But he avoided them, and went to sit with Mentor, Antiphus, and Halitherses, old friends of his father's house, and they made him tell them all that had happened to him. Then Piraeus came up with Theoclymenus, whom he had escorted through the town to the place of assembly, whereon Telemachus at once joined them. Piraeus was first to speak: "Telemachus," said he, "I wish you would send some of your women to my house to take away the presents Menelaus gave you."

"We do not know, Piraeus," answered Telemachus, "what may happen. If the suitors kill me in my own house and divide my property among them, I would rather you had the presents than that any of those people should get hold of them. If on the other hand I manage to kill them, I shall be much obliged if you will kindly bring me my presents."

With these words he took Theoclymenus to his own house. When they got there they laid their cloaks on the benches and seats, went into the baths, and washed themselves. When the maids had washed and anointed them, and had given them cloaks and shirts, they took their seats at table. A maidservant then brought them water in a beautiful golden ewer, and poured it into a silver basin for them to wash their hands; and she drew a clean table beside them. An upper servant brought them bread and offered them many good things of what there was in the house. Opposite them sat Penelope, reclining on a couch by one of the bearing-posts of the cloister, and spinning. Then they laid their hands on the good things that were before them, and as soon as they had had enough to eat and drink Penelope said:

"Telemachus, I shall go upstairs and lie down on that sad couch, which I have not ceased to water with my tears, from the day Odysseus set out for Troy with the sons of Atreus. You failed, however, to make it clear to me, before the suitors came back to the house, whether or no you had been able to hear anything about the return of your father."

"I will tell you the truth," replied her son. "We went to Pylos and saw Nestor, who took me to his house and treated me as hospitably as though I were a son of his own who had just returned after a long absence; so also did his sons; but he said he had not heard a word from any human being about Odysseus, whether he was alive or dead. He sent me, therefore, with a chariot and horse to Menelaus. There I saw Helen, for whose sake so many, both Argives and Trojans, were in heaven's wisdom doomed to suffer. Menelaus asked me what it was that had brought me to Sparta, and I told him the whole truth, whereon he said, 'So, then, these cowards would usurp a brave man's bed? A hind might as well lay her newborn young in the lair of a lion, and then go off to feed in the forest or in some grassy dell. The lion, when he comes back to his lair, will make short work with the pair of them, and so will Odysseus with these suitors. By father Zeus, Athene, and Apollo, if Odysseus is still the man that he was when he wrestled with Philomeleides in Lesbos, and threw him so heavily that all the Greeks cheered him—if he is still such, and were to come near these suitors, they would have a short shrift and a sorry wedding. As regards your question, however, I will not prevaricate or deceive you, but what the old man of the sea told me, so much will I tell you in full. He said he could see Odysseus on an island sorrowing bitterly in the house of the nymph Calypso, who was keeping him prisoner, and he could not reach his home, for he had no ships or sailors to take him over the sea.' This was what Menelaus told me, and when I had heard his story I came away. The gods then gave me a fair wind and soon brought me safe home again."

With these words he moved the heart of Penelope. Then Theoclymenus said to her:

"Madam, wife of Odysseus, Telemachus does not understand these things. Listen therefore to me, for I can divine them surely, and will hide nothing from you. May Zeus the king of heaven be my witness, and the rites of hospitality, with that hearth of Odysseus to which I now come, that Odysseus himself is even now in Ithaca, and, either going about the country or staying in one place, is inquiring into all these evil deeds and preparing a day of reckon-

ing for the suitors. I saw an omen when I was on the ship which
meant this, and I told Telemachus about it."

"May it be even so," answered Penelope; "if your words come
true, you shall have such gifts and such good will from me that all
who see you shall congratulate you."

Thus did they converse. Meanwhile, the suitors were throwing
discs, or aiming with spears at a mark on the leveled ground in
front of the house and behaving with all their old insolence. But
when it was now time for dinner, and the flock of sheep and goats
had come into the town from all the country round,[1] with their
shepherds as usual, then Medon, who was their favorite servant,
and who waited upon them at table, said, "Now then, my young
masters, you have had enough sport, so come inside that we may
get dinner ready. Dinner is not a bad thing, at dinner time."

They left their sports as he told them, and when they were within
the house, they laid their cloaks on the benches and seats inside, and
then sacrificed some sheep, goats, pigs, and a heifer, all of them fat
and well grown.[2] Thus they made ready for their meal. In the meantime Odysseus and the swineherd were about starting for the town,
and the swineherd said: "Stranger, I suppose you still want to go
to town today, as my master said you were to do. For my own part,
I should have liked you to stay here as a station hand, but I must
do as my master tells me, or he will scold me later on, and a scolding from one's master is a very serious thing. Let us then be off, for
it is now broad day; it will be night again directly and then you will
find it colder."

"I know, and understand you," replied Odysseus; "you need say
no more. Let us be going, but if you have a stick ready cut, let me
have it to walk with, for you say the road is a very rough one."

As he spoke he threw his shabby old tattered wallet over his shoulders, by the cord from which it hung, and Eumaeus gave him a

[1] That is, to be milked, as in South Italian and Sicilian towns at the present day.
(B.)
[2] The butchering and making ready the carcasses took place partly in the outer yard
and partly in the open part of the inner court. (B.)

stick to his liking. The two then started, leaving the station in charge of the dogs and herdsmen who remained behind. The swineherd led the way and his master followed after, looking like some broken-down old tramp as he leaned upon his staff, and his clothes were all in rags. When they had got over the rough steep ground and were nearing the city, they reached the fountain from which the citizens drew their water. This had been made by Ithacus, Neritus, and Polyctor. There was a grove of water-loving poplars planted in a circle all round it, and the clear cold water came down to it from a rock high up, while above the fountain there was an altar to the nymphs, at which all wayfarers used to sacrifice. Here Melanthius son of Dolius overtook them as he was driving down some goats, the best in his flock, for the suitors' dinner, and there were two shepherds with him. When he saw Eumaeus and Odysseus, he reviled them with outrageous and unseemly language, which made Odysseus very angry.

"There you go," cried he, "and a precious pair you are. See how heaven brings birds of the same feather to one another. Where, pray, master swineherd, are you taking this poor miserable object? It would make anyone sick to see such a creature at table. A fellow like this never won a prize for anything in his life, but will go about rubbing his shoulders against every man's doorpost, and begging, not for swords and cauldrons[3] like a man, but only for a few scraps not worth begging for. If you would give him to me for a hand on my station, he might do to clean out the folds, or bring a bit of sweet feed to the kids, and he could fatten his thighs as much as he pleased on whey; but he has taken to bad ways and will not go about any kind of work; he will do nothing but beg victuals all the town over, to feed his insatiable belly. I say, therefore—and it shall surely be—if he goes near Odysseus' house he will get his head broken by the stools they will fling at him, till they turn him out."

On this, as he passed, he gave Odysseus a kick on the hip out of

[3] From this and other passages in the *Odyssey* it appears that we are in an age anterior to the use of coined money—an age when cauldrons, tripods, swords, cattle, chattels of all kinds, measures of corn, wine, or oil, etc., not to say pieces of gold, silver, bronze, or even iron, wrought more or less, but unstamped, were the nearest approach to a currency that had as yet been reached. (B.)

pure wantonness, but Odysseus stood firm, and did not budge from the path. For a moment he doubted whether or no to fly at Melanthius and kill him with his staff, or fling him to the ground and beat his brains out. He resolved, however, to endure it and keep himself in check, but the swineherd looked straight at Melanthius and rebuked him, lifting up his hands and praying to heaven as he did so.

"Fountain nymphs," he cried, "children of Zeus, if ever Odysseus burned you thighbones covered with fat whether of lambs or kids, grant my prayer that heaven may send him home. He would soon put an end to the swaggering threats with which such men as you go about insulting people—gadding all over the town while your flocks are going to ruin through bad shepherding."

Then Melanthius the goatherd answered: "You ill-conditioned cur, what are you talking about? Some day or other I will put you on board ship and take you to a foreign country, where I can sell you and pocket the money you will fetch. I wish I were as sure that Apollo would strike Telemachus dead this very day, or that the suitors would kill him, as I am that Odysseus will never come home again."

With this he left them to come on at their leisure, while he went quickly forward and soon reached the house of his master. When he got there he went in and took his seat among the suitors opposite Eurymachus, who liked him better than any of the others. The servants brought him a portion of meat, and an upper womanservant set bread before him that he might eat. Presently Odysseus and the swineherd came up to the house and stood by it, amid a sound of music, for Phemius was just beginning to sing to the suitors. Then Odysseus took hold of the swineherd's hand, and said:

"Eumaeus, this house of Odysseus is a very fine place. No matter how far you go you will find few like it. One building keeps following on after another. The outer court has a wall with battlements all round it; the doors are double folding, and of good workmanship; it would be a hard matter to take it by force of arms. I perceive, too, that there are many people banqueting within it, for there is a smell of roast meat, and I hear a sound of music, which the gods have made to go along with feasting."

Then Eumaeus said: "You have perceived aright, as indeed you generally do; but let us think what will be our best course. Will you go inside first and join the suitors, leaving me here behind you, or will you wait here and let me go in first? But do not wait long, or someone may see you loitering about outside, and throw something at you. Consider this matter, I pray."

And Odysseus answered: "I understand and heed. Go in first and leave me here where I am. I am quite used to being beaten and having things thrown at me. I have been so much buffeted about in war and by sea that I am case-hardened, and this too may go with the rest. But a man cannot hide away the cravings of a hungry belly; this is an enemy which gives much trouble to all men. It is because of this that ships are fitted out to sail the seas, and to make war upon other people."

As they were thus talking, a dog that had been lying asleep raised his head and pricked up his ears. This was Argos, whom Odysseus had bred before setting out for Troy. but he had never had any work out of him. In the old days he used to be taken out by the young men when they went hunting wild goats, or deer, or hares, but now that his master was gone he was lying neglected on the heaps of mule and cow dung that lay in front of the stable doors till the men should come and draw it away to manure the great close; and he was full of fleas. As soon as he saw Odysseus standing there, he dropped his ears and wagged his tail, but he could not get close up to his master. When Odysseus saw the dog on the other side of the yard, he dashed a tear from his eyes without Eumaeus seeing it, and said:

"Eumaeus, what a noble hound that is over yonder on the manure heap; his build is splendid. Is he as fine a fellow as he looks, or is he only one of those dogs that come begging about a table and are kept merely for show?"

"This hound," answered Eumaeus, "belonged to him who has died in a far country. If he were what he was when Odysseus left

for Troy, he would soon show you what he could do. There was
not a wild beast in the forest that could get away from him when
he was once on its tracks. But now he has fallen on evil times, for
his master is dead and gone, and the women take no care of him.
Servants never do their work when their master's hand is no longer
over them, for Zeus takes half the goodness out of a man when he
makes a slave of him."

N. B.

As he spoke he went inside the buildings to the cloister where the
suitors were, but Argos died as soon as he had recognized his master.

Telemachus saw Eumaeus long before anyone else did, and
beckoned him to come and sit beside him. So he looked about and
saw a seat lying near where the carver sat serving out their portions
to the suitors; he picked it up, brought it to Telemachus' table, and
sat down opposite him. Then the servant brought him his portion,
and gave him bread from the bread-basket.

Immediately afterwards Odysseus came inside, looking like a poor
miserable old beggar, leaning on his staff and with his clothes all in
rags. He sat down upon the threshold of ash-wood just inside the
doors leading from the outer to the inner court, and against a bearing-post of cypress wood which the carpenter had skillfully planed,
and had made to join truly with rule and line. Telemachus took a
whole loaf from the bread-basket, with as much meat as he could
hold in his two hands, and said to Eumaeus, "Take this to the
stranger, and tell him to go the round of the suitors, and beg from
them. A beggar must not be shamefaced."

So Eumaeus went up to him and said, "Stranger, Telemachus
sends you this, and says you are to go the round of the suitors begging, for beggars must not be shamefaced."

Odysseus answered, "May King Zeus grant all happiness to Telemachus, and fulfill the desire of his heart."

Then with both hands he took what Telemachus had sent him,
and laid it on the dirty old wallet at his feet. He went on eating it
while the bard was singing, and had just finished his dinner as he
left off. The suitors applauded the bard, whereon Athene went up
to Odysseus and prompted him to beg pieces of bread from each one

of the suitors, that he might see what kind of people they were, and tell the good from the bad. But come what might she was not going to save a single one of them. Odysseus, therefore, went on his round, going from left to right, and stretched out his hands to beg as though he were a real beggar. Some of them pitied him, and were curious about him, asking one another who he was and where he came from; whereon the goatherd Melanthius said, "Suitors of my noble mistress, I can tell you something about him, for I have seen him before. The swineherd brought him here, but I know nothing about the man himself, nor where he comes from."

On this Antinous began to abuse the swineherd. "You precious idiot," he cried, "what have you brought this man to town for? Have we not tramps and beggars enough already to pester us as we sit at meat? Do you think it a small thing that such people gather here to waste your master's property—and must you needs bring this man as well?"

And Eumaeus answered: "Antinous, your birth is good but your words evil. It was no doing of mine that he came here. Who is likely to invite a stranger from a foreign country, unless it be one of those who can do public service as a seer, a healer of hurts, a carpenter, or a bard who can charm us with his singing? Such men are welcome all the world over, but no one is likely to ask a beggar who will only worry him. You are always harder on Odysseus' servants than any of the other suitors are, and above all on me, but I do not care so long as Telemachus and Penelope are alive and here."

But Telemachus said, "Hush, do not answer him. Antinous has the bitterest tongue of all the suitors, and he makes the others worse."

Then turning to Antinous he said: "Antinous, you take as much care of my interests as though I were your son. Why should you want to see this stranger turned out of the house? Heaven forbid. Take something and give it him yourself; I do not grudge it; I bid you take it. Never mind my mother, or any of the other servants in the house. But I know you will not do what I say, for you are more fond of eating things yourself than of giving them to other people."

"What do you mean, Telemachus," replied Antinous, "by this swaggering talk? If all the suitors were to give him as much as I will, he would not come here again for another three months."

As he spoke he drew the stool on which he rested his dainty feet from under the table and made as though he would throw it at Odysseus, but the other suitors all gave him something, and filled his wallet with bread and meat. He was about, therefore, to go back to the threshold and eat what the suitors had given him, but he first went up to Antinous and said:

"Sir, give me something. You are not, surely, the poorest man here. You seem to be a chief, foremost among them all; therefore you should be the better giver, and I will tell far and wide of your bounty. I too was a rich man once, and had a fine house of my own. In those days I gave to many a tramp such as I now am, no matter who he might be or what he wanted. I had any number of servants, and all the other things which people have who live well and are accounted wealthy, but it pleased Zeus to take all away from me. He sent me with a band of roving robbers to Egypt; it was a long voyage and I was undone by it. I stationed my ships in the river Aegyptus, and bade my men stay by them and keep guard over them, while I sent out scouts to reconnoiter from every point of vantage.

"But the men disobeyed my orders, took to their own devices, and ravaged the land of the Egyptians, killing the men, and taking their wives and children captives. The alarm was soon carried to the city, and when they heard the war-cry, the people came out at daybreak till the plain was filled with soldiers horse and foot, and with the gleam of armor. Then Zeus spread panic among my men, and they would no longer face the enemy, for they found themselves surrounded. The Egyptians killed many of us, and took the rest alive to do forced labor for them. As for myself, they gave me to a friend who met them, to take to Cyprus, Dmetor by name, son of Iasus, who was a great man in Cyprus. Thence I am come hither in a state of great misery."

Then Antinous said: "What god can have sent such a pestilence to plague us during our dinner? Get out, into the open part of the court, or I will give you Egypt and Cyprus over again for your insolence and importunity. You have begged of all the others, and they have given you lavishly, for they have abundance round them, and it is easy to be free with other people's property when there is plenty of it."

On this Odysseus began to move off, and said: "Your looks, my fine sir, are better than your breeding. If you were in your own house, you would not spare a poor man so much as a pinch of salt, for though you are in another man's, and surrounded with abundance, you cannot find it in you to give him even a piece of bread."

This made Antinous very angry, and he scowled at him saying, "You shall pay for this before you get clear of the court." With these words he threw a footstool at him, and hit him on the right shoulder blade near the top of his back. Odysseus stood firm as a rock and the blow did not even stagger him, but he shook his head in silence as he brooded on his revenge. Then he went back to the threshold and sat down there, laying his well-filled wallet at his feet.

"Listen to me," he cried, "you suitors of Queen Penelope, that I may speak even as I am minded. A man knows neither ache nor pain if he gets hit while fighting for his money, or for his sheep or his cattle. Even so Antinous has hit me while in the service of my miserable belly, which is always getting people into trouble. Still, if the poor have gods and avenging deities at all, I pray them that Antinous may come to a bad end before his marriage."

"Sit where you are, and eat your victuals in silence, or be off elsewhere," shouted Antinous. "If you say more, I will have you dragged hand and foot through the courts, and the servants shall flay you alive."

The other suitors were much displeased at this, and one of the young men said, "Antinous, you did ill in striking that poor wretch of a tramp. It will be worse for you if he should turn out to be some god. And we know the gods go about disguised in all sorts of ways as people from foreign countries, and travel about the world to see who do amiss and who righteously."

Thus said the suitors, but Antinous paid them no heed. Meanwhile Telemachus was furious about the blow that had been given to his father, and though no tear fell from him, he shook his head in silence and brooded on his revenge.

Now when Penelope heard that the beggar had been struck in the banqueting cloister, she said before her maids, "Would that Apollo would so strike you, Antinous," and her waiting woman Eurynome answered, "If our prayers were answered not one of the suitors would ever again see the sun rise." Then Penelope said, "Nurse, I hate every single one of them, for they mean nothing but mischief, but I hate Antinous like the darkness of death itself. A poor unfortunate tramp has come begging about the house for sheer want. Everyone else has given him something to put in his wallet, but Antinous has hit him on the right shoulder blade with a footstool."

Thus did she talk with her maids as she sat in her own room, and in the meantime Odysseus was getting his dinner. Then she called for the swineherd and said, "Eumaeus, go and tell the stranger to come here. I want to see him and ask him some questions. He seems to have traveled much, and he may have seen or heard something of my unhappy husband."

To this you answered, O swineherd Eumaeus: "If these Achaeans, madam, would only keep quiet, you would be charmed with the history of his adventures. I had him three days and three nights with me in my hut, which was the first place he reached after running away from his ship, and he has not yet completed the story of his misfortunes. If he had been the most heaven-taught minstrel in the whole world, on whose lips all hearers hang entranced, I could not have been more charmed as I sat in my hut and listened to him. He says there is an old friendship between his house and that of Odysseus, and that he comes from Crete where the descendants of Minos live, after having been driven hither and thither by every kind of misfortune. He also declares that he has heard of Odysseus as being alive and near at hand among the Thesprotians, and that he is bringing great wealth home with him."

"Call him here, then," said Penelope, "that I too may hear his story. As for the suitors, let them take their pleasure indoors or out as they will, for they have nothing to fret about. Their corn and wine remain unwasted in their houses with none but servants to consume them, while they keep hanging about our house day after day, sacrificing our oxen, sheep, and fat goats for their banquets, and never giving so much as a thought to the quantity of wine they drink. No estate can stand such recklessness, for we have now no Odysseus to protect us. If we were to come again, he and his son would soon have their revenge."

As she spoke Telemachus sneezed so loudly that the whole house resounded with it. Penelope laughed when she heard this, and said to Eumaeus, "Go and call the stranger. Did you not hear how my son sneezed just as I was speaking? This can only mean that all the suitors are going to be killed, and that not one of them shall escape. Furthermore I say, and I lay my saying to your heart: if I am satisfied that the stranger is speaking the truth I shall give him a shirt and cloak of good wear."

When Eumaeus heard this he went straight to Odysseus and said: "Father stranger, my mistress Penelope, mother of Telemachus, has sent for you. She is in great grief, but she wishes to hear anything you can tell her about her husband, and if she is satisfied that you are speaking the truth, she will give you a shirt and cloak, which are the very things that you are most in want of. As for bread, you can get enough of that to fill your belly, by begging about the town, and letting those give that will."

"I will tell Penelope," answered Odysseus, "nothing but what is strictly true. I know all about her husband, and have been partner with him in affliction, but I am afraid of passing through this crowd of cruel suitors, for their pride and insolence reach heaven. Just now, moreover, as I was going about the house without doing any harm, a man gave me a blow that hurt me very much, but neither Telemachus nor anyone else defended me. Tell Penelope, therefore, to be patient and wait till sundown. Let her give me a seat close up to the fire, for my clothes are worn very thin. You know they are, for you have seen them ever since I first asked you to help me. She can then ask me about the return of her husband."

The swineherd went back when he heard this, and Penelope said as she saw him cross the threshold, "Why do you not bring him here, Eumaeus? Is he afraid that someone will ill-treat him, or is he shy of coming inside the house at all? Beggars should not be shame-faced."

To this you answered, O swineherd Eumaeus, "The stranger is quite reasonable. He is avoiding the suitors, and is only doing what anyone else would do. He asks you to wait till sundown, and it will be much better, madam, that you should have him all to yourself, when you can hear him and talk to him as you will."

"The man is no fool," answered Penelope, "it would very likely be as he says, for there are no such abominable people in the whole world as these men are."

When she had done speaking Eumaeus went back to the suitors, for he had explained everything. Then he went up to Telemachus and said in his ear so that none could overhear him, "My dear sir, I will now go back to the pigs, to see after your property and my own business. You will look to what is going on here, but above all be careful to keep out of danger, for there are many who bear you ill will. May Zeus bring them to a bad end before they do us a mischief."

"Very well," replied Telemachus, "go home when you have had your dinner, and in the morning come here with the victims we are to sacrifice for the day. Leave the rest to heaven and me."

On this Eumaeus took his seat again, and when he had finished his dinner he left the courts and the cloister with the men at table, and went back to his pigs. As for the suitors, they presently began to amuse themselves with singing and dancing, for it was now getting on towards evening.

BOOK XVIII

Odysseus is insulted by Irus, a beggar, who challenges him to fight. While the suitors look on, Odysseus thrashes Irus soundly. Penelope upbraids her son for allowing the stranger to be ill-treated. The suitor Eurymachus gibes at Odysseus, and hurls a footstool at him. Telemachus censures the suitors for their behavior, and they go home to bed.

NOW THERE CAME A CERTAIN COMMON TRAMP who used to go begging all over the city of Ithaca, and was notorious as an incorrigible glutton and drunkard. This man had no strength or stay in him, but he was a great hulking fellow to look at. His real name, the one his mother gave him, was Arnaeus, but the young men of the place called him Irus, because he used to run errands for anyone who would send him.[1] As soon as he came he began to insult Odysseus, and to try and drive him out of his own house.

"Be off, old man," he cried, "from the doorway, or you shall be dragged out neck and heels. Do you not see that they are all giving me the wink, and wanting me to turn you out by force, only I do not like to do so? Get up then, and go of yourself, or we shall come to blows."

[1] Iris was the messenger of the gods.

Odysseus frowned on him and said: "My friend, I do you no manner of harm; people give you a great deal, but I am not jealous. There is room enough in this doorway for the pair of us, and you need not grudge me things that are not yours to give. You seem to be just such another tramp as myself, but perhaps the gods will give us better luck by and by. Do not, however, talk too much about fighting, or you will incense me, and old though I am, I shall cover your mouth and chest with blood. I shall have more peace tomorrow if I do, for you will not come to the house of Odysseus any more."

Irus was very angry and answered: "You filthy glutton, you run on trippingly like an old fish-fag. I have a good mind to lay both hands about you, and knock your teeth out of your head like so many boar's tusks. Get ready, therefore, and let these people here stand by and look on. You will never be able to fight one who is so much younger than yourself."

Thus roundly did they rate one another on the smooth pavement in front of the doorway,[2] and when Antinous saw what was going on he laughed heartily and said to the others, "This is the finest sport that you ever saw; heaven never yet sent anything like it into this house. The stranger and Irus have quarreled and are going to fight. Let us set them on to do so at once."

The suitors all came up laughing, and gathered round the two ragged tramps. "Listen to me," said Antinous, "there are some goats' paunches down at the fire, which we have filled with blood and fat, and set aside for supper. He who is victorious and proves himself to be the better man shall have his pick of the lot. He shall be free of our table and we will not allow any other beggar about the house at all."

The others all agreed, but Odysseus, to throw them off the scent, said, "Sirs, an old man like myself, worn out with suffering, cannot hold his own against a young one. But my irrepressible belly urges me on, though I know it can only end in my getting a drubbing. You must swear, however, that none of you will give me a foul blow to favor Irus and secure him the victory."

[2] The doorway leading from the inner to the outer court. (B.)

They swore as he told them, and when they had completed their oath Telemachus put in a word and said, "Stranger, if you have a mind to settle with this fellow, you need not be afraid of anyone here. Whoever strikes you will have to fight more than one. I am host, and the other chiefs, Antinous and Eurymachus, both of them men of understanding, are of the same mind as I am."

Everyone assented, and Odysseus girded his old rags about his loins, thus baring his stalwart thighs, his broad chest and shoulders, and his mighty arms. Athene came up to him and made his limbs even stronger still. The suitors were beyond measure astonished, and one would turn towards his neighbor saying, "The stranger has brought such a thigh out of his old rags that there will soon be nothing left of Irus."

Irus began to be very uneasy as he heard them, but the servants girded him by force, and brought him into the open part of the court in such a fright that his limbs were all of a tremble. Antinous scolded him and said, "You swaggering bully, you ought never to have been born at all if you are afraid of such an old broken-down creature as this tramp is. I say, therefore—and it shall surely be—if he beats you and proves himself the better man, I shall pack you off on board ship to the mainland and send you to king Echetus, who kills everyone that comes near him. He will cut off your nose and ears, and draw out your entrails for the dogs to eat."

This frightened Irus still more, but they brought him into the middle of the court, and the two men raised their hands to fight. Then Odysseus considered whether he should let drive so hard at him as to make an end of him then and there, or whether he should give him a lighter blow that should only knock him down. In the end he deemed it best to give the lighter blow for fear the Achaeans should begin to suspect who he was. Then they began to fight, and Irus hit Odysseus on the right shoulder, but Odysseus gave Irus a blow on the neck under the ear that broke in the bones of his skull, and the blood came gushing out of his mouth. He fell groaning in the dust, gnashing his teeth and kicking on the ground. The suitors threw up their hands and nearly died of laughter, as Odysseus caught hold of him by the foot and dragged him into the outer court as far as the gate-house. There he propped him up against the wall and put his staff in his hands. "Sit here," said he, "and keep the dogs and pigs off. You are a pitiful creature, and if you try to make yourself king of the beggars any more you shall fare still worse."

Then he threw his dirty old wallet, all tattered and torn, over his shoulder with the cord by which it hung, and went back to sit down upon the threshold. But the suitors went within the cloisters, laughing and saluting him, "May Zeus, and all the other gods," said they, "grant you whatever you want for having put an end to the importunity of this insatiable tramp. We will take him over to the mainland presently, to king Echetus, who kills everyone that comes near him."

Odysseus hailed this as of good omen, and Antinous set a great goat's paunch before him filled with blood and fat. Amphinomus took two loaves out of the bread-basket and brought them to him, pledging him as he did so in a golden goblet of wine. "Good luck to you," he said, "father stranger. You are very badly off at present, but I hope you will have better times by and by."

To this Odysseus answered: "Amphinomus, you seem to be a man of good understanding, as indeed you may well be, seeing whose son you are. I have heard your father well spoken of; he is Nisus of Dulichium, a man both brave and wealthy. They tell me you are his son, and you appear to be a considerable person. Listen, therefore, and take heed to what I am saying. Man is the vainest of all creatures that have their being upon earth. As long as heaven vouchsafes him health and strength, he thinks that he shall come to no harm hereafter, and even when the blessed gods bring sorrow upon him, he bears it as he needs must, and makes the best of it; for God almighty gives men their daily minds day by day. I know all about it, for I was a rich man once, and did much wrong in the stubbornness of my pride, and in the confidence that my father and my brothers would support me. Therefore let a man fear God in all things always, and take the good that heaven may see fit to send him without vainglory. Consider the infamy of what these suitors are doing. See how they are wasting the estate, and doing dishonor to the wife, of one who is certain to return some day, and that, too, not long hence. Nay, he will be here soon. May heaven send you home quietly first that you may not meet with him in the day of his coming, for once he is here the suitors and he will not part bloodlessly."

With these words he made a drink offering, and when he had drunk he put the gold cup again into the hands of Amphinomus, who walked away serious and bowing his head, for he foreboded evil. But even so he did not escape destruction, for Athene had doomed him to fall by the hand of Telemachus. So he took his seat again at the place from which he had come.

Then Athene put it into the mind of Penelope to show herself to the suitors, that she might make them still more enamoured of her, and win still further honor from her son and husband. So she feigned a mocking laugh and said, "Eurynome, I have changed my mind, and have a fancy to show myself to the suitors although I detest them. I should like also to give my son a hint that he had better not have anything more to do with them. They speak fairly enough but they mean mischief."

"My dear child," answered Eurynome, "all that you have said is true. Go and tell your son about it, but first wash yourself and anoint your face. Do not go about with your cheeks all covered with tears. It is not right that you should grieve so incessantly; for Telemachus, whom you always prayed that you might live to see with a beard, is already grown up."

"I know, Eurynome," replied Penelope, "that you mean well, but do not try and persuade me to wash and to anoint myself, for heaven robbed me of all my beauty on the day my husband sailed. Nevertheless, tell Autonoe and Hippodamia that I want them. They must be with me when I am in the cloister. I am not going among the men alone; it would not be proper for me to do so."

On this the old woman went out of the room to bid the maids go to their mistress. In the meantime Athene bethought her of another matter, and sent Penelope off into a sweet slumber; so she lay down on her couch and her limbs became heavy with sleep. Then the goddess shed grace and beauty over her that all the Achaeans might admire her. She washed her face with the ambrosial loveliness that Aphrodite wears when she goes dancing with the Graces; she made her taller and of a more commanding figure, while as for her complexion it was whiter than sawn ivory. When Athene had done all this she went away, whereon the maids came in from the women's room and woke Penelope with the sound of their talking.

"What an exquisitely delicious sleep I have been having," said she, as she passed her hands over her face, "in spite of all my misery. I wish Artemis would let me die so sweetly now at this very moment, that I might no longer waste in despair for the loss of my dear husband, who possessed every kind of good quality and was the most distinguished man among the Achaeans."

With these words she came down from her upper room, not alone but attended by two of her maidens, and when she reached the suitors she stood by one of the bearing-posts supporting the roof of the cloister, holding a veil before her face, and with a staid maidservant on either side of her. As they beheld her the suitors were so overpowered and became so desperately enamoured of her that each one prayed he might win her for his own bedfellow.

"Telemachus," said she, addressing her son, "I fear you are no longer so discreet and well conducted as you used to be. When you were younger you had a greater sense of propriety; now, however, that you have grown up, though a stranger to look at you would take you for the son of a well-to-do father as far as size and good looks go, your conduct is by no means what it should be. What is all this disturbance that has been going on, and how came you to allow a stranger to be so disgracefully ill-treated? What would have happened if he had suffered serious injury while a suppliant in our house? Surely this would have been very discreditable to you."

"I am not surprised, my dear mother, at your displeasure," replied Telemachus, "I understand all about it and know when things are not as they should be, which I could not do when I was younger. I cannot, however, behave with perfect propriety at all times. First one and then another of these wicked people here keeps driving me out of my mind, and I have no one to stand by me. After all, however, this fight between Irus and the stranger did not turn out as the suitors meant it to do, for the stranger got the best of it. I wish Father Zeus, Athene, and Apollo would break the neck of every one of these wooers of yours, some inside the house and some out; and I wish they might all be as limp as Irus is over yonder in the gate of the outer court. See how he nods his head like a drunken man. He has had such a thrashing that he cannot stand on his feet nor get back to his home, wherever that may be, for he has no strength left in him."

Thus did they converse. Eurymachus then came up and said, "Queen Penelope, daughter of Icarius, if all the Achaeans in Iasian Argos could see you at this moment, you would have still more suitors in your house by tomorrow morning, for you are the most admirable woman in the whole world both as regards personal beauty and strength of understanding."

To this Penelope replied: "Eurymachus, heaven robbed me of all my beauty whether of face or figure when the Argives set sail for Troy and my dear husband with them. If he were to return and look after my affairs, I should both be more respected and show a better presence to the world. As it is, I am oppressed with care, and with the afflictions which heaven has seen fit to heap upon me. My husband foresaw it all, and when he was leaving home he took my right wrist in his hand—'Wife,' he said, 'we shall not all of us come safe home from Troy, for the Trojans fight well both with bow and spear. They are excellent also at fighting from chariots, and nothing decides the issue of a fight sooner than this. I know not, therefore, whether heaven will send me back to you, or whether I may not fall over there at Troy. In the meantime do you look after things here. Take care of my father and mother as at present, and even more so during my absence, but when you see our son growing a beard, then marry whom you will, and leave this your present home.' This is what he said and now it is all coming true. A night will come when I shall have to yield myself to a marriage which I detest, for Zeus has taken from me all hope of happiness. This further grief, moreover, cuts me to the very heart. You suitors are not wooing me after the custom of my country. When men are courting a woman who they think will be a good wife to them and who is of noble birth, and when they are each trying to win her for himself, they usually bring oxen and sheep to feast the friends of the lady, and they make her magnificent presents, instead of eating up other people's property without paying for it."

This was what she said, and Odysseus was glad when he heard her trying to get presents out of the suitors, and flattering them with fair words which he knew she did not mean.

Then Antinous said, "Queen Penelope, daughter of Icarius, take as many presents as you please from anyone who will give them to you. It is not well to refuse a present. But we will not go about our business or stir from where we are, till you have married the best man among us, whoever he may be."

The others applauded what Antinous had said, and each one sent his servant to bring his present. Antinous' man returned with a large and lovely dress most exquisitely embroidered. It had twelve beautifully made brooch pins of pure gold with which to fasten it. Eurymachus immediately brought her a magnificent chain of gold and amber beads that gleamed like sunlight. Eurydamas' two men returned with some earrings fashioned into three brilliant pendants which glistened most beautifully; while King Pisander son of Polyctor gave her a necklace of the rarest workmanship, and everyone else brought her a beautiful present of some kind.

Then the queen went back to her room upstairs, and her maids brought the presents after her. Meanwhile, the suitors took to singing and dancing, and stayed till evening came. They danced and sang till it grew dark; they then brought in three braziers[3] to give light, and piled them up with chopped firewood very old and dry, and they lit torches from them, which the maids held up turn and turn about. Then Odysseus said:

"Maids, servants of Odysseus, who has so long been absent, go to

---

[3] These, I imagine, must have been in the open part of the inner courtyard, where the maids also stood, and threw the light of their torches into the covered cloister that ran all round it. The smoke would otherwise have been intolerable. (B.)

the queen inside the house. Sit with her and amuse her, or spin, and pick wool. I will hold the light for all these people. They may stay till morning, but shall not beat me, for I can stand a great deal."

The maids looked at one another and laughed, while pretty Melantho began to gibe at him contemptuously. She was daughter to Dolius, but had been brought up by Penelope, who used to give her toys to play with, and looked after her when she was a child. But in spite of all this she showed no consideration for the sorrows of her mistress, and used to misconduct herself with Eurymachus, with whom she was in love.

"Poor wretch," said she, "are you gone clean out of your mind? Go and sleep in some smithy, or place of public gossips, instead of chattering here. Are you not ashamed of opening your mouth before your betters—so many of them too? Has the wine been getting into your head, or do you always babble in this way? You seem to have lost your wits because you beat the tramp Irus; take care that a better man than he does not come and cudgel you about the head till he pack you bleeding out of the house."

"Vixen," replied Odysseus, scowling at her, "I will go and tell Telemachus what you have been saying, and he will have you torn limb from limb."

With these words he scared the women, and they went off into the body of the house. They trembled all over, for they thought he would do as he said. But Odysseus took his stand near the burning braziers, holding up torches and looking at the people—brooding the while on things that should surely come to pass.

But Athene would not let the suitors for one moment cease their insolence, for she wanted Odysseus to become even more bitter against them; she therefore set Eurymachus son of Polybus on to gibe at him, which made the others laugh. "Listen to me," said he, "you suitors of Queen Penelope, that I may speak even as I am minded. It is not for nothing that this man has come to the house of Odysseus. I believe the light has not been coming from the torches, but from his own head—for his hair is all gone, every bit of it."

Then turning to Odysseus he said, "Stranger, will you work as a servant, if I send you to the wolds and see that you are well paid? Can you build a stone fence, or plant trees? I will have you fed all the year round and provide you with shoes and clothing. Will you go, then? Not you; for you have got into bad ways, and do not want to work! You had rather fill your belly by going round the country begging."

"Eurymachus," answered Odysseus, "if you and I were to work one against the other in early summer when the days are at their longest—give me a good scythe, and take another yourself, and let us see which will fast the longer or mow the stronger, from dawn till dark when the mowing grass is about. Or if you will plow against me, let us each take a yoke of tawny oxen, well-mated and of great strength and endurance: turn me into a four-acre field, and see whether you or I can drive the straighter furrow. If, again, war were to break out this day, give me a shield, a couple of spears and a helmet fitting well upon my temples—you would find me foremost in the fray, and would cease your gibes about my belly. You are insolent and cruel, and think yourself a great man because you live in a little world, and that a bad one. If Odysseus comes to his own again, the doors of his house are wide, but you will find them narrow when you try to fly through them."

Eurymachus was furious at all this. He scowled at him and cried: "You wretch, I will soon pay you out for daring to say such things to me, and in public too! Has the wine been getting into your head or do you always babble in this way? You seem to have lost your wits because you beat the tramp Irus." With this he caught hold of a footstool, but Odysseus sought protection at the knees of Amphinomus of Dulichium, for he was afraid. The stool hit the cup-bearer on his right hand and knocked him down: the man fell with a cry flat on his back, and his wine jug fell ringing to the ground. The suitors in the covered cloister were now in an uproar, and one would turn towards his neighbor, saying, "I wish the stranger had gone somewhere else. Bad luck to him, for all the trouble he gives us. We cannot permit such disturbance about a beggar; if such ill counsels are to prevail we shall have no more pleasure at our banquet."

On this Telemachus came forward and said, "Sirs, are you mad? Can you not carry your meat and your liquor decently? Some evil spirit has possessed you. I do not wish to drive any of you away, but you have had your suppers, and the sooner you all go home to bed the better."

The suitors bit their lips and marveled at the boldness of his speech; but Amphinomus the son of Nisus, who was son to Aretias, said, "Do not let us take offense; it is reasonable, so let us make no answer. Neither let us do violence to the stranger nor to any of Odysseus' servants. Let the cupbearer go round with the drink offerings, that we may make them and go home to our rest. As for the stranger, let us leave Telemachus to deal with him, for it is to his house that he has come."

Thus did he speak, and his saying pleased them well. So Mulius of Dulichium, servant to Amphinomus, mixed them a bowl of wine and water and handed it round to each of them man by man, whereon they made their drink offerings to the blessed gods. Then, when they had made their drink offerings and had drunk each one as he was minded, they took their several ways each of them to his own abode.

BOOK XIX

Inventing a plausible excuse, Telemachus and Odysseus remove all armor from the court to the storeroom. Penelope talks with Odysseus, not knowing him, and he tries to encourage her by foretelling the early return of the wanderer. The old nurse Euryclea washes Odysseus' feet and recognizes him by a scar on his leg. She is overjoyed, but he commands her to keep silent as to her discovery. Penelope tells him of the archery test she is to set for the suitors.

ODYSSEUS WAS LEFT IN THE CLOISTER, pondering on the means whereby with Athene's help he might be able to kill the suitors. Presently he said to Telemachus: "Telemachus, we must get the armor together and take it down inside. Make some excuse when the suitors ask you why you have removed it. Say that you have taken it to be out of the way of the smoke, inasmuch as it is no longer what it was when Odysseus went away, but has become soiled and begrimed with soot. Add to this more particularly that you are afraid Zeus may set them on to quarrel over their wine, and that they may do each other some harm which may disgrace both banquet and wooing, for the sight of arms sometimes tempts people to use them."

Telemachus approved of what his father had said, so he called
nurse Euryclea and said, "Nurse, shut the women up in their room,
while I take the armor that my father left behind him down into the
storeroom. No one looks after it now my father is gone, and it has
got all smirched with soot during my own boyhood. I want to take
it down where the smoke cannot reach it."

"I wish, child," answered Euryclea, "that you would take the
management of the house into your own hands altogether, and look
after all the property yourself. But who is to go with you and light
you to the storeroom? The maids would have done so, but you
would not let them."

"The stranger," said Telemachus, "shall show me a light. When
people eat my bread they must earn it, no matter where they come
from."

Euryclea did as she was told, and bolted the women inside their
room. Then Odysseus and his son made all haste to take the helmets, shields, and spears inside; and Athene went before them with
a gold lamp in her hand that shed a soft and brilliant radiance.
Whereon Telemachus said, "Father, my eyes behold a great marvel:
the walls, with the rafters, crossbeams, and the supports on which
they rest are all aglow as with a flaming fire. Surely there is some
god here who has come down from heaven."

"Hush," answered Odysseus, "hold your peace and ask no questions, for this is the manner of the gods. Get you to your bed, and
leave me here to talk with your mother and the maids. Your mother
in her grief will ask me all sorts of questions."

On this Telemachus went by torchlight to the other side of the
inner court, to the room in which he always slept. There he lay in
his bed till morning, while Odysseus was left in the cloister pondering on the means whereby with Athene's help he might be able
to kill the suitors.

Then Penelope came down from her room looking like Aphrodite
or Artemis, and they set her a seat inlaid with scrolls of silver and
ivory near the fire in her accustomed place. It had been made by

Icmalius and had a footstool all in one piece with the seat itself, and it was covered with a thick fleece; on this she now sat, and the maids came from the women's room to join her. They set about removing the tables at which the wicked suitors had been dining, and took away the bread that was left, with the cups from which they had drunk. They emptied the embers out of the braziers and heaped much wood upon them to give both light and heat. But Melantho began to rail at Odysseus a second time and said, "Stranger, do you mean to plague us by hanging about the house all night and spying upon the women? Be off, you wretch, outside, and eat your supper there, or you shall be driven out with a firebrand."

Odysseus scowled at her and answered: "My good woman, why should you be so angry with me? Is it because I am not clean, and my clothes are all in rags, and because I am obliged to go begging about after the manner of tramps and beggars generally? I too was a rich man once, and had a fine house of my own; in those days I gave to many a tramp such as I now am, no matter who he might be nor what he wanted. I had any number of servants, and all the other things which people have who live well and are accounted wealthy, but it pleased Zeus to take all away from me. Therefore, woman, beware lest you too come to lose that pride and place in which you now wanton above your fellows. Have a care lest you get out of favor with your mistress, and lest Odysseus should come home, for there is still a chance that he may do so. Moreover, though he be dead as you think he is, yet by Apollo's will he has left a son behind him, Telemachus, who will note anything done amiss by the maids in the house, for he is now no longer in his boyhood."

Penelope heard what he was saying and scolded the maid. "Impudent baggage," said she, "I see how abominably you are behaving, and you shall smart for it. You knew perfectly well, for I told you myself, that I was going to see the stranger and ask him about my husband, for whose sake I am in such continual sorrow."

Then she said to her head waiting-woman Eurynome, "Bring a

seat with a fleece upon it, for the stranger to sit upon while he tells his story, and listens to what I have to say. I wish to ask him some questions."

Eurynome brought the seat at once and set a fleece upon it, and as soon as Odysseus had sat down Penelope began by saying, "Stranger, I shall first ask you who and whence are you? Tell me of your town and parents."

"Madam," answered Odysseus, "who on the face of the whole earth can dare to chide with you? Your fame reaches the firmament of heaven itself. You are like some blameless king, who upholds righteousness, as the monarch over a great and valiant nation. The earth yields its wheat and barley, the trees are loaded with fruit, the ewes bring forth lambs, and the sea abounds with fish by reason of his virtues, and his people do good deeds under him. Nevertheless, as I sit here in your house, ask me some other question and do not seek to know my race and family, or you will recall memories that will yet more increase my sorrow. I am full of heaviness, but I ought not to sit weeping and wailing in another person's house, nor is it well to be thus grieving continually. I shall have one of the servants or even yourself complaining of me, and saying that my eyes swim with tears because I am heavy with wine."

Then Penelope answered: "Stranger, heaven robbed me of all beauty, whether of face or figure, when the Argives set sail for Troy and my dear husband with them. If he were to return and look after my affairs I should be both more respected and should show a better presence to the world. As it is, I am oppressed with care, and with the afflictions which heaven has seen fit to heap upon me. The chiefs from all our islands—Dulichium, Same, and Zacynthus, as also from Ithaca itself, are wooing me against my will and are wasting my estate. I can therefore show no attention to strangers, or suppliants, or to people who say that they are skilled artisans, but am all the time brokenhearted about Odysseus. They want me to marry again at once, and I have to invent stratagems in order to deceive them.

"In the first place heaven put it in my mind to set up a great tambour-frame in my room, and to begin working upon an enormous piece of fine needlework. Then I said to them, "Sweethearts, Odysseus is indeed dead, still, do not press me to marry again immediately. Wait—for I would not have my skill in needlework perish unrecorded—till I have finished making a pall for the hero Laertes, to be ready against the time when death shall take him. He is very rich, and the women of the place will talk if he is laid out without a pall.' This was what I said, and they assented; whereon I used to keep working at my great web all day long, but at night I would unpick the stitches again by torch light. I fooled them in this way for three years without their finding it out, but as time wore on and I was now in my fourth year, in the waning of moons, and many days had been accomplished, those good-for-nothing hussies my maids betrayed me to the suitors, who broke in upon me and caught me; they were very angry with me, so I was forced to finish my work whether I would or no.

"And now I do not see how I can find any further shift for getting out of this marriage. My parents are putting great pressure upon me, and my son chafes at the ravages the suitors are making upon his estate, for he is now old enough to understand all about it and is perfectly able to look after his own affairs, for heaven has blessed him with an excellent disposition. Still, notwithstanding all this, tell me who you are and where you come from—for you must have had father and mother of some sort; you cannot be the son of an oak or of a rock."

Then Odysseus answered: "Madam, wife of Odysseus, since you persist in asking me about my family, I will answer, no matter what it costs me. People must expect to be pained when they have been exiles as long as I have, and suffered as much among as many peoples. Nevertheless, as regards your question I will tell you all you ask. There is a fair and fruitful island in mid-ocean called Crete. It is thickly peopled and there are ninety cities in it. The people speak many different languages which overlap one another, for there are Achaeans, brave Eteocretans, Dorians of three-fold race, and noble Pelasgi. There is a great town there, Cnossus, where

Minos reigned who every nine years had a conference with Zeus himself. Minos was father to Deucalion, whose son I am, for Deucalion had two sons, Idomeneus and myself. Idomeneus sailed for Troy, and I, who am the younger, am called Aethon; my brother, however, was at once the older and the more valiant of the two.

"Hence it was in Crete that I saw Odysseus and showed him hospitality, for the winds took him there as he was on his way to Troy, carrying him out of his course from cape Malea and leaving him in Amnisus off the cave of Ilithuia, where the harbors are difficult to enter and he could hardly find shelter from the winds that were then raging. As soon as he got there he went into the town and asked for Idomeneus, claiming to be his old and valued friend, but Idomeneus had already set sail for Troy some ten or twelve days earlier, so I took him to my own house and showed him every kind of hospitality, for I had abundance of everything. Moreover, I fed the men who were with him with barley meal from the public store, and got subscriptions of wine and oxen for them to sacrifice to their heart's content. They stayed with me twelve days, for there was a gale blowing from the north so strong that one could hardly keep one's feet on land. I suppose some unfriendly god had raised it for them, but on the thirteenth day the wind dropped, and they got away."

Many a plausible tale did Odysseus further tell her, and Penelope wept as she listened, for her heart was melted. As the snow wastes upon the mountain tops when the winds from southeast and west have breathed upon it and thawed it till the rivers run bank full with water, even so did her cheeks overflow with tears for the husband who was all the time sitting by her side. Odysseus felt for her and was sorry for her, but he kept his eyes as hard as horn or iron without letting them so much as quiver, so cunningly did he restrain his tears. Then, when she had relieved herself by weeping, she turned to him again and said: "Now, stranger, I shall put you to the test and see whether or no you really did entertain my husband and his men, as you say you did. Tell me, then, how he was dressed, what kind of a man he was to look at, and so also with his companions."

"Madam," answered Odysseus, "it is such a long time ago that I can hardly say. Twenty years are come and gone since he left my home, and went elsewhither; but I will tell you as well as I can recollect. Odysseus wore a mantle of purple wool, double lined, and it was fastened by a gold brooch with two catches for the pin. On the face of this there was a device that showed a dog holding ɑ spotted fawn between his forepaws, and watching it as it lay panting upon the ground. Everyone marveled at the way in which these things had been done in gold, the dog looking at the fawn, and strangling it, while the fawn was struggling convulsively to escape. As for the shirt that he wore next his skin, it was so soft that it fitted him like the skin of an onion, and glistened in the sunlight to the admiration of all the women who beheld it.

"Furthermore I say, and lay my saying to your heart, that I do not know whether Odysseus wore these clothes when he left home, or whether one of his companions had given them to him while he was on his voyage; or possibly someone at whose house he was staying made him a present of them, for he was a man of many friends and had few equals among the Achaeans. I myself gave him a sword of bronze and a beautiful purple mantle, double lined, with a shirt that went down to his feet, and I sent him on board his ship with every mark of honor. He had a servant with him, a little older than himself, and I can tell you what he was like; his shoulders were hunched, he was dark, and he had thick curly hair. His name was Eurybates, and Odysseus treated him with greater familiarity than he did any of the others, as being the most like-minded with himself."

Penelope was moved still more deeply as she heard the indisputable proofs that Odysseus laid before her; and when she had again found relief in tears she said to him: "Stranger, I was already disposed to pity you, but henceforth you shall be honored and made welcome in my house. It was I who gave Odysseus the clothes you speak of. I took them out of the storeroom and folded them up myself, and I gave him also the gold brooch to wear as an ornament. Alas! I shall never welcome him home again. It was by an ill fate that he ever set out for that detested city whose very name I cannot bring myself even to mention."

Then Odysseus answered: "Madam, wife of Odysseus, do not disfigure yourself further by grieving thus bitterly for your loss, though I can hardly blame you for doing so. A woman who has loved her husband and borne him children would naturally be grieved at losing him, even though he were a worse man than Odysseus, who they say was like a god. Still, cease your tears and listen to what I can tell you. I will hide nothing from you, and can say with perfect truth that I have lately heard of Odysseus as being alive and on his way home. He is among the Thesprotians, and is bringing back much valuable treasure that he has begged from one and another of them. But his ship and all his crew were lost as they were leaving the Thrinacian island, for Zeus and the sun-god were angry with him because his men had slaughtered the sun-god's cattle, and they were all drowned to a man. But Odysseus stuck to the keel of the ship and was drifted on to the land of the Phaeacians, who are near of kin to the immortals, and who treated him as though he had been a god, giving him many presents, and wishing to escort him home safe and sound. In fact Odysseus would have been here long ago, had he not thought better to go from land to land gathering wealth; for there is no man living who is so wily as he is; there is no one can compare with him. Pheidon, king of the Thesprotians, told me all this, and he swore to me—making drink offerings in his house as he did so— that the ship was by the water side and the crew found who would take Odysseus to his own country. He sent me off first, for there happened to be a Thesprotian ship sailing for the wheat-growing island of Dulichium, but he showed me all the treasure Odysseus had got together, and he had enough lying in the house of King Pheidon to keep his family for ten generations. The king said Odysseus had gone to Dodona that he might learn Zeus' mind from the high oak tree, and know whether after so long an absence he should return to Ithaca openly or in secret. So you may know he is safe and will be here shortly; he is close at hand and cannot remain away from home much longer. Furthermore, I will confirm my words with an oath, and call Zeus who is the first and mightiest of all gods to witness, as also that hearth of Odysseus to which I have now come, that all I have spoken shall surely come to pass. Odysseus will return in this self same year; with the end of this moon and the beginning of the next he will be here."

"May it be even so," answered Penelope. "If your words come true, you shall have such gifts and such good will from me that all who see you shall congratulate you; but I know very well how it will all be. Odysseus will not return, neither will you get your escort hence, for so surely as that Odysseus ever was, there are now no longer any such masters in the house as he was, to receive honorable strangers or to further them on their way home. And now, you maids, wash his feet for him, and make him a bed on a couch with rugs and blankets, that he may be warm and quiet till morning. Then, at daybreak wash him and anoint him again, that he may sit in the cloister and take his meals with Telemachus. It shall be the worse for any one of these hateful people who is uncivil to him; like it or not, he shall have no more to do in this house. For how, sir, shall you be able to learn whether or no I am superior to others of my sex both in goodness of heart and understanding, if I let you dine in my cloisters squalid and ill clad? Men live but for a little season; if they are hard, and deal hardly, people wish them ill so long as they are alive, and speak contemptuously of them when they are dead, but he that is righteous and deals righteously, the people tell of his praise among all lands, and many shall call him blessed."

Odysseus answered: "Madam, I have foresworn rugs and blankets from the day that I left the snowy ranges of Crete to go on shipboard. I will lie as I have lain on many a sleepless night hitherto. Night after night have I passed in any rough sleeping place, and waited for morning. Nor, again, do I like having my feet washed. I shall not let any of the young hussies about your house touch my feet; but, if you have any old and respectable woman who has gone through as much trouble as I have, I will allow her to wash them."

To this Penelope said: "My dear sir, of all the guests who ever yet came to my house there never was one who spoke in all things with such admirable propriety as you do. There happens to be in the house a most respectable old woman—the same who received my poor dear husband in her arms the night he was born, and nursed him in infancy. She is very feeble now, but she shall wash your feet. Come here," said she, "Euryclea, and wash your master's age-mate; I suppose Odysseus' hands and feet are very much the same now as his are, for trouble ages all of us dreadfully fast."

On these words the old woman covered her face with her hands. She began to weep and made lamentation, saying, "My dear child, I cannot think whatever I am to do for you. I am certain no one was ever more god-fearing than yourself, and yet Zeus hates you. No one in the whole world ever burned him more thighbones, nor gave him finer hecatombs when you prayed you might come to a green old age yourself and see your son grow up to take your place after you: yet see how he has prevented you alone from ever getting back to your own home! I have no doubt the women in some foreign palace which Odysseus has got to are gibing at him as all these sluts here have been gibing at you. I do not wonder at your not choosing to let them wash you after the manner in which they have insulted you. I will wash your feet myself gladly enough, as Penelope has said that I am to do so; I will wash them both for Penelope's sake and for your own, for you have raised the most lively feelings of compassion in my mind. And let me say this moreover, which pray attend to: we have had all kinds of strangers in distress come here before now, but I make bold to say that no one ever yet came who was so like Odysseus in figure, voice, and feet as you are."

"Those who have seen us both," answered Odysseus, "have always said we were wonderfully like each other, and now you have noticed it too."

Then the old woman took the cauldron in which she was going to wash his feet, and poured plenty of cold water into it, adding hot till the bath was warm enough. Odysseus sat by the fire, but ere long he turned away from the light, for it occurred to him that when the old woman had hold of his leg she would recognize a certain scar which it bore, whereon the whole truth would come out. And indeed as soon as she began washing her master, she at once knew the scar as one that had been given him by a wild boar when he was hunting on Mount Parnassus with his excellent grandfather Autolycus—who was the most accomplished thief and perjurer in the whole world— and with the sons of Autolycus. Hermes himself had endowed him with his gift, for he used to burn the thighbones of goats and kids to him, so he took pleasure in his companionship. It happened once that Autolycus had gone to Ithaca and had found the child of his daughter just born. As soon as he had done supper Euryclea set the infant upon his knees and said, "Autolycus, you must find a name for your grandson; you greatly wished that you might have one."

"Son-in-law and daughter," replied Autolycus, "call the child thus. I am highly displeased with a large number of people in one place and another, both men and women; so name the child 'Odysseus,' or the child of anger. When he grows up and comes to visit his mother's family on Mount Parnassus, where my possessions lie, I will make him a present and will send him on his way rejoicing."

Odysseus, therefore, went to Parnassus to get the presents from Autolycus, who with his sons shook hands with him and gave him welcome. His grandmother Amphithea threw her arms about him, and kissed his head, and both his beautiful eyes, while Autolycus desired his sons to get dinner ready, and they did as he told them. They brought in a five-year-old bull, flayed it, made it ready and divided it into joints; these they then cut carefully up into smaller pieces and spitted them; they roasted them sufficiently and served the portions round. Thus through the livelong day to the going down of the sun they feasted, and every man had his full share so that all were satisfied; but when the sun set and it came on dark, they went to bed and enjoyed the boon of sleep.

When the child of morning, rosy-fingered Dawn, appeared, the sons of Autolycus went out with their hounds hunting, and Odysseus went too. They climbed the wooded slopes of Parnassus and soon reached its breezy upland valleys; but as the sun was beginning to beat upon the fields, fresh-risen from the slow still currents of Oceanus, they came to a mountain dell. The dogs were in front searching for the tracks of the beast they were chasing, and after them came the sons of Autolycus, among whom was Odysseus, close behind the dogs, and he had a long spear in his hand. Here was the lair of a huge boar among some thick brush-wood, so dense that the wind and rain could not get through it, nor could the sun's rays pierce it, and the ground underneath lay thick with fallen leaves. The boar heard the noise of the men's feet, and the hounds baying on every side as the huntsmen came up to them, so he rushed from his lair, raised the bristles on his neck, and stood at bay with fire flashing from his eyes. Odysseus was the first to raise his spear and try to drive it into the brute, but the boar was too quick for him, and charged him sideways, ripping him above the knee with a gash that tore deep though it did not reach the bone. As for the boar, Odysseus hit him on the right shoulder, and the point of the spear went right through him, so that he fell groaning in the dust until the life went out of him. The sons of Autolycus busied themselves with the carcass of the boar, and bound Odysseus' wound; then, after saying a spell to stop the bleeding, they went home as fast as they could. But when Autolycus and his sons had thoroughly healed Odysseus, they made him some splendid presents, and sent him back to Ithaca with much mutual good will. When he got back, his father and mother were rejoiced to see him, and asked him all about it, and how he had hurt himself to get the scar; so he told them how the boar had ripped him when he was out hunting with Autolycus and his sons on Mount Parnassus.

As soon as Euryclea had got the scarred limb in her hands and had well hold of it, she recognized it and dropped the foot at once. The leg fell into the bath, which rang out and was overturned, so that all the water was spilt on the ground. Euryclea's eyes between her joy and her grief filled with tears, and she could not speak, but she caught Odysseus by the beard and said, "My dear child, I am sure you must be Odysseus himself, only I did not know you till I had actually touched and handled you."

As she spoke she looked towards Penelope, as though wanting to tell her that her dear husband was in the house, but Penelope was unable to look in that direction and observe what was going on, for Athene had diverted her attention. So Odysseus caught Euryclea by the throat with his right hand and with his left drew her close to him, and said, "Nurse, do you wish to be the ruin of me, you who nursed me at your own breast, now that after twenty years of wandering I am at last come to my own home again? Since it has been borne in upon you by heaven to recognize me, hold your tongue, and do not say a word about it to anyone else in the house, for if you do I tell you—and it shall surely be—that if heaven grants me to take the lives of these suitors, I will not spare you, though you are my own nurse, when I am killing the other women."

"My child," answered Euryclea, "what are you talking about? You know very well that nothing can either bend or break me. I will hold my tongue like a stone or a piece of iron. Furthermore let me say, and lay my saying to your heart, when heaven has delivered the suitors into your hand, I will give you a list of the women in the house who have been ill-behaved and of those who are guiltless."

And Odysseus answered, "Nurse, you ought not to speak in that way; I am well able to form my own opinion about one and all of them. Hold your tongue and leave everything to heaven."

As he said this Euryclea left the cloister to fetch some more water, for the first had been all spilt. And when she had washed him and anointed him with oil, Odysseus drew his seat nearer to the fire to warm himself, and hid the scar under his rags. Then Penelope began talking to him and said:

"Stranger, I should like to speak with you briefly about another matter. It is indeed nearly bedtime—for those, at least, who can sleep in spite of sorrow. As for myself, heaven has given me a life of such unmeasurable woe, that even by day when I am attending to my duties and looking after the servants, I am still weeping and lamenting during the whole time; then, when night comes, and we all of us go to bed, I lie awake thinking, and my heart becomes a prey to the most incessant and cruel tortures. As the dun nightingale, daughter of Pandareus, sings in the early spring from her seat in shadiest covert hid, and with many a plaintive trill pours out the tale how by mishap she killed her own child Itylus, son of king Zethus, even so does my mind toss and turn in its uncertainty whether I ought to stay with my son here, and safeguard my substance, my bondsmen, and the greatness of my house, out of regard to public opinion and the memory of my late husband, or whether it is not now time for me to go with the best of these suitors who are wooing me and making me such magnificent presents. As long as my son was still young, and unable to understand, he would not hear of my leaving my husband's house, but now that he is full grown he begs and prays me to do so, being incensed at the way in which the suitors are eating up his property.

"Listen, then, to a dream that I have had and interpret it for me if you can. I have twenty geese about the house that eat mash out of a trough, and of which I am exceedingly fond. I dreamed that a great eagle came swooping down from a mountain, and dug his curved beak into the neck of each of them till he had killed them all. Presently he soared off into the sky, and left them lying dead about the yard; whereon I wept in my dream till all my maids gathered round me, so piteously was I grieving because the eagle had killed my geese. Then he came back again, and perching on a projecting rafter spoke to me with human voice, and told me to leave off crying. 'Be of good courage,' he said, 'daughter of Icarius; this is no dream, but a vision of good omen that shall surely come to pass. The geese are the suitors, and I am no longer an eagle, but your own husband, who am come back to you, and who will bring these suitors to a disgraceful end.' On this I woke, and when I looked out I saw my geese at the trough eating their mash as usual."

"This dream, madam," replied Odysseus, "can admit but of one interpretation, for has not Odysseus himself told you how it shall be fulfilled? The death of the suitors is portended, and not one single one of them will escape."

And Penelope answered: "Stranger, dreams are very curious and unaccountable things, and they do not by any means invariably come true. There are two gates through which these unsubstantial fancies proceed; the one is of horn, and the other ivory. Those that come through the gate of ivory are fatuous, but those from the gate of horn mean something to those that see them. I do not think, however, that my own dream came through the gate of horn, though I and my son should be most thankful if it proves to have done so. Furthermore I say—and lay my saying to your heart—the coming dawn will usher in the ill-omened day that is to sever me from the house of Odysseus, for I am about to hold a tournament of axes. My husband used to set up twelve axes in the court, one in front of the other, like the stays upon which a ship is built; he would then go back from them and shoot an arrow through the whole twelve. I shall make the suitors try to do the same thing, and whichever of them can string the bow most easily, and send his arrow through all the twelve axes, him will I follow, and quit this house of my lawful husband, so goodly and so abounding in wealth. But even so, I doubt not that I shall remember it in my dreams."

Then Odysseus answered, "Madam, wife of Odysseus, you need not defer your tournament, for Odysseus will return ere ever they can string the bow, handle it how they will, and send their arrows through the iron."

To this Penelope said: "As long, sir, as you will sit here and talk to me, I can have no desire to go to bed. Still, people cannot do permanently without sleep, and heaven has appointed us dwellers on earth a time for all things. I will therefore go upstairs and recline upon that couch which I have never ceased to flood with my tears from the day Odysseus set out for the city with a hateful name."

She then went upstairs to her own room, not alone, but attended by her maidens, and when there, she lamented her dear husband till Athene shed sweet sleep over her eyelids.

BOOK XX

Both Odysseus and Penelope pass a restless night. In the morning Odysseus is heartened by omens from Zeus. At the feast Telemachus seats the ragged Odysseus in an honorable place, but he is again abused by the suitors. The stranger Theoclymenus, seeing signs of impending disaster, takes his leave.

ODYSSEUS SLEPT IN THE CLOISTER UPON AN undressed bullock's hide, on the top of which he threw several skins of the sheep the suitors had eaten, and Eurynome threw a cloak over him after he had laid himself down. There, then, Odysseus lay wakefully brooding upon the way in which he should kill the suitors; and by and by, the women who had been in the habit of misconducting themselves with them left the house giggling and laughing with one another. This made Odysseus very angry, and he doubted whether to get up and kill every single one of them then and there, or to let them sleep one more and last time with the suitors. His heart growled within him, and as a bitch with puppies growls and shows her teeth when she sees a stranger, so did his heart growl with anger at the evil deeds that were being done. But he beat his breast and said, "Heart, be still! You had worse than this to bear on the day when the terrible Cyclops ate your brave companions; yet you bore it in silence till your cunning got you safe out of the cave, though you made sure of being killed."

Thus he chided with his heart, and checked it into endurance, but he tossed about as one who turns a paunch full of blood and fat in front of a hot fire, doing it first on one side and then on the other, that he may get it cooked as soon as possible. Even so did he turn himself about from side to side, thinking all the time how, single handed as he was, he should contrive to kill so large a body of men as the wicked suitors. But by and by Athene came down from heaven in the likeness of a woman, and hovered over his head saying, "My poor unhappy man, why do you lie awake in this way? This is your house; your wife is safe inside it, and so is your son who is just such a young man as any father may be proud of."

"Goddess," answered Odysseus, "all that you have said is true, but I am in some doubt as to how I shall be able to kill these wicked suitors single handed, seeing what a number of them there always are. And there is this further difficulty, which is still more considerable. Supposing that with Zeus' and your assistance I succeed in killing them, I must ask you to consider where I am to escape from their avengers when it is all over."

"For shame," replied Athene, "why, anyone else would trust a worse ally than myself, even though that ally were only a mortal and less wise than I am. Am I not a goddess, and have I not protected you throughout in all your troubles? I tell you plainly that even though there were fifty bands of them surrounding us and eager to kill us, you should take all their sheep and cattle, and drive them away with you. But go to sleep; it is a very bad thing to lie awake all night, and you shall be out of your troubles before long."

As she spoke she shed sleep over his eyes, and then went back to Olympus.

While Odysseus was thus yielding himself to a very deep slumber that eased the burden of his sorrows, his admirable wife awoke, and sitting up in her bed began to cry. When she had relieved herself by weeping she prayed to Artemis saying, "Great Goddess Artemis, daughter of Zeus, drive an arrow into my heart and slay me; or let some whirlwind snatch me up and bear me through paths of darkness till it drop me into the mouths of overflowing Oceanus, as it did the daughters of Pandareus. The daughters of Pandareus lost their father and mother, for the gods killed them, so they were left orphans. But Aphrodite took care of them, and fed them on cheese, honey, and sweet wine. Hera taught them to excell all women in beauty of form and understanding; Artemis gave them an imposing presence, and Athene endowed them with every kind of accomplishment. But one day when Aphrodite had gone up to Olympus to see Zeus about getting them married (for well does he know both what shall happen and what not happen to everyone) the storm winds came and spirited them away to become handmaids to the dread Furies. Even so I wish that the gods who live in heaven would hide me from mortal sight, or that fair Artemis might strike me, for I would fain go even beneath the sad earth if I might do so still looking towards Odysseus only, and without having to yield myself to a worse man than he was. Besides, no matter how much people may grieve by day, they can put up with it so long as they can sleep at night, for when the eyes are closed in slumber people forget good and ill alike; whereas my misery haunts me even in my dreams. This very night methought there was one lying by my side who was like Odysseus as he was when he went away with his host, and I rejoiced, for I believed that it was no dream, but the very truth itself."

On this the day broke, but Odysseus heard the sound of her weeping, and it puzzled him, for it seemed as though she already knew him and was by his side. Then he gathered up the cloak and the fleeces on which he had lain, and set them on a seat in the cloister, but he took the bullock's hide out into the open. He lifted up his hands to heaven, and prayed, saying, "Father Zeus, since you have seen fit to bring me over land and sea to my own home after all the afflictions you have laid upon me, give me a sign out of the mouth of some one or other of those who are now waking within the house, and let me have another sign of some kind from outside."

Thus did he pray. Zeus heard his prayer and forthwith thundered high up among the clouds from the splendor of Olympus, and Odysseus was glad when he heard it. At the same time within the house, a miller-woman from hard by in the mill room lifted up her voice and gave him another sign. There were twelve miller-women whose business it was to grind wheat and barley which are the staff of life. The others had ground their task and had gone to take their rest, but this one had not yet finished, for she was not so strong as they were, and when she heard the thunder she stopped grinding and gave the sign to her master. "Father Zeus," said she, "you who rule over heaven and earth, you have thundered from a clear sky without so much as a cloud in it, and this means something for somebody. Grant the prayer, then, of me your poor servant who calls upon you, and let this be the very last day that the suitors dine in the house of Odysseus. They have worn me out with the labor of grinding meal for them, and I hope they may never have another dinner anywhere at all."

Odysseus was glad when he heard the omens conveyed to him by the woman's speech, and by the thunder, for he knew they meant that he should avenge himself on the suitors.

Then the other maids in the house rose and lit the fire on the hearth. Telemachus also rose and put on his clothes. He girded his sword about his shoulder, bound his sandals on his comely feet, and took a doughty spear with a point of sharpened bronze; then he went to the threshold of the cloister and said to Euryclea, "Nurse, did you make the stranger comfortable both as regards bed and board, or did you let him shift for himself?—for my mother, good woman though she is, has a way of paying great attention to second-rate people, and of neglecting others who are in reality much better men."

"Do not find fault, child," said Euryclea, "when there is no one to find fault with. The stranger sat and drank his wine as long as he liked. Your mother did ask him if he would take any more bread and he said he would not. When he wanted to go to bed she told the servants to make one for him, but he said he was such a wretched outcast that he would not sleep on a bed and under blankets. He insisted on having an undressed bullock's hide and some sheepskins put for him in the cloister, and we threw a cloak over him."

Then Telemachus went out of the court to the place where the Achaeans were meeting in assembly. He had his spear in his hand, and he was not alone, for his two dogs went with him. But Euryclea called the maids and said, "Come, wake up; set about sweeping the cloisters and sprinkling them with water to lay the dust. Put the covers on the seats; wipe down the tables, some of you, with a wet sponge; clean out the mixing-jugs and the cups, and go for water from the fountain at once. The suitors will be here directly; they will be here early, for it is a feast day."

Thus did she speak, and they did even as she had said. Twenty of them went to the fountain for water, and the others set themselves busily to work about the house. The men who were in attendance on the suitors also came up and began chopping firewood. By and by the women returned from the fountain, and the swineherd came after them with the three best pigs he could pick out. These he let feed about the premises, and then he said good-humoredly to Odysseus, "Stranger, are the suitors treating you any better now, or are they as insolent as ever?"

"May heaven," answered Odysseus, "requite to them the wickedness with which they deal high-handedly in another man's house without any sense of shame."

Thus did they converse. Meanwhile, Melanthius the goatherd came up, for he too was bringing in his best goats for the suitors' dinner, and he had two shepherds with him. They tied the goats up under the gatehouse, and then Melanthius began gibing at Odysseus. "Are you still here, stranger," said he, "to pester people by begging about the house? Why can you not go elsewhere? You and I shall not come to an understanding before we have given each other a taste of our fists. You beg without any sense of decency. Are there not feasts elsewhere among the Achaeans, as well as here?"

Odysseus made no answer, but bowed his head and brooded. Then a third man, Philoetius, joined them, who was bringing in a barren heifer and some goats. These were brought over by the boatmen who are there to take people over when anyone comes to them. So Philoetius made his heifer and his goats secure under the gatehouse, and then went up to the swineherd. "Who, swineherd," said he, "is this stranger that is lately come here? Is he one of your men? What is his family? Where does he come from? Poor fellow, he looks as if he had been some great man, but the gods give sorrow to whom they will—even to kings if it so pleases them."

As he spoke he went up to Odysseus and saluted him with his right hand. "Good day to you, father stranger," said he, "you seem to be very poorly off now, but I hope you will have better times by and by. Father Zeus, of all gods you are the most malicious. We are your own children, yet you show us no mercy in all our misery and afflictions. A sweat came over me when I saw this man, and my eyes filled with tears, for he reminds me of Odysseus, who I fear is going about in just such rags as this man's are, if indeed he is still among the living. If he is already dead and in the house of Hades, then, alas! for my good master, who made me his stockman when I was quite young among the Cephallenians, and now his cattle are countless. No one could have done better with them than I have, for they have bred like ears of corn; nevertheless, I have to keep bringing them in for others to eat, who take no heed of his son though he is in the house, and fear not the wrath of heaven, but are already eager to divide Odysseus' property among them because he has been away so long. I have often thought—only it would not be right while his son is living—of going off with the cattle to some foreign country. Bad as this would be, it is still harder to stay here and be ill-treated about other people's herds. My position is intolerable, and I should long since have run away and put myself under the protection of some other chief, only that I believe my poor master will yet return, and send all these suitors flying out of the house."

"Stockman," answered Odysseus, "you seem to be a very well-disposed person, and I can see that you are a man of sense. There-

fore I will tell you, and will confirm my words with an oath: by
Zeus, the chief of all gods, and by that hearth of Odysseus to which
I am now come, Odysseus shall return before you leave this place,
and if you are so minded you shall see him killing the suitors who
are now masters here."

"If Zeus were to bring this to pass," replied the stockman, "you
should see how I would do my very utmost to help him."

And in like manner Eumaeus prayed that Odysseus might return
home.

Thus did they converse. Meanwhile the suitors were hatching a
plot to murder Telemachus: but a bird flew near them on their left
hand—an eagle with a dove in its talons. On this Amphinomus said,
"My friends, this plot of ours to murder Telemachus will not succeed; let us go to dinner instead."

The others assented, so they went inside and laid their cloaks on
the benches and seats. They sacrificed the sheep, goats, pigs, and the
heifer, and when the inward meats were cooked they served them
round. They mixed the wine in the mixing-bowls, and the swineherd
gave every man his cup, while Philoetius handed round the bread
in the bread-baskets, and Melanthius poured them out their wine.
Then they laid their hands upon the good things that were before
them.

Telemachus purposely made Odysseus sit in the part of the cloister
that was paved with stone;[1] he gave him a shabby-looking seat at
a little table to himself, and had his portion of the inward meats
brought to him, with his wine in a gold cup. "Sit there," said he, "and
drink your wine among the great people. I will put a stop to the
gibes and blows of the suitors, for this is no public house, but belongs to Odysseus, and has passed from him to me. Therefore, suitors,
keep your hands and your tongues to yourselves, or there will be
mischief."

The suitors bit their lips, and marveled at the boldness of his
speech; then Antinous said, "We do not like such language but we

---

[1] This, I take it, was immediately in front of the main entrance from the inner
courtyard into the body of the house. (B.)

will put up with it, for Telemachus is threatening us in good earnest.
If Zeus had let us we should have put a stop to his brave talk ere
now."

Thus spoke Antinous, but Telemachus heeded him not. Meanwhile the heralds were bringing the holy hecatomb through the city,
and the Achaeans gathered under the shady grove of Apollo.

Then they roasted the outer meat, drew it off the spits, gave every
man his portion, and feasted to their hearts' content; those who
waited at table gave Odysseus exactly the same portion as the others
had, for Telemachus had told them to do so.

But Athene would not let the suitors for one moment drop their
insolence, for she wanted Odysseus to become still more bitter against
them. Now there happened to be among them a ribald fellow, whose
name was Ctesippus, and who came from Same. This man, confident
in his great wealth, was paying court to the wife of Odysseus, and
said to the suitors, "Hear what I have to say. The stranger has already
had as large a portion as anyone else. This is well, for it is not right
or reasonable to ill-treat any guest of Telemachus who comes here.
I will, however, make him a present on my own account, that he
may have something to give to the bath-woman, or to some other of
Odysseus' servants."

As he spoke he picked up a heifer's foot from the meat-basket in
which it lay, and threw it at Odysseus, but Odysseus turned his head
a little aside, and avoided it, smiling grimly Sardinian fashion as he
did so, and it hit the wall, not him. On this Telemachus spoke
fiercely to Ctesippus. "It is a good thing for you," said he, "that the
stranger turned his head so that you missed him. If you had hit him
I should have run you through with my spear, and your father would
have had to see about getting you buried rather than married in this
house. So let me have no more unseemly behavior from any of you,
for I am grown up now to the knowledge of good and evil and
understand what is going on, instead of being the child that I have
been heretofore. I have long seen you killing my sheep and making
free with my corn and wine. I have put up with this, for one man
is no match for many, but do me no further violence. Still, if you

wish to kill me, kill me; I would far rather die than see such dis-graceful scenes day after day—guests insulted, and men dragging the women servants about the house in an unseemly way."

They all held their peace till at last Agelaus son of Damastor said: "No one should take offense at what has just been said, nor gainsay it, for it is quite reasonable. Leave off, therefore, ill-treating the stranger, or anyone else of the servants who are about the house. I would say, however, a friendly word to Telemachus and his mother, which I trust may commend itself to both. 'As long,' I would say, 'as you had ground for hoping that Odysseus would one day come home, no one could complain of your waiting and suffering the suitors to be in your house. It would have been better that he should have returned, but it is now sufficiently clear that he will never do so. Therefore talk all this quietly over with your mother, and tell her to marry the best man, and the one who makes her the most advan-tageous offer. Thus you will yourself be able to manage your own inheritance, and to eat and drink in peace, while your mother will look after some other man's house, not yours.' "

To this Telemachus answered: "By Zeus, Agelaus, and by the sorrows of my unhappy father, who has either perished far from Ithaca, or is wandering in some distant land, I throw no obstacles in the way of my mother's marriage. On the contrary, I urge her to choose whomsoever she will, and I will give her numberless gifts into the bargain, but I dare not insist point-blank that she shall leave the house against her own wishes. Heaven forbid that I should do this."

Athene now made the suitors fall to laughing immoderately, and set their wits wandering; but they were laughing with a forced laughter. Their meat became smeared with blood, their eyes filled with tears, and their hearts were heavy with forebodings. Theo-clymenus saw this and said, "Unhappy men, what is it that ails you? There is a shroud of darkness drawn over you from head to foot, your cheeks are wet with tears. The air is alive with wailing voices; the walls and roof-beams drip blood; the gate of the cloisters and the court beyond them are full of ghosts trooping down into the night of hell. The sun is blotted out of heaven, and a blighting gloom is over all the land."

Thus did he speak, and they all of them laughed heartily. Eurymachus then said, "This stranger who has lately come here has lost his senses. Servants, turn him out into the streets, since he finds it so dark here."

But Theoclymenus said, "Eurymachus, you need not send anyone with me. I have eyes, ears, and a pair of feet of my own, to say nothing of an understanding mind. I will take these out of the house with me, for I see mischief overhanging you, from which not one of you men who are insulting people and plotting ill deeds in the house of Odysseus will be able to escape."

He left the house as he spoke, and went back to Piraeus who gave him welcome, but the suitors kept looking at one another and provoking Telemachus by laughing at the strangers. One insolent fellow said to him, "Telemachus, you are not happy in your guests. First you have this importunate tramp, who comes begging bread and wine and has no skill for work or for hard fighting, but is perfectly useless, and now here is another fellow who is setting himself up as a prophet. Let me persuade you, for it will be much better, to put them on board ship and send them off to the Sicels to sell for what they will bring."

Telemachus gave him no heed, but sat silently watching his father, expecting every moment that he would begin his attack upon the suitors.

Meanwhile the daughter of Icarius, wise Penelope, had had a rich seat placed for her facing the court and cloisters, so that she could hear what everyone was saying. The dinner indeed had been prepared amid much merriment; it had been both good and abundant, for they had sacrificed many victims. But the supper was yet to come, and nothing can be conceived more gruesome than the meal which a goddess and a brave man were soon to lay before them—for they had brought their doom upon themselves.

BOOK XXI

*The banquet being over, Penelope brings forth Odysseus'
bow, which first Telemachus and then the suitors try to
string without success. Odysseus, going outside, reveals
himself to Eumaeus and Philoetus, the stockman. They bar
the outer doors and send the women to their quarters, in
preparation for the fray. Odysseus now strings the bow with
ease and shoots it with perfection. The suitors watch him,
fearful and dismayed.*

ATHENE NOW PUT IT IN PENELOPE'S MIND TO
make the suitors try their skill with the bow and with the
iron axes, in contest among themselves, as a means of bringing about their destruction. She went upstairs and got the storeroom
key, which was made of bronze and had a handle of ivory. She then
went with her maidens into the storeroom at the end of the house,
where her husband's treasures of gold, bronze, and wrought iron
were kept, and where was also his bow, and the quiver full of deadly
arrows that had been given him by a friend whom he had met in
Sparta—Iphitus the son of Eurytus. The two fell in with one another in Messene at the house of Ortilochus, where Odysseus was
staying in order to recover a debt that was owing from the whole

people; for the Messenians had carried off three hundred sheep from Ithaca, and had sailed away with them and with their shepherds. In quest of these Odysseus took a long journey while still quite young, for his father and the other chieftains sent him on a mission to recover them. Iphitus had gone there also to try and get back twelve brood mares that he had lost, and the mule foals that were running with them. These mares were the death of him in the end, for when he went to the house of Zeus' son, mighty Heracles, who performed such prodigies of valor, Heracles to his shame killed him, though he was his guest. For he feared not heaven's vengeance, nor yet respected his own table which he had set before Iphitus, but killed him in spite of everything, and kept the mares himself.

It was when claiming these that Iphitus met Odysseus, and gave him the bow which mighty Eurytus had been used to carry, and which on his death had been left by him to his son. Odysseus gave him in return a sword and a spear, and this was the beginning of a fast friendship, although they never visited at one another's houses, for Zeus' son Heracles killed Iphitus ere they could do so. This bow, then, given him by Iphitus, had not been taken with him by Odysseus when he sailed for Troy; he had used it so long as he had been at home, but had left it behind as having been a keepsake from a valued friend.

Penelope presently reached the oak threshold of the storeroom. The carpenter had planed this duly, and had drawn a line on it so as to get it straight; he had then set the doorposts into it and hung the doors. She loosed the strap from the handle of the door, put in the key, and drove it straight home to shoot back the bolts that held the doors; these flew open with a noise like a bull bellowing in a meadow, and Penelope stepped upon the raised platform, where the chests stood in which the fair linen and clothes were laid by along with fragrant herbs. Reaching thence, she took down the bow with its bow case from the peg on which it hung. She sat down with it on her knees, weeping bitterly as she took the bow out of its case. When her tears had relieved her, she went to the cloister where the suitors were, carrying the bow and the quiver, with the many deadly arrows that were inside it. Along with her came her maidens, bearing a chest that contained much iron and bronze which her husband had won as prizes. When she reached the suitors, she stood by one of the bearing-posts supporting the roof of the cloister, holding a veil before her face, and with a maid on either side of her. Then she said:

"Listen to me you suitors, who persist in abusing the hospitality of this house because its owner has been long absent, and without other pretext than that you want to marry me. This, then, being the prize that you are contending for, I will bring out the mighty bow of Odysseus, and whosoever of you shall string it most easily and send his arrow through each one of twelve axes, him will I follow and quit this house of my lawful husband, so goodly, and so abounding in wealth. But even so I doubt not that I shall remember it in my dreams."

As she spoke, she told Eumaeus to set the bow and the pieces of iron before the suitors, and Eumaeus wept as he took them to do as she had bidden him. Hard by, the stockman wept also when he saw his master's bow, but Antinous scolded them. "You country louts," said he, "silly simpletons; why should you add to the sorrows of your mistress by crying in this way? She has enough to grieve her in the loss of her husband. Sit still, therefore, and eat your dinners in silence, or go outside if you want to cry, and leave the bow behind you. We suitors shall have to contend for it with might and main, for we shall find it no light matter to string such a bow as this is. There is not a man of us all who is such another as Odysseus; for I have seen him and remember him, though I was then only a child."

This was what he said, but all the time he was expecting to be able to string the bow and shoot through the iron, whereas in fact he was to be the first that should taste of the arrows from the hands of Odysseus, whom he was dishonoring in his own house—egging the others on to do so also.

Then Telemachus spoke. "Great heavens!" he exclaimed. "Zeus must have robbed me of my senses. Here is my dear and excellent mother saying she will quit this house and marry again, yet I am laughing and enjoying myself as though there were nothing happening. But, suitors, as the contest has been agreed upon, let it go forward. It is for a woman whose peer is not to be found in Pylos, Argos, or Mycene, nor yet in Ithaca nor on the mainland. You know this as well as I do; what need have I to speak in praise of my mother? Come on, then, make no excuses for delay, but let us see whether you can string the bow or no. I too will make trial of it, for if I can string it and shoot through the iron, I shall not suffer my mother to quit this house with a stranger, nor if I can win the prizes which my father won before me."

As he spoke he sprang from his seat, threw his crimson cloak from him, and took his sword from his shoulder. First he set the axes in a row, in a long groove which he had dug for them, and had made straight by line.[1] Then he stamped the earth tight round them, and everyone was surprised when they saw him set them up so orderly, though he had never seen anything of the kind before. This done, he went on to the pavement to make trial of the bow. Thrice did he tug at it, trying with all his might to draw the string, and thrice he had to leave off, though he had hoped to string the bow and shoot through the iron. He was trying for the fourth time, and would have strung it had not Odysseus made a sign to check him in spite of all his eagerness. So he said:

"Alas! I shall either be always feeble and of no prowess, or I am too young, and have not yet reached my full strength so as to be able to hold my own if anyone attacks me. You others, therefore, who are stronger than I, make trial of the bow and get this contest settled."

On this he put the bow down, letting it lean against the door that led into the house with the arrow standing against the top of the bow. Then he sat down on the seat from which he had risen, and Antinous said:

"Come on, each of you in his turn, going towards the right from the place at which the cupbearer begins when he is handing round the wine."

[1] It is evident that the open part of the court had no flooring, but the natural soil. (B.)

The rest agreed, and Leiodes son of Oenops was the first to rise. He was sacrificial priest to the suitors, and sat in the corner near the mixing-bowl. He was the only man who hated their evil deeds and was indignant with the others. He was now the first to take the bow and arrow, so he went on to the pavement to make his trial. But he could not string the bow, for his hands were weak and unused to hard work; they therefore soon grew tired, and he said to the suitors: "My friends, I cannot string it; let another have it. This bow shall take the life and soul out of many a chief among us, for it is better to die than to live after having missed the prize that we have so long striven for, and which has brought us so long together. Some one of us is even now hoping and praying that he may marry Penelope, but when he has seen this bow and tried it, let him woo and make bridal offerings to some other woman, and let Penelope marry whoever makes her the best offer and whose lot it is to win her."

On this he put the bow down, letting it lean against the door,[2] with the arrow standing against the tip of the bow. Then he took his seat again on the seat from which he had risen; and Antinous rebuked him, saying:

"Leiodes, what are you talking about? Your words are monstrous and intolerable, it makes me angry to listen to you. Shall, then, this bow take the life of many a chief among us, merely because you cannot bend it yourself? True, you were not born to be an archer, but there are others who will soon string it."

Then he said to Melanthius the goatherd, "Look sharp, light a fire in the court, and set a seat hard by with a sheepskin on it; bring us also a large ball of lard, from what they have in the house. Let us warm the bow and grease it. We will then make trial of it again, and bring the contest to an end."

Melanthius lit the fire, and set a seat covered with sheepskins beside it. He also brought a great ball of lard from what they had in the house, and the suitors warmed the bow and again made trial of it, but they were none of them nearly strong enough to string it. Nevertheless there still remained Antinous and Eurymachus, who

---

[2] The door that led into the body of the house.

were the ringleaders among the suitors and much the foremost among them all.

Then the swineherd and the stockman left the cloisters together, and Odysseus followed them. When they had got outside the gates and the outer yard, Odysseus said to them quietly:

"Stockman, and you swineherd, I have something in my mind which I am in doubt whether to say or no; but I think I will say it. What manner of men would you be to stand by Odysseus, if some god should bring him back here all of a sudden? Say which you are disposed to do—to side with the suitors, or with Odysseus?"

"Father Zeus," answered the stockman, "would indeed that you might so ordain it. If some god were but to bring Odysseus back, you should see with what might and main I would fight for him."

In like words Eumaeus prayed to all the gods that Odysseus might return. When, therefore, he saw for certain what mind they were of, Odysseus said: "It is I, Odysseus, who am here. I have suffered much, but at last, in the twentieth year, I am come back to my own country. I find that you two alone of all my servants are glad that I should do so, for I have not heard any of the others praying for my return. To you two, therefore, will I unfold the truth as it shall be. If heaven shall deliver the suitors into my hands, I will find wives for both of you, will give you house and holding close to my own, and you shall be to me as though you were brothers and friends of Telemachus. I will now give you convincing proofs that you may know me and be assured. See, here is the scar from the boar's tooth that ripped me when I was out hunting on Mount Parnassus with the sons of Autolycus."

As he spoke he drew his rags aside from the great scar, and when they had examined it thoroughly, they both of them wept about Odysseus, threw their arms round him, and kissed his head and shoulders, while Odysseus kissed their hands and faces in return. The sun would have gone down upon their mourning if Odysseus had not checked them and said:

"Cease your weeping, lest someone should come outside and see us, and tell those who are within. When you go in, do so separately, not both together; I will go first, and do you follow afterwards. Let this moreover be the token between us; the suitors will all of them try to prevent me from getting hold of the bow and quiver. Do you therefore, Eumaeus, place it in my hands when you are carrying it about, and tell the women to close the doors of their apartment. If they hear any groaning or uproar as of men fighting about the house, they must not come out; they must keep quiet, and stay where they are at their work. And I charge you, Philoetius, to make fast the doors of the outer court, and to bind them securely at once."

When he had thus spoken, he went back to the house and took the seat that he had left. Presently, his two servants followed him inside.

At this moment the bow was in the hands of Eurymachus, who was warming it by the fire, but even so he could not string it, and he was greatly grieved. He heaved a deep sigh and said, "I grieve for myself and for us all. I grieve that I shall have to forego the marriage, but I do not care nearly so much about this, for there are plenty of other women in Ithaca and elsewhere. What I feel most is the fact of our being so inferior to Odysseus in strength that we cannot string his bow. This will disgrace us in the eyes of those who are yet unborn."

"It shall not be so, Eurymachus," said Antinous, "and you know it yourself. Today is the feast of Apollo throughout all the land; who can string a bow on such a day as this? Put it on one side! As for the axes, they can stay where they are, for no one is likely to come to the house and take them away. Let the cupbearer go round with his cups, that we may make our drink offerings and drop this matter of the bow. We will tell Melanthius to bring us in some goats tomorrow—the best he has; we can then offer thighbones to Apollo the mighty archer, and again make trial of the bow, so as to bring the contest to an end."

The rest approved his words, and thereon menservants poured water over the hands of the guests, while pages filled the mixing-bowls with wine and water and handed it round after giving every man his drink offering. Then, when they had made their offerings and had drunk each as much as he desired, Odysseus craftily said: "Suitors of the illustrious queen, listen that I may speak even as I am minded. I appeal more especially to Eurymachus, and to Antinous who has just spoken with so much reason. Cease shooting for the present and leave the matter to the gods, but in the morning let heaven give victory to whom it will. For the moment, however, give me the bow that I may prove the power of my hands among you all, and see whether I still have as much strength as I used to have, or whether travel and neglect have made an end of it."

This made them all very angry, for they feared he might string the bow. Antinous therefore rebuked him fiercely, saying: "Wretched creature, you have not so much as a grain of sense in your whole body. You ought to think yourself lucky in being allowed to dine unharmed among your betters, without having any smaller portion served you than we others have had, and in being allowed to hear our conversation. No other beggar or stranger has been allowed to hear what we say among ourselves. The wine must have been doing you a mischief, as it does with all those who drink immoderately. It was wine that inflamed the Centaur Eurytion when he was staying with Peirithous among the Lapithae. When the wine had got into his head, he went mad and did ill deeds about the house of Peirithous; this angered the heroes who were there assembled, so they rushed at him and cut off his ears and nostrils; then they dragged him through the doorway of the house. So he went away crazed, and bore the burden of his crime, bereft of understanding. Henceforth, therefore, there was war between mankind and the centaurs, but he brought it upon himself through his own drunkenness. In like manner I can tell you that it will go hardly with you if you string the bow. You will find no mercy from anyone here, for we shall at once ship you off to King Echetus, who kills everyone that comes near him; you will never get away alive. So drink and keep quiet without getting into a quarrel with men younger than yourself."

Penelope then spoke to him. "Antinous," said she, "it is not right that you should ill-treat any guest of Telemachus who comes to this house. If the stranger should prove strong enough to string the mighty bow of Odysseus, can you suppose that he would take me home with him and make me his wife? Even the man himself can have no such idea in his mind. None of you need let that disturb his feasting; it would be out of all reason."

"Queen Penelope," answered Eurymachus, "we do not suppose that this man will take you away with him; it is impossible. But we are afraid lest some of the baser sort, men or women among the Achaeans, should go gossiping about and say, 'These suitors are a feeble folk; they are paying court to the wife of a brave man whose bow not one of them was able to string. Yet a beggarly tramp who came to the house strung it at once and sent an arrow through the iron.' This is what will be said, and it will be a scandal against us."

"Eurymachus," Penelope answered, "people who persist in eating up the estate of a great chieftain and dishonoring his house must not expect others to speak well of them. Why then should you mind if men talk as you think they will? This stranger is strong and well-built; he says moreover that he is of noble birth. Give him the bow, and let us see whether he can string it or no. I say—and it shall surely be—that if Apollo vouchsafes him the glory of stringing it, I will give him a cloak and shirt of good wear, with a javelin to keep off dogs and robbers, and a sharp sword. I will also give him sandals, and will see him sent safely wherever he wants to go."

Then Telemachus said: "Mother, I am the only man either in Ithaca or in the islands that are over against Elis who has the right to let anyone have the bow or to refuse it. No one shall force me one way or the other, not even though I choose to make the stranger a present of the bow outright, and let him take it away with him. Go, then, within the house and busy yourself with your daily duties, your loom, your distaff, and the ordering of your servants. This bow is a man's matter, and mine above all others, for it is I who am master here."

She went wondering back into the house, and laid her son's saying in her heart. Then going upstairs with her handmaids into her room, she mourned her dear husband till Athene sent sweet sleep over her eyelids.

The swineherd now took up the bow and was for taking it to Odysseus, but the suitors clamored at him from all parts of the cloisters, and one of them said, "You idiot, where are you taking the bow to? Are you out of your wits? If Apollo and the other gods will grant our prayer, your own boarhounds shall get you into some quiet little place, and worry you to death."

Eumaeus was frightened at the outcry they all raised, so he put the bow down then and there. But Telemachus shouted out at him from the other side of the cloisters, and threatened him, saying, "Father Eumaeus, bring the bow on in spite of them, or young as I am I will pelt you with stones back to the country, for I am the better man of the two. I wish I was as much stronger than all the other suitors in the house as I am than you. I would soon send some of them off sick and sorry, for they mean mischief."

Thus did he speak, and they all of them laughed heartily, which put them in a better humor with Telemachus. So Eumaeus brought the bow on and placed it in the hands of Odysseus. When he had done this, he called Euryclea apart and said to her, "Euryclea, Telemachus says you are to close the doors of the women's apartments. If they hear any groaning or uproar as of men fighting about the house, they are not to come out, but are to keep quiet and stay where they are at their work."

Euryclea did as she was told and closed the doors of the women's apartments.

Meanwhile Philoetius slipped quietly out and made fast the gates of the outer court. There was a ship's cable of byblus fiber lying in the gatehouse, so he made the gates fast with it. Then he came in again, resuming the seat that he had left, and keeping an eye on Odysseus, who had now got the bow in his hands, and was turning it every way about, and proving it all over to see whether the worms had been eating into its two horns during his absence. Then would one turn towards his neighbor saying, "This is some tricky old bow-fancier. Either he has got one like it at home, or he wants to make one; in such workmanlike style does the old vagabond handle it."

Another said, "I hope he may be no more successful in other things than he is likely to be in stringing this bow."

But Odysseus, when he had taken it up and examined it all over strung it as easily as a skilled bard strings a new peg of his lyre and makes the twisted gut fast at both ends. Then he took it in his right hand to prove the string, and it sang sweetly under his touch like the twittering of a swallow. The suitors were dismayed, and turned color as they heard it; at that moment, moreover, Zeus thundered loudly as a sign and the heart of Odysseus rejoiced as he heard the omen that the son of scheming Cronus had sent him.

He took an arrow that was lying upon the table—for those which the Achaeans were so shortly to taste were all inside the quiver. He laid it on the center-piece of the bow, and drew the notch of the arrow and the string toward him, still seated on his seat. When he had taken aim he let fly, and his arrow pierced every one of the handle-holes of the axes from the first onwards till it had gone right through them,[3] and into the outer courtyard. Then he said to Telemachus:

"Your guest has not disgraced you, Telemachus. I did not miss what I aimed at, and I was not long in stringing my bow. I am still strong, and not as the suitors twit me with being. Now, however, it is time for the Achaeans to prepare supper while there is still daylight, and then otherwise to disport themselves with song and dance, which are the crowning ornaments of a banquet."

As he spoke he made a sign with his eyebrows, and Telemachus girded on his sword, grasped his spear, and stood armed beside his father's seat.

[3] I suppose the iron part of the axe to have been wedged into the handle, or bound securely to it—the handle being half buried in the ground. The axe would be placed edgeways towards the archer, and he would have to shoot his arrow through the hole into which the handle was fitted when the axe was in use. Twelve axes were placed in a row all at the same height, all exactly in front of one another, all edgeways to Odysseus whose arrow passed through all the holes from the first onward. (B.)

BOOK XXII

*Odysseus tears off his rags and begins the slaughter of the
suitors. Telemachus brings armor from the storeroom, and
Athene appears to help her favorite. The suitors try to defend
themselves, but all finally are slain. Odysseus learns from
Euryclea which of the housemaids have been guilty of mis-
behavior and these are hung. The banqueting cloister is then
thoroughly cleansed and purified.*

THEN ODYSSEUS TORE OFF HIS RAGS, AND SPRANG
on to the broad pavement with his bow and his quiver full
of arrows. He shed the arrows on to the ground at his feet and
said, "The mighty contest is at an end. I will now see whether
Apollo will vouchsafe it to me to hit another mark which no man
has yet hit."

On this he aimed a deadly arrow at Antinous, who was about to
take up a two-handled gold cup to drink his wine and already had
it in his hands. He had no thought of death—who amongst all the
revelers would think that one man, however brave, would stand
alone among so many and kill him? The arrow struck Antinous in
the throat, and the point went clean through his neck, so that he
fell over and the cup dropped from his hand, while a thick stream

of blood gushed from his nostrils. He kicked the table from him and upset the things on it, so that the bread and roasted meats were all soiled as they fell over on to the ground. The suitors were in an uproar when they saw that a man had been hit. They sprang in dismay one and all of them from their seats and looked everywhere towards the walls, but there was neither shield nor spear, and they rebuked Odysseus very angrily. "Stranger," said they, "you shall pay for shooting people in this way. You shall see no other contest; you are a doomed man. He whom you have slain was the foremost youth in Ithaca, and the vultures shall devour you for having killed him."

Thus they spoke, for they thought that he had killed Antinous by mistake, and did not perceive that death was hanging over the head of every one of them. But Odysseus glared at them and said:

"Dogs, did you think that I should not come back from Troy? You have wasted my substance, have forced my womenservants to lie with you, and have wooed my wife while I was still living. You have feared neither God nor man, and now you shall die."

They turned pale with fear as he spoke, and every man looked round about to see whether he might fly for safety, but Eurymachus alone spoke.

"If you are Odysseus," said he, "then what you have said is just. We have done much wrong on your lands and in your house. But Antinous who was the head and front of the offending lies low already. It was all his doing. It was not that he wanted to marry Penelope; he did not so much care about that. What he wanted was something quite different, and Zeus has not vouchsafed it to him; he wanted to kill your son and to be chief man in Ithaca. Now, therefore, that he has met the death which was his due, spare the lives of your people. We will make everything good among ourselves, and pay you in full for all that we have eaten and drunk. Each one of us shall pay you a fine worth twenty oxen, and we will keep on giving you gold and bronze till your heart is softened. Until we have done this no one can complain of your being enraged against us."

Odysseus again glared at him and said: "Though you should give

me all you have in the world both now and all that you ever shall
have, I will not stay my hand till I have paid all of you in full. You
must fight, or fly for your lives; and fly, not a man of you shall."

Their hearts sank as they heard him, but Eurymachus again
spoke saying:

"My friends, this man will give us no quarter. He will stand
where he is and shoot us down till he has killed every man among
us. Let us then show fight; draw your swords, and hold up the tables
to shield you from his arrows. Let us have at him with a rush, to
drive him from the pavement and doorway. We can then get
through into the town, and raise such an alarm as shall soon stay his
shooting."

As he spoke he drew his keen blade of bronze, sharpened on both
sides, and with a loud cry sprang towards Odysseus, but Odysseus
instantly shot an arrow into his breast that caught him by the nipple
and fixed itself in his liver. He dropped his sword and fell doubled
up over his table. The cup and all the meats went over on to the
ground as he smote the earth with his forehead in the agonies of
death, and he kicked the stool with his feet until his eyes were
closed in darkness.

Then Amphinomus drew his sword and made straight at Odysseus to try to get him away from the door, but Telemachus was
too quick for him, and struck him from behind. The spear caught
him between the shoulders and went right through his chest, so that
he fell heavily to the ground and struck the earth with his forehead.
Then Telemachus sprang away from him, leaving his spear still in
the body, for he feared that if he stayed to draw it out, some one of
the Achaeans might come up and hack at him with his sword, or
knock him down, so he set off at a run, and immediately was at his
father's side. Then he said:

"Father, let me bring you a shield, two spears, and a brass helmet
for your temples. I will arm myself as well, and will bring other
armor for the swineherd and the stockman, for we had better be
armed."

"Run and fetch them," answered Odysseus, "while my arrows

hold out, or when I am alone they may get me away from the door."

Telemachus did as his father said, and ran off to the storeroom where the armor was kept. He chose four shields, eight spears, and four brass helmets with horsehair plumes. He brought them with all speed to his father, and armed himself first, while the stockman and the swineherd also put on their armor, and took their places near Odysseus. Meanwhile Odysseus, as long as his arrows lasted, had been shooting the suitors one by one, and they fell thick on one another. When his arrows gave out, he set the bow to stand against the end wall of the house by the doorpost, and hung a shield four hides thick about his shoulders; on his comely head he set his helmet, well wrought with a crest of horsehair that nodded menacingly above it, and he grasped two redoubtable bronze-shod spears.

Now there was a window in the wall, while at one end of the pavement[1] there was an exit leading to a narrow passage, and this exit was closed by a well-made door. Odysseus told Philoetius to stand by this door and guard it, for only one person could attack it at a time. But Agelaus shouted out, "Cannot someone go up to the window and tell the people outside what is going on? Help would come at once, and we should soon make an end of this man and his shooting."

"This may not be, Agelaus," answered Melanthius, "the mouth of the narrow passage is dangerously near the entrance to the outer court. One brave man could prevent any number from getting in. But I know what I will do, I will bring you arms from the storeroom, for I am sure it is there that Odysseus and his son have put them."

On this the goatherd Melanthius went by back passages to the storeroom of Odysseus' house. There he chose twelve shields, with as many helmets and spears, and brought them back as fast as he could to give them to the suitors. Odysseus' heart began to fail him when he saw the suitors putting on their armor and brandishing their spears. He saw the greatness of the danger, and said to Tele-

---

[1] The pavement on which Odysseus was standing.

machus, "Some one of the women inside is helping the suitors against us, or it may be Melanthius."

Telemachus answered: "The fault, father, is mine, and mine only. I left the storeroom door open, and they have kept a sharper lookout than I have. Go, Eumaeus, put the door to, and see whether it is one of the women who is doing this, or whether, as I suspect, it is Melanthius the son of Dolius."

Thus did they converse. Meanwhile Melanthius was again going to the storeroom to fetch more armor, but the swineherd saw him and said to Odysseus who was beside him, "Odysseus, noble son of Laertes, it is that scoundrel Melanthius, just as we suspected, who is going to the storeroom. Say, shall I kill him, if I can get the better of him, or shall I bring him here that you may take your own revenge for all the many wrongs that he has done in your house?"

Odysseus answered: "Telemachus and I will hold these suitors in check, no matter what they do. Go back, both of you, and bind Melanthius' hands and feet behind him. Throw him into the storeroom and make the door fast behind you; then fasten a noose about his body, and string him close up to the rafters from a high bearing-post, that he may linger on in an agony."

Thus did he speak, and they did even as he had said. They went to the storeroom, which they entered before Melanthius saw them, for he was busy searching for arms in the innermost part of the room, so the two took their stand on either side of the door and waited. By and by Melanthius came out with a helmet in one hand, and an old dry-rotted shield in the other, which had been borne by Laertes when he was young, but which had been long since thrown aside, and the straps had become unsewn. On this the two seized him, dragged him back by the hair, and threw him struggling to the ground. They bent his hands and feet well behind his back, and bound them tight with a painful bond as Odysseus had told them; then they fastened a noose about his body and strung him up from a high pillar till he was close up to the rafters. And over him did you then vaunt, O swineherd Eumaeus, saying, "Melanthius, you will pass the night on a soft bed as you deserve. You will know very well when morning comes from the streams of Oceanus, and it is time for you to be driving in your goats for the suitors to feast on."

There, then, they left him in very cruel bondage, and having put on their armor they closed the door behind them and went back to take their places by the side of Odysseus; whereon the four men stood in the cloister, fierce and full of fury. Nevertheless, those who were in the body of the court were still both brave and many. Then Zeus' daughter Athene came up to them, having assumed the voice and form of Mentor. Odysseus was glad when he saw her and said, "Mentor, lend me your help, and forget not your old comrade, or the many good turns he has done you. Besides, you are my age-mate."

But all the time he felt sure it was Athene, and the suitors from the other side raised an uproar when they saw her. Agelaus was the first to reproach her. "Mentor," he cried, "do not let Odysseus beguile you into siding with him and fighting the suitors. This is what we will do: when we have killed these people, father and son, we will kill you too. You shall pay for it with your head, and when we have killed you, we will take all you have, indoors or out, and bring it into hotch-pot with Odysseus' property. We will not let your sons live in your house, nor your daughters, nor shall your widow continue to live in the city of Ithaca."

This made Athene still more furious, so she scolded Odysseus very angrily. "Odysseus," she said, "your strength and prowess are no longer what they were when you fought for nine long years among the Trojans about the noble lady Helen. You killed many a man in those days, and it was through your stratagem that Priam's city was taken. How comes it that you are so lamentably less valiant now that you are on your own ground, face to face with the suitors in your own house? Come on, my good fellow, stand by my side and see how Mentor son of Alcimus shall fight your foes and requite your kindnesses conferred upon him."

But she would not give him full victory as yet, for she wished still further to prove his own prowess and that of his brave son, so she flew up to one of the rafters in the roof of the cloister and sat upon it in the form of a swallow.

Meanwhile Agalaus son of Damastor, Eurynomus, Amphimedon, Demoptolemus, Pisander, and Polybus son of Polyctor bore the brunt of the fight upon the suitors' side. Of all those who were still fighting for their lives they were by far the most valiant, for the others had already fallen under the arrows of Odysseus. Agelaus shouted to them and said: "My friends, he will soon have to leave off, for Mentor has gone away after having done nothing for him but brag. They are standing at the doors unsupported. Do not aim at him all at once, but six of you throw your spears first, and see if you cannot cover yourselves with glory by killing him. When he has fallen we need not be uneasy about the others."

They threw their spears as he bade them, but Athene made them all of no effect. One hit the doorpost; another went against the door; the pointed shaft of another struck the wall. As soon as they had avoided all the spears of the suitors Odysseus said to his own men, "My friends, I should say we too had better let drive into the middle of them, or they will crown all the harm they have done us by killing us outright."

They therefore aimed straight in front of them and threw their spears. Odysseus killed Demoptolemus, Telemachus Euryades, Eumaeus Elatus, while the stockman killed Pisander. These all bit the dust, and as the others drew back into a corner Odysseus and his men rushed forward and regained their spears by drawing them from the bodies of the dead.

The suitors now aimed a second time, but again Athene made their weapons for the most part without effect. One hit a bearing-post of the cloister; another went against the door; while the pointed shaft of another struck the wall. Still, Amphimedon just took a piece of the top skin from off Telemachus' wrist, and Ctesippus managed to graze Eumaeus' shoulder above his shield; but the spear went on and fell to the ground. Then Odysseus and his men let drive into the crowd of suitors. Odysseus hit Eurydamas, Telemachus Amphimedon, and Eumaeus Polybus. After this the stockman hit

Ctesippus in the breast, and taunted him saying, "Foul-mouthed son of Polytherses, do not be so foolish as to talk wickedly another time, but let heaven direct your speech, for the gods are far stronger than men. I make you a present of this advice to repay you for the foot which you gave Odysseus when he was begging about in his own house."

Thus spoke the stockman, and Odysseus struck the son of Damastor with a spear in close fight, while Telemachus hit Leocritus son of Evenor in the belly, and the dart went clean through him, so that he fell forward full on his face upon the ground. Then Athene from her seat on the rafter held up her deadly aegis, and the hearts of the suitors quailed. They fled to the other end of the court like a herd of cattle maddened by the gadfly in early summer when the days are at their longest. As eagle-beaked, crook-taloned vultures from the mountains swoop down on the smaller birds that cower in flocks upon the ground, and kill them, for they cannot either fight or fly, and lookers-on enjoy the sport—even so did Odysseus and his men fall upon the suitors and smite them on every side. They made a horrible groaning as their brains were being battered in, and the ground seethed with their blood.

Leiodes then caught the knees of Odysseus and said, "Odysseus, I beseech you have mercy upon me and spare me. I never wronged any of the women in your house either in word or deed, and I tried to stop the others. I saw them, but they would not listen, and now they are paying for their folly. I was their sacrificing priest. If you kill me, I shall die without having done anything to deserve it, and shall have got no thanks for all the good that I did."

Odysseus looked sternly at him and answered, "If you were their sacrificing priest, you must have prayed many a time that it might be long before I got home again, and that you might marry my wife and have children by her. Therefore you shall die."

With these words he picked up the sword that Agelaus had dropped when he was being killed, and which was lying upon the ground. Then he struck Leiodes on the back of his neck, so that his head fell rolling in the dust while he was yet speaking.

The minstrel Phemius son of Terpes—he who had been forced by the suitors to sing to them—now tried to save his life. He was standing near towards the window and held his lyre in his hand. He did not know whether to fly out of the cloister and sit down by the altar of Zeus that was in the outer court, and on which both Laertes and Odysseus had offered up the thighbones of many an ox, or whether to go straight up to Odysseus and embrace his knees, but in the end he deemed it best to embrace Odysseus' knees. So he laid his lyre on the ground between the mixing-bowl and the silver-studded seat; then going up to Odysseus he caught hold of his knees and said: "Odysseus, I beseech you have mercy on me and spare me. You will be sorry for it afterwards if you kill a bard who can sing both for gods and men as I can. I make all my lays myself, and heaven visits me with every kind of inspiration. I would sing to you as though you were a god; do not therefore be in such a hurry to cut my head off. Your own son Telemachus will tell you that I did not want to frequent your house and sing to the suitors after their meals, but they were too many and too strong for me, so they made me."

Telemachus heard him, and at once went up to his father. "Hold!" he cried. "The man is guiltless, do him no hurt; and we will spare Medon too, who was always good to me when I was a boy, unless Philoetius or Eumaeus has already killed him, or he has fallen in your way when you were raging about the court."

Medon caught these words of Telemachus, for he was crouching under a seat beneath which he had hidden by covering himself up with a freshly flayed heifer's hide, so he threw off the hide, went up to Telemachus, and laid hold of his knees.

"Here I am, my dear sir," said he. "Stay your hand therefore, and tell your father, or he will kill me in his rage against the suitors for having wasted his substance and been so foolishly disrespectful to yourself."

Odysseus smiled at him and answered, "Fear not! Telemachus has saved your life, that you may know in future, and tell other people, how greatly better good deeds prosper than evil ones. Go, therefore, outside the cloisters into the outer court, and be out of the way

that supported the roof of the domed room, and secured it all around the building, at a good height, lest any of the women's feet should touch the ground. And as thrushes or doves beat against a net that has been set for them in a thicket just as they were getting to their nest, and a terrible fate awaits them, even so did the women have to put their heads in nooses one after the other and die most miserably. Their feet moved convulsively for a while, but not for very long.

As for Melanthius, they took him through the cloister into the inner court. There they cut off his nose and his ears; they drew out his vitals and gave them to the dogs raw, and then in their fury they cut off his hands and his feet.

When they had done this they washed their hands and feet and went back into the house, for all was now over. And Odysseus said to the dear old nurse Euryclea, "Bring me sulphur, which cleanses all pollution, and fetch fire also that I may burn it, and purify the cloisters. Go, moreover, and tell Penelope to come here with her attendants, and also all the maidservants that are in the house."

"All that you have said is true," answered Euryclea, "but let me bring you some clean clothes—a shirt and cloak. Do not keep these rags on your back any longer. It is not right."

"First light me a fire," replied Odysseus.

She brought the fire and sulphur, as he had bidden her, and Odysseus thoroughly purified the cloisters and both the inner and outer courts. Then she went inside to call the women and tell them what had happened; whereon they came from their apartments with torches in their hands, and pressed round Odysseus to embrace him, kissing his head and shoulders and taking hold of his hands. It made him feel as if he should like to weep, for he remembered every one of them.

BOOK XXIII

Euryclea now tells her mistress that the beggar who has rid the house of the plague of suitors is Odysseus. Unbelieving, Penelope questions him, and is at last convinced that it is indeed he. They embrace and converse happily through much of the night. The following day, Odysseus, accompanied by Telemachus and their faithful retainers, goes to tell his father Laertes of his return.

EURYCLEA NOW WENT UPSTAIRS LAUGHING, TO tell her mistress that her dear husband had come home. Her aged knees became young again and her feet were nimble for joy as she went up to her mistress and bent over her head to speak to her. "Wake up, Penelope, my dear child," she exclaimed, "and see with your own eyes something that you have been wanting this long time past. Odysseus has at last indeed come home again, and has killed the suitors who were giving so much trouble in his house, eating up his estate and ill-treating his son."

"My good nurse," answered Penelope, "you must be mad. The gods sometimes send some very sensible people out of their minds, and make foolish people become sensible. This is what they must have been doing to you; for you always used to be a reasonable person. Why should you thus mock me when I have trouble enough already—talking such nonsense, and waking me up out of a sweet sleep that had taken possession of my eyes and closed them? I have never slept so soundly from the day my poor husband went to that city with the ill-omened name. Go back again into the women's room! If it had been anyone else who had woke me up to bring me such absurd news, I should have sent her away with a severe scolding. As it is, your age shall protect you."

"My dear child," answered Euryclea, "I am not mocking you. It is quite true as I tell you that Odysseus is come home again. He was the stranger whom they all kept on treating so badly in the cloister. Telemachus knew all the time that he was come back, but kept his father's secret that he might have his revenge on all these wicked people."

Then Penelope sprang up from her couch, threw her arms round Euryclea, and wept for joy. "But my dear nurse," said she, "explain this to me: if he has really come home as you say, how did he manage to overcome the wicked suitors single handed, seeing what a number of them there always were?"

"I was not there," answered Euryclea, "and do not know; I only heard them groaning while they were being killed. We sat crouching and huddled up in a corner of the women's room with the doors closed, till your son came to fetch me because his father sent him. Then I found Odysseus standing over the corpses that were lying on the ground all round him, one on top of the other. You would have enjoyed it if you could have seen him standing there all bespattered with blood and filth, and looking just like a lion. But the corpses are now all piled up in the gatehouse that is in the outer court, and Odysseus has lit a great fire to purify the house with sulphur. He has sent me to call you, so come with me that you may both be happy together after all; for now at last the desire of your heart has been fulfilled. Your husband is come home to find both wife and son alive and well, and to take his revenge in his own house on the suitors who behaved so badly to him."

"My dear nurse," said Penelope, "do not exult too confidently over all this. You know how delighted everyone would be to see Odysseus come home—more particularly myself, and the son who has been born to both of us; but what you tell cannot be really true. It is some god who is angry with the suitors for their great wickedness, and has made an end of them; for they respected no man in the whole world, neither rich nor poor, who came near them, and they have come to a bad end in consequence of their iniquity. Odysseus is dead far away from the Achaean land; he will never return home again."

Then nurse Euryclea said: "My child, what are you talking about? But you were always hard of belief, and have made up your mind that your husband is never coming, although he is in the house and by his own fireside at this very moment. Besides, I can give you another proof. When I was washing him I perceived the scar which the wild boar gave him, and I wanted to tell you about it, but in his wisdom he would not let me, and clapped his hands over my mouth. So come with me and I will make this bargain with you—if I am deceiving you, you may have me killed by the most cruel death you can think of."

"My dear nurse," said Penelope, "however wise you may be, you can hardly fathom the counsels of the gods. Nevertheless, we will go in search of my son, that I may see the corpses of the suitors, and the man who has killed them."

On this she came down from her upper room, and while doing so she considered whether she should keep at a distance from her husband and question him, or whether she should at once go up to him and embrace him. When, however, she had crossed the stone floor of the cloister, she sat down opposite Odysseus by the fire, against the wall at right angles to that by which she had entered, while Odysseus sat near one of the bearing-posts, looking upon the ground, and waiting to see what his brave wife would say to him when she saw him. For a long time she sat silent and as one lost in amazement. At one moment she looked him full in the face, but then again directly, she was misled by his shabby clothes and failed to recognize him, till Telemachus began to reproach her and said:

"Mother—but you are so hard that I cannot call you by such a name—why do you keep away from my father in this way? Why do you not sit by his side and begin talking to him and asking him questions? No other woman could bear to keep away from her husband when he had come back to her after twenty years of absence, and after having gone through so much. But your heart always was as hard as a stone."

Penelope answered: "My son, I am so lost in astonishment that I can find no words in which either to ask questions or to answer them. I cannot even look him straight in the face. Still, if he really is Odysseus come back to his own home again, we shall get to understand one another better by and by, for there are tokens with which we two are alone acquainted, and which are hidden from all others."

Odysseus smiled at this, and said to Telemachus: "Let your mother put me to any proof she likes; she will make up her mind about it presently. She rejects me for the moment and believes me to be somebody else, because I am covered with dirt and have such bad clothes on. Let us, however, consider what we had better do next. When one man has killed another, even though he was not one who would leave many friends to take up his quarrel, the man who has killed him must still say good-by to his friends and fly the country; whereas we have been killing the stay of a whole town, and all the picked youth of Ithaca. I would have you consider this matter."

"Look to it yourself, father," answered Telemachus, "for they say you are the wisest counselor in the world, and that there is no other mortal man who can compare with you. We will follow you with right good will, nor shall you find us fail you in so far as our strength holds out."

"I will say what I think will be best," answered Odysseus. "First wash and put your shirts on; tell the maids also to go to their own room and dress. Phemius shall then strike up a dance tune on his lyre, so that if people outside hear, or any of the neighbors, or someone going along the street happens to notice it, they may think there is a wedding in the house, and no rumors about the death of the suitors will get about in the town, before we can escape to the woods upon my own land. Once there, we will settle which of the courses heaven vouchsafes us shall seem wisest."

Thus did he speak, and they did even as he had said. First they washed and put their shirts on, while the women got ready. Then Phemius took his lyre and set them all longing for sweet song and stately dance. The house re-echoed with the sound of men and women dancing, and the people outside said, "I suppose the queen has been getting married at last. She ought to be ashamed of herself for not continuing to protect her husband's property until he comes home."

This was what they said, but they did not know what it was that had been happening. The upper servant Eurynome washed and anointed Odysseus in his own house and gave him a shirt and cloak, while Athene made him look taller and stronger than before. She also made the hair grow thick on the top of his head, and flow down in curls like hyacinth blossoms; she glorified him about the head and shoulders just as a skillful workman who has studied art of all kinds under Hephaestus or Athene—and his work is full of beauty— enriches a piece of silver plate by gilding it. He came from the bath looking like one of the immortals, and sat down opposite his wife on the seat he had left. "My dear," said he, "heaven has endowed you with a heart more unyielding than woman ever yet had. No other woman could bear to keep away from her husband when he had come back to her after twenty years of absence, and after having gone through so much. But come, nurse, get a bed ready for me. I will sleep alone, for this woman has a heart as hard as iron."

"My dear," answered Penelope, "I have no wish to set myself up, nor to depreciate you, but I am not struck by your appearance, for I very well remember what kind of a man you were when you set sail from Ithaca. Nevertheless, Euryclea, take his bed outside the bedchamber that he himself built. Bring the bed outside this room, and put bedding upon it with fleeces, good coverlets, and blankets."

She said this to try him, but Odysseus was very angry and said:

"Wife, I am much displeased at what you have just been saying. Who has been taking my bed from the place in which I left it? He must have found it a hard task, no matter how skilled a workman he was, unless some god came and helped him to shift it. There is no man living, however strong and in his prime, who could move it from its place, for it is a marvelous curiosity which I made with my very own hands. There was a young olive growing within the precincts of the house, in full vigor, and about as thick as a bearing-post. I built my room round this with strong walls of stone and a roof to cover them, and I made the doors strong and well-fitting. Then I cut off the top boughs of the olive tree and left the stump standing. This I dressed roughly from the root upwards and then worked with carpenter's tools well and skillfully, straightening my work by drawing a line on the wood, and making it into a bed-prop. I then bored a hole down the middle, and made it the center-post of my bed, at which I worked till I had finished it, inlaying it with gold and silver; after this I stretched a hide of crimson leather from one side of it to the other. So you see I know all about it, and I desire to learn whether it is still there, or whether anyone has been removing it by cutting down the olive tree at its roots."

When she heard the sure proofs Odysseus now gave her, she fairly broke down. She flew weeping to his side, flung her arms about his neck, and kissed him. "Do not be angry with me, Odysseus," she cried, "you, who are the wisest of mankind. We have suffered, both of us. Heaven has denied us the happiness of spending our youth and growing old, together; do not then be aggrieved or take it amiss that I did not embrace you thus as soon as I saw you. I have been shuddering all the time through fear that someone might come here and deceive me with a lying story; for there are many very wicked people going about. Zeus' daughter Helen would never have yielded herself to a man from a foreign country, if she had known that the sons of Achaeans would come after her and bring her back. Heaven put it in her heart to do wrong, and she gave no thought to that sin, which has been the source of all our sorrows. Now, however, that you have convinced me by showing that you know all about our bed (which no human being has ever seen but you and I and a single maidservant, the daughter of Actor, who was given me by my father on my marriage and who keeps the doors of our room), hard of belief though I have been, I can mistrust no longer."

Then Odysseus in his turn melted, and wept as he clasped his dear and faithful wife to his bosom. As the sight of land is welcome to men who are swimming towards the shore, when Poseidon has wrecked their ship with the fury of his winds and waves—a few alone reach the land, and these, covered with brine, are thankful when they find themselves on firm ground and out of danger— even so was her husband welcome to her as she looked upon him, and she could not tear her two fair arms from about his neck. Indeed they would have gone on indulging their sorrow till rosy-fingered morn appeared, had not Athene determined otherwise, and held night back in the far west, while she would not suffer Dawn to leave Oceanus, nor to yoke the two steeds Lampus and Phaethon that bear her onward to break the day upon mankind.

At last, however, Odysseus said: "Wife, we have not yet reached the end of our troubles. I have an unknown amount of toil still to undergo. It is long and difficult, but I must go through with it, for thus the shade of Teiresias prophesied concerning me, on the day when I went down into Hades to ask about my return and that of my companions. But now let us go to bed, that we may lie down and enjoy the blessed boon of sleep."

"You shall go to bed as soon as you please," replied Penelope, "now that the gods have sent you home to your own good house and to your country. But as heaven has put it in your mind to speak of it, tell me about the task that lies before you. I shall have to hear about it later, so it is better that I should be told at once."

"My dear," answered Odysseus, "why should you press me to tell you? Still I will not conceal it from you, though you will not like it. I do not like it myself, for Teiresias bade me travel far and wide, carrying an oar, till I came to a country where the people have never heard of the sea, and do not even mix salt with their food.

They know nothing about ships, nor oars that are as the wings of a ship. He gave me this certain token which I will not hide from you. He said that a wayfarer should meet me and ask me whether it was a winnowing shovel that I had on my shoulder. On this, I was to fix my oar in the ground and sacrifice a ram, a bull, and a boar to Poseidon; after which I was to go home and offer hecatombs to all the gods in heaven, one after the other. As for myself, he said that death should come to me from the sea, and that my life should ebb away very gently when I was full of years and peace of mind, and my people should bless me. All this, he said, should surely come to pass."

And Penelope said, "If the gods are going to vouchsafe you a happier time in your old age, you may hope then to have some respite from misfortune."

Thus did they converse. Meanwhile Eurynome and the nurse took torches and made the bed ready with soft coverlets. As soon as they had laid them, the nurse went back into the house to go to her rest, leaving the bedchamber woman Eurynome to show Odysseus and Penelope to bed by torchlight. When she had conducted them to their room she went back, and they then came joyfully to the rites of their own old bed. Telemachus, Philoetius, and the swineherd now left off dancing, and made the women leave off also. They then laid themselves down to sleep in the cloisters.

When Odysseus and Penelope had had their fill of love, they fell talking with one another. She told him how much she had had to bear in seeing the house filled with a crowd of wicked suitors who had killed so many sheep and oxen on her account, and had drunk so many casks of wine. Odysseus in his turn told her what he had suffered, and how much trouble he had himself given to other people. He told her everything, and she was so delighted to listen that she never went to sleep till he had ended his whole story.

He began with his victory over the Cicones, and how he thence reached the fertile land of the Lotus-eaters. He told her all about the Cyclops and how he had punished him for having so ruthlessly eaten his brave comrades; how he then went on to Aeolus, who received him hospitably and furthered him on his way, but even so he was not to reach home, for to his great grief a hurricane carried him out to sea again; how he went on to the Laestrygonian city Telepylos, where the people destroyed all his ships with their crews, save himself and his own ship only. Then he told of cunning Circe and her craft, and how he sailed to the chill house of Hades, to consult the ghost of the Theban prophet Teiresias, and how he saw his old comrades in arms, and his mother who bore him and brought him up when he was a child; how he then heard the wondrous singing of the Sirens, and went on to the wandering rocks and terrible Charybdis and to Scylla, whom no man had ever yet passed in safety; how his men then ate the cattle of the sun-god, and how Zeus therefore struck the ship with his thunderbolts, so that all his men perished together, himself alone being left alive; how at last he reached the Ogygian island and the nymph Calypso, who kept him there in a cave, and fed him, and wanted him to marry her, in which case she intended making him immortal so that he should never grow old, but she could not persuade him to let her do so; and how after much suffering he had found his way to the Phaeacians, who had treated him as though he had been a god, and sent him back in a ship to his own country after having given him gold, bronze, and raiment in great abundance. This was the last thing about which he told her, for here a deep sleep took hold upon him and eased the burden of his sorrows.

Then Athene bethought her of another matter. When she deemed that Odysseus had had enough both of his wife and of repose, she bade gold-enthroned Dawn rise out of Oceanus that she might shed light upon mankind. On this, Odysseus rose from his comfortable bed and said to Penelope: "Wife, we have both of us had our full share of troubles, you, here, in lamenting my absence, and I in being prevented from getting home though I was longing all the time to do so. Now, however, that we have at last come together, take care of the property that is in the house. As for the sheep and goats which the wicked suitors have eaten, I will take many myself by force from other people, and will compel the

Achaeans to make good the rest till they shall have filled all my yards. I am now going to the wooded lands out in the country to see my father who has so long been grieved on my account, and to yourself I will give these instructions, though you have little need of them. At sunrise it will at once get abroad that I have been killing the suitors; go upstairs, therefore, and stay there with your women. See nobody and ask no questions."

As he spoke he girded on his armor. Then he roused Telemachus, Philoetius and Eumaeus, and told them all to put on their armor also. This they did, and armed themselves. When they had done so, they opened the gates and sallied forth, Odysseus leading the way. It was now daylight, but Athene nevertheless concealed them in darkness and led them quickly out of the town.

BOOK XXIV

The ghosts of the suitors gather miserably in the house of Hades and tell of their deaths to the spirits of Agamemnon and Achilles. Meanwhile, Odysseus finds his father working humbly in his orchard and reveals himself to him. Certain men of Ithaca, bent on avenging the suitors, march to attack Odysseus. The battle begins, but Athene stops it, bidding them make a covenant of peace.

THEN HERMES OF CYLLENE SUMMONED THE ghosts of the suitors, and in his hand he held the fair golden wand with which he seals men's eyes in sleep or wakes them just as he pleases; with this he roused the ghosts and led them, while they followed whining and gibbering behind him. As bats fly squealing in the hollow of some great cave, when one of them has fallen out of the cluster in which they hang, even so did the ghosts whine and squeal as Hermes the healer of sorrow led them down into the dark abode of death. When they had passed the waters of Oceanus and the rock Leucas, they came to the gates of the sun and the land of dreams, whereon they reached the meadow of asphodel where dwell the souls and shadows of them that can labor no more.

ognized Amphimedon son of Melaneus, who lived in Ithaca and had been his host, so it began to talk to him.

"Amphimedon," it said, "what has happened to all you fine young men—all of an age too—that you are come down here under the ground? One could pick no finer body of men from any city. Did Poseidon raise his winds and waves against you when you were at sea, or did your enemies make an end of you on the mainland when you were cattle-lifting or sheep-stealing, or while fighting in defense of their wives and city? Answer my question, for I have been your guest. Do you not remember how I came to your house with Menelaus, to persuade Odysseus to join us with his ships against Troy? It was a whole month ere we could resume our voyage, for we had hard work to persuade Odysseus to come with us."

And the ghost of Amphimedon answered: "Agamemnon son of Atreus, king of men, I remember everything that you have said, and will tell you fully and accurately about the way in which our end was brought about. Odysseus had been long gone, and we were courting his wife, who did not say point-blank that she would not marry, nor yet bring matters to an end, for she meant to compass our destruction. This, then, was the trick she played us. She set up a great tambour frame in her room and began to work on an enormous piece of fine needlework. 'Sweethearts,' said she, 'Odysseus is indeed dead, still, do not press me to marry again immediately. Wait—for I would not have my skill in needlework perish unrecorded—till I have completed a pall for the hero Laertes, against the time when death shall take him. He is very rich, and the women of the place will talk if he is laid out without a pall.' This is what she said, and we assented; whereupon we could see her working upon her great web all day long, but at night she would unpick the stitches again by torchlight. She fooled us in this way for three years without our finding it out. But as time wore on and she was now in her fourth year, in the waning of moons and many days had been accomplished, one of her maids who knew what she was doing told us, and we caught her in the act of undoing her work, so she had to finish it whether she would or no. And when she showed us the robe she had made, after she had had it washed, its splendor was as that of the sun or moon.

"Then some malicious god conveyed Odysseus to the upland farm where his swineherd lives. Thither presently came also his son, returning from a voyage to Pylos, and the two came to the town when they had hatched their plot for our destruction. Telemachus came first, and then after him, accompanied by the swineherd, came Odysseus, clad in rags and leaning on a staff as though he were some miserable old beggar. He came so unexpectedly that none of us knew him, not even the older ones among us, and we reviled him and threw things at him. He endured both being struck and insulted without a word, though he was in his own house; but when the will of aegis-bearing Zeus inspired him, he and Telemachus took the armor and hid it in an inner chamber, bolting the doors behind them. Then he cunningly made his wife offer his bow and a quantity of iron to be contended for by us ill-fated suitors. And this was the beginning of our end, for not one of us could string the bow—nor nearly do so. When it was about to reach the hands of Odysseus, we all of us shouted out that it should not be given him, no matter what he might say, but Telemachus insisted on his having it. When he had got it in his hands he strung it with ease and sent his arrow through the iron. Then he stood on the floor of the cloister and poured his arrows on the ground, glaring fiercely about him. First he killed Antinous, and then, aiming straight before him, he let fly his deadly darts and they fell thick on one another. It was plain that some one of the gods was helping them, for they fell upon us with might and main throughout the cloisters, and there was a hideous sound of groaning as our brains were being battered in, and the ground seethed with our blood. This, Agamemnon, is how we came by our end, and our bodies are lying still uncared for in the house of Odysseus. For our friends at home do not yet know what has happened, so that they cannot lay us out and wash the black blood from our wounds, making moan over us according to the offices due to the departed."

"Happy Odysseus son of Laertes," replied the ghost of Agamem-

when we bade you check the folly of your sons who were doing much wrong in the wantonness of their hearts—wasting the substance and dishonoring the wife of a chieftain who they thought would not return. Now, however, let it be as I say, and do as I tell you. Do not go out against Odysseus, or you may find that you have been drawing down evil on your own heads."

This was what he said, and more than half raised a loud shout, and at once left the assembly. But the rest stayed where they were, for the speech of Halitherses displeased them, and they sided with Eupeithes. They therefore hurried off for their armor, and when they had armed themselves, they met together in front of the city, and Eupeithes led them on in their folly. He thought he was going to avenge the murder of his son, whereas in truth he was never to return, but was himself to perish in the attempt.

Then Athene said to Zeus, "Father, son of Cronus, king of kings, answer me this question: What do you propose to do? Will you set them fighting still further, or will you make peace between them?"

And Zeus answered: "My child, why should you ask me? Was it not by your own arrangement that Odysseus came home and took his revenge upon the suitors? Do whatever you like, but I will tell you what I think will be the most reasonable arrangement. Now that Odysseus is revenged, let them swear to a solemn covenant, in virtue of which he shall continue to rule, while we cause the others to forgive and forget the massacre of their sons and brothers. Let them then all become friends as heretofore, and let peace and plenty reign."

This was what Athene was already eager to bring about, so down she darted from off the topmost summits of Olympus.

Now when Laertes and the others had done dinner, Odysseus began by saying, "Some of you go out and see if they are not getting close up to us." So one of Dolius' sons went as he was bid. Standing on the threshold he could see them all quite near, and said to Odysseus, "Here they are, let us put on our armor at once."

They put on their armor as fast as they could—that is to say Odysseus, his three men, and the six sons of Dolius. Laertes also and

Dolius did the same—warriors by necessity in spite of their gray hair. When they had all put on their armor, they opened the gate and sallied forth, Odysseus leading the way.

Then Zeus' daughter Athene came up to them, having assumed the form and voice of Mentor. Odysseus was glad when he saw her, and said to his son Telemachus, "Telemachus, now that you are about to fight in an engagement which will show every man's mettle, be sure not to disgrace your ancestors, who were eminent for their strength and courage all the world over."

"You say truly, my dear father," answered Telemachus, "and you shall see, if you will, that I am in no mind to disgrace your family."

Laertes was delighted when he heard this. "Good heavens," he exclaimed, "what a day I am enjoying! I do indeed rejoice at it. My son and grandson are vying with one another in the matter of valor."

On this Athene came close up to him and said, "Son of Arceisius —best friend I have in the world—pray to the blue-eyed damsel, and to Zeus her father; then poise your spear and hurl it."

As she spoke she infused fresh vigor into him, and when he had prayed to her he poised his spear and hurled it. He hit Eupeithes' helmet, and the spear went right through it, for the helmet stayed it not, and his armor rang rattling round him as he fell heavily to the ground. Meantime Odysseus and his son fell upon the front line of the foe and smote them with their swords and spears. Indeed, they would have killed every one of them, and prevented them from ever getting home again, only Athene raised her voice aloud, and made everyone pause. "Men of Ithaca," she cried, "cease this dreadful war, and settle the matter at once without further bloodshed."

On this pale fear seized everyone; they were so frightened that their arms dropped from their hands and fell upon the ground at the sound of the goddess' voice, and they fled back to the city for their lives. But Odysseus gave a great cry, and gathering himself together swooped down like a soaring eagle. Then the son of Cronus sent a thunderbolt of fire that fell just in front of Athene, so she said to Odysseus, "Odysseus, noble son of Laertes, stop this warful strife, or Zeus will be angry with you."

Thus spoke Athene, and Odysseus obeyed her gladly. Then Athene assumed the form and voice of Mentor, and presently made a covenant of peace between the two contending parties.

THE END.

30 TALES TO GIVE YOU

Goosebumps®

R.L. STINE

SCHOLASTIC INC.

New York   Toronto   London   Auckland   Sydney
Mexico City   New Delhi   Hong Kong   Buenos Aires

The *Goosebumps* book series created by Parachute Press, Inc.

ISBN 0-439-68948-1

12 11 10 9 8 7 6 5 4 3 2 1   4 5 6 7 8 9/0

Printed in the U.S.A.   23

First Scholastic book club printing, November 2004

CONTENTS

TALES TO GIVE YOU

Goosebumps®

THE HOUSE OF
NO RETURN

We were afraid to go too close to the house. So we stayed down at the street, staring up at it. Staring across the bare, sloping front yard.

No grass would grow in that yard. The trees, gnarled and bent, were all dead. Not even weeds sprouted in the dry, cracked dirt.

At the top of the sloping yard, the house seemed to stare back at us. The two upstairs windows gaped like two unblinking black eyes.

The house was wide and solid-looking. Built of bricks. Many years ago, the bricks had been painted white. But now the paint was faded and peeling. Spots of red brick showed through like bloodstains.

The window shutters were cracked. Several had fallen off. The beams of the front porch tilted dangerously. A strong wind could blow the porch over.

No one lived there. The house had been empty for years and years.

1

No one *could* live there.

The house was haunted. Everyone in town said it was.

Everyone knew the legend of the house: If you spent the night inside it, you would never come out.

That's why we brought kids there. That's why we dared them to go inside.

You couldn't join our Danger Club unless you stayed inside the house — by yourself — for an hour.

Staring up at the house, bathed in a haze of pale moonlight, I shivered. I zipped my windbreaker up to my chin and crossed my arms over my chest.

"How long has he been in there, Robbie?" Nathan asked me.

Lori and I both raised our wrists to check our watches. "Only ten minutes," I told Nathan.

"Fifty minutes to go," Lori said. "Think he'll make it?"

"Doug is pretty brave," I replied thoughtfully, watching the moon disappear behind a cloud. "He might last another five minutes!" I said, grinning.

Lori and Nathan snickered.

The three of us felt safe down here by the street.

Poor Doug probably didn't feel too safe right now. He was shut inside the dark house. Trying to stay there an hour so he could join our club.

I turned and saw a light rolling silently over

the street, coming toward us. A white, ghostly light.

My breath caught in my throat.

It's a car, I realized, as it floated closer. A car with only one headlight. The first car we'd seen on this street all night.

The beam from the headlight washed over my two friends and me, forcing us to shield our eyes. As it passed, we turned back to the house — and heard a shrill scream.

A wail of terror.

"Here he comes!" Nathan cried.

Sure enough, Doug burst out through the front door. He stumbled off the crumbling porch and came tearing across the dead, bare yard.

His hands waved wildly in front of him. His head was tilted back, and his mouth was frozen open in one long, high shriek of fright.

"Doug — what did you see?" I called. "Did you really see a ghost?"

"S-something touched my *face*!" he wailed. He ran right past Nathan, Lori, and me, screaming his head off.

"Probably only a spiderweb," I murmured.

"Robbie — we've got to stop him!" Lori cried.

"Doug! Hey — Doug!" We called his name and chased after him, our sneakers slapping loudly on the pavement.

Waving his arms frantically and screaming, leaning into the wind, Doug kept running.

3

We couldn't catch him. "He'll run home," I said breathlessly. I stopped and leaned over, pressing my hands against my knees, trying to catch my breath.

Up ahead, we could still hear poor Doug's frightened wail.

"Guess he doesn't join the club," I said, still breathing hard.

"What do we do now?" Nathan asked, glancing back at the house.

"I guess we find another victim," I replied.

Chris Wakely seemed like a perfect victim.

His family had moved to town last summer, and Chris started in my sixth-grade class in September. Chris had pale blue eyes and very short, white-blond hair. He was kind of shy, but he seemed like a really nice guy.

One day after school, I saw Chris walking home and I hurried to catch up with him. It was a windy October day. All around us, red and yellow leaves were falling from the trees. It looked like it was raining leaves.

I said hi to Chris and started telling him about our club. I asked if he'd like to join.

"It's only for brave people," I explained. "In order to join, you have to spend an hour at night inside the house on Willow Hill."

Chris stopped walking and turned to me,

4

squinting at me with those pale blue eyes. "Isn't that house supposed to be haunted?" he asked.

I laughed. "You don't believe in ghosts — do you?"

He didn't smile. His expression turned serious. The light seemed to fade in his eyes. "I'm not very brave," he said softly.

We started to walk again. Our sneakers crunched on the leaves strewn over the sidewalk. "We'd really like you to join the club," I told him. "You're brave enough to spend one hour in an empty house, aren't you?"

He shrugged and lowered his eyes. "I — I don't think so," he stammered. "I've always been afraid of monsters and things," he admitted. "I believed there was a monster living under my bed until I was eight!"

I laughed. But his expression remained solemn. He wasn't kidding.

"When I go to a scary movie," Chris continued, "I have to duck under the seat when the scary parts come on."

Lori and Nathan came running up to us. "Are you going to do it?" Nathan asked Chris. "Are you going to join the club?"

Chris shoved his hands deep into his jeans pockets. "Did you guys spend an hour in the house?" he asked.

I shook my head. "We don't have to," I told

him. "We started the club, so we don't have to go in the house. We already know we like danger. New members have to prove themselves."

Chris chewed thoughtfully at his lower lip. We turned the corner and kept walking. The house was up the hill, at the end of the block.

We stopped in front of it and stared across the bare front yard. "See? It doesn't look scary at all in the daytime," I said.

Chris swallowed hard. "Needs a paint job," he muttered. "And how come all the trees died?"

"No one to take care of them," Nathan said.

"How about it, Chris?" I urged. "We really need new members."

"Yeah," Lori agreed. "A club isn't much fun with only three kids in it."

Chris had his eyes on the house. He kept his hands jammed into his jeans pockets. I thought I saw him shiver. But it might have been the wind rustling his jacket.

"W-will you come in with me?" he asked.

"No way," I replied, shaking my head.

"We can't," Lori told him. "The idea of the club is to show how brave you are."

"We won't come in," Nathan said. "But we'll wait out front for you."

"Come on, Chris," I urged. "Do it. It'll be fun! It's almost Halloween. Get in the spirit!"

He swallowed a couple of times, staring up at the house. Then he shook his head. "I really don't

6

want to," he murmured in a low voice, so low I could barely hear him. "Guess I'm kind of a scaredy-cat."

I started to plead with him. But I could see he was really embarrassed. So I didn't say any more.

Chris waved good-bye and hurried off toward his house. Lori, Nathan, and I watched him until he disappeared around the corner.

"Now what?" Nathan asked.

We held a club meeting at my house two nights later. It was a pretty boring meeting. None of us could think of another cool kid to join our club. And we couldn't think of anything fun to do.

"Halloween is Saturday," I moaned. "We should be able to think of something scary to do."

"What are you going to dress up as?" Lori asked Nathan.

"Freddy Krueger," Nathan replied. "I already bought the metal fingernails."

"Weren't you Freddy Krueger last year?" I asked him.

"So? I *like* being Freddy Krueger!" Nathan insisted.

"You and every other kid in school," Lori muttered.

Lori planned to dress as a vampire. And I had my monster costume all ready.

"We need more club members," Lori said, sighing. "You can't have a club with just three people."

"Chris would be perfect," I replied. "If only he weren't such a scaredy-cat."

"You know," Nathan started, rubbing his chin thoughtfully, "it would be really good for Chris to get over his fears."

"Huh? What do you mean?" I asked.

"I mean we could help Chris out," Nathan replied, smiling. "We could help him be brave."

I still didn't understand. "Nathan — what are you saying?"

His smile grew wider. "We could *force* him to go into the house."

I called Chris later that night and invited him to go trick-or-treating with us. He said yes. He sounded grateful to have some kids to go around with. He had only been at our school two months, and he hadn't made many friends.

The three of us met at my house on Halloween. Nathan clicked his long metal nails and kept cackling and grinning like Freddy Krueger. I was a very cool monster, with eyeballs on springs popping from my purple head. Lori kept talking in a weird vampire voice.

"Where's Chris?" Nathan asked, looking around. "Is he meeting us here?"

"Yeah. Where is he?" Lori demanded.

We were all a little tense. We were playing a mean trick on Chris. But we knew he'd feel good about things by the end of the night.

8

The doorbell rang, and we all ran to answer it. Chris stood in the porch light, his face an ugly green. He raised both hands to show them to us. They were covered in green, too.

"What are *you* supposed to be — a pea pod?" I joked.

Chris looked hurt. "No. I'm a corpse."

"Very scary," I said. I handed out trick-or-treat bags. "Let's get going." I led the way down the driveway and up the street.

We stopped at several houses and collected candy. It was a cool, windy night with a tiny sliver of a moon. Gusts of wind kept fluttering our costumes and making our trick-or-treat bags fly up.

We were approaching the house on Willow Hill. I had a heavy feeling in my stomach. My hands suddenly felt ice cold.

I hope Chris can stay in the house for a whole hour, I thought. He's such a nice guy. I'd really like him to be in the club.

Such a nice guy. And we were about to do such a mean thing to him.

But he'll quickly get over it, I told myself. And he'll be glad we made him test his bravery.

The eerie house came into view. I saw Chris glance at it, then quickly turn to cross the street. He didn't want to go near it. Especially on Halloween night.

But Nathan and I grabbed him by the arms.

9

Chris cried out in surprise. "Hey — let go! What are you guys doing?"

Chris struggled to pull free. But Nathan and I were much bigger than him, and stronger.

Lori led the way over the bare, dirt yard, up the sloping hill to the dark, silent house. Chris tried to swing both arms, tried desperately to break free. But Nathan and I dragged him onto the tilting porch, up to the front door.

"No! Please!" Chris pleaded. "Please — don't do this! Don't!"

I turned to him. Even under the green makeup, I could see the terror on his face. The poor guy was totally freaked!

"Chris, you'll be okay," I said softly, soothingly. "Go inside. It'll be fun. We'll wait for you. I promise."

"You'll be proud of yourself," Lori told him, helping to push him up to the door. "And then you'll be in our club."

Lori started to push open the heavy door. Nathan and I moved to shove Chris inside. But to my surprise, he reached out and grabbed my arm.

"Come in with me — please!" he begged, his eyes wide with fright. "Please! I'm too scared! I'm just too scared!" He held on tightly to my arm. "Let's all go in together — okay?"

I glanced at Lori and Nathan. "No way," I replied. "You've got to prove your bravery, Chris. See you in an hour."

10

We gave him a hard shove inside the house. Then we slammed the heavy door behind him.

"He seems so . . . scared," Lori said, her voice muffled by the vampire fangs.

"He'll be okay," I said. "Let's wait for him down by the street."

We took our places at the bottom of the driveway, and waited.

And waited.

We checked our watches after ten minutes. After twenty minutes. After half an hour.

"Chris is doing great!" I whispered, my eyes on the dark windows of the house. "I didn't think he'd last *two* minutes."

"He's a lot braver than I thought," Nathan said from behind his Freddy Krueger mask.

We huddled close together, staring up at the house as the wind shook the trees all around us. Heavy clouds rolled over the moon, covering us in darkness.

We waited ten minutes more. Then ten minutes more.

"He's going to do it," I said, checking my watch again. "He's going to stay in there for a whole hour."

"Let's really give him a big cheer when he comes out," Lori suggested.

As the hour ended, we counted off the last thirty seconds out loud, one by one. Then we took a few steps up the driveway, eager to congratulate

Chris and welcome him to the Danger Club.

But the front door didn't open. The house remained dark and silent.

Ten more minutes passed.

"I think he's showing off," I said.

No one laughed. We kept our eyes raised to the house.

Ten more minutes. Then ten more.

"Where *is* he?" I cried shrilly.

"Something is wrong," Lori said, taking the plastic vampire fangs out of her mouth. "Something is wrong, Robbie."

"Chris should be out of there by now," Nathan agreed in a trembling voice.

I felt a chill run down my back. All of my muscles were tightening in dread. I knew my friends were right. Something bad had happened inside that house. Something very bad.

"We have to go in there," Lori urged. "We have to find Chris. We have to get him out."

All three of us exchanged frightened glances. We didn't want to walk up that driveway. We didn't want to go inside that dark house.

But we didn't have a choice.

"Maybe we should wait a few more minutes," I suggested, trying to stop my legs from shaking. "Maybe he doesn't have a watch. Maybe he's — "

"Come on, Robbie." Lori gave me a hard tug. "Chris isn't coming out. We have to go get him."

The wind swirled around us, fluttering our costumes as we made our way up to the front door. I started to open the door, but my hand was so sweaty, the doorknob slid under my grasp.

Finally, Nathan and I pushed open the heavy door. The rusty hinges creaked as we opened the door and peered into the solid blackness.

"Chris?" I called. "Chris — you can come out now!" My voice sounded tiny and hollow.

No reply.

"Chris? Chris? Where are you?" All three of us began calling him.

The floor groaned and creaked beneath us as we took a few steps into the living room. The wind rattled the old windowpanes.

"Chris — can you hear us? Chris?"

No reply.

A loud crash made all three of us cry out.

The front door had slammed behind us.

"J-just the wind, guys," I choked out.

It was much darker with the door closed. But it didn't stay dark for long. Pale light flickered at the top of the stairs. It looked at first like dozens of fireflies clustered together.

I gasped as the light flared brighter. And floated down the stairs, like a shimmering cloud.

"Let's get out!" I cried.

Too late.

The shimmering cloud spread around us. And inside it I saw two frightening figures — a ghostly

13

man and woman, hazy and transparent except for their red, glowing eyes.

Their terrifying eyes sparkled like fiery coals as they circled us, floating silently.

I can see right through both of them! I realized. This house really is haunted.

"Wh-where's Chris?" I managed to blurt out.

The man's voice was a dry whisper, the sound of wind through dead leaves. "Your friend? He went out the back door," the ghost replied. "About an hour ago."

"We didn't want to let him go," the woman whispered, her red eyes glowing brighter. "But he made a bargain with us." She snickered, a dry, dead laugh. "He promised that if we let him go, three kids would come in to take his place."

"And here you are," said the ghostly man, flashing an ugly, toothless smile. "Here you are."

"Don't look so frightened, kids," the woman rasped, floating closer. "You might as well make yourselves at home. You're all going to be here — *forever!*"

TEACHER'S PET

Do you like snakes?

If you're in Mr. Blankenship's class, you *have* to like snakes — or you're in *major* trouble!

Let me start at the beginning, on the first day of school last September. Benjy, my best friend, was shouting to me from my front porch. "Becca, move it! We'll be late!"

I grabbed my black denim jacket and tucked my ponytail under my New York Yankees baseball cap. I hurried, even though I knew Benjy would never leave without me.

Benjy and I had walked to school together every day since kindergarten. Some people think it's weird that a girl and a guy are best friends. But Benjy and I don't care. We've always liked to do the same sort of stuff — like play basketball and baseball, and cook. (Benjy would kill me if he knew I told anyone about that!)

Benjy and I were starting sixth grade. At our

school, sixth-graders get to do great stuff — like go on a camp-out for a whole week!

We were supposed to have Ms. Wenger this year, the coolest teacher in the whole school. Ms. Wenger is the kind of teacher who takes the whole class in-line skating so that when someone falls down, she can talk to us about gravity!

Benjy and I figured this would be just about the best school year ever.

So you can imagine our surprise when we walked into our classroom and saw the teacher writing his name on the board. The teacher wasn't Ms. Wenger. It was a man named Mr. Blankenship.

Benjy and I both groaned in disappointment. Mr. Blankenship was a strange-looking dude. He was really, really tall and really, really skinny. And he was almost completely bald.

His clothes were pretty bad, too. Especially the weird turtleneck sweater he was wearing with the beige, brown, and black diamonds all over it.

He greeted Benjy and me at the door and asked our names.

"I'm Becca Thompson," I said.

"Benjy Connor," Benjy said.

"I'm just getting things together right now. Why don't you two join the others and take a tour around the room?" Mr. Blankenship suggested.

The room looked pretty dull — not cool the way Ms. Wenger would have done it. Mr. Blankenship had set up the typical stuff — reading corner, computer corner, and a corny "Welcome Back" bulletin board.

The only unusual things were the five or six glass tanks placed around the classroom. I walked over to one of the tanks and pressed my nose up against the glass. Not much to see — some rocks, a pile of dried grass, a stick, and . . .

"*Aaagh!*" I uttered a shriek.

Then I just stood there, pointing at the long, skinny, hissing creature. I hate snakes. I can't help it. I just hate them!

I hate those tiny, black eyes that sort of stare right through you. That's what scares me the most — those eyes.

I wanted to turn away from the snake's angry glare, but I couldn't. I seemed to be paralyzed. Frozen stiff. And my heart was pounding so hard, I thought it was going to pop out of my chest!

It was Benjy who broke the snake's spell over me. He came over and shoved me out of the way to get a better view. "Oh. A snake," he said calmly. But I knew that Benjy is just as afraid of snakes as I am.

"I see you've met one of my little pals," Mr. Blankenship said to us, smiling. "We're going to study snakes this year. Fascinating creatures. Fascinating."

Leaning over the cage, Mr. Blankenship turned to me. "Did you know that snakes can live for months without food? Of course, they'd much rather swallow a tasty little mouse instead. Watch."

He reached into a smaller cage hidden behind a bookshelf and grabbed a small white mouse by the tail. The mouse tried to wriggle free, but Mr. Blankenship held tight to its slender pink tail.

He dangled the thrashing, wriggling mouse over the snake's tank for a few seconds. Then he dropped it right next to the snake.

I didn't want to watch. But I couldn't help myself.

The snake snapped open its jaws, and swallowed the little white mouse — whole! I let out a groan as I watched the pink tail slide past the snake's teeth like a spaghetti noodle.

I felt really sick to my stomach. But there was no way I was giving Mr. Blankenship the satisfaction of knowing he had totally grossed me out.

"Who's next?" Mr. Blankenship asked, rubbing his long, slender hands together. "Who's hungry?"

That's when I realized that *all* of the glass cages in the room were filled with Mr. Blankenship's slimy, slithering, hissing little "pals."

Benjy and I tried to like Mr. Blankenship's class. But it wasn't easy. For one thing, he kept adding more and more snakes. Soon, one entire wall was filled with glass tanks.

The snakes slithered silently, their black eyes

following Mr. Blankenship. "There are more snakes than kids in here!" I whispered to Benjy one day.

It seemed as if Mr. Blankenship could talk about nothing else! In science, we studied about the hatching of snake eggs. For history, we read stories about ancient beliefs in serpents. For geometry, we made chalk drawings of snakeskin patterns.

One enormous glass cage behind Mr. Blankenship's desk stood empty. Benjy and I wondered what he planned to put in there. "A giant python!" Benjy guessed.

I shuddered. I didn't want to think about it.

Every time I peered into a glass cage and saw a snake staring back at me, I panicked. I knew the snakes hated being cooped up in those tanks. Something in their eyes told me that if they ever got out, they would go for the first human they saw.

I hoped it wasn't me!

One night I was lying in bed, trying to get to sleep. Pale moonlight washed over my room from the open window. I saw a shadow move against the wall.

Uttering a frightened gasp, I clicked on my bed-table lamp.

And saw a snake slithering out of my backpack on the floor.

How had it escaped from its tank? How had it crept into my backpack?

Frozen in terror, I watched it slither over my shag rug, making its way to my bed.

I screamed and forced myself to sit up. I tried to scramble away. But I felt something warm and dry curl around my arm.

"Uh-uh-uh-uh — !" I was making this weird gasping sound. I felt something like a rope tightening around my ankle. Another snake slithered over my pillow. Two more snakes crawled over my pajama legs.

"Helllllp!" My frantic plea escaped my lips in a hushed whisper.

The snakes tightened themselves around me, curling around my waist, my arms, my legs. One of them slithered through my hair.

I started to shudder and shake. I shook so hard, I woke myself up.

What a horrible nightmare!

Mr. Blankenship and his room full of snakes were ruining my life. But what could I do?

The next day I tried to switch my seat to one far away from the snake tanks. But the tanks were everywhere, on the shelves, on the tables, stacked along the window ledges. Every day there seemed to be more of them.

I tried hard not to think about the snakes around the room. I tried to concentrate on our geography lesson — the snakes of New Mexico.

But just as Mr. Blankenship began to discuss the heat of the desert, I heard a *thud*. Then Melissa Potter let out a shrill scream.

"I'm sorry!" she cried. "I bumped a cage. I let out one of the mice!"

"Where? Where did it go?" Mr. Blankenship cried excitedly.

"There it goes!" Benjy cried, pointing. The little white mouse scampered across the floor. Kids screamed and laughed.

But Mr. Blankenship had a serious, angry expression on his face. "Grab it! Grab it — quick!" he shouted.

"It's over there!" shouted Carl Jansen, pointing to the window in the corner. Mr. Blankenship always left that window open so his snake pals could get fresh air.

Mr. Blankenship dived across the room. The mouse scuttled onto the window ledge. Mr. Blankenship grabbed for the tail. Missed. The mouse vanished out the window.

Our teacher turned beet-red. Even the top of his bald head was red. "Now look what you've done!" he screamed at Melissa. "You let a perfectly good snake dinner get away!

"You will all have to be taught to be more careful," Mr. Blankenship bellowed. "Perhaps an extra homework assignment will help you remember. I want three pages on the feeding habits of

21

the eastern diamondback rattler. And I want it tomorrow!"

"What is his problem?" I whispered to Benjy.

"Becca!" Mr. Blankenship shouted. "I heard that! *You* will write a *ten*-page essay!"

"But — but — !" I sputtered.

"And you will clean the snake cages for the next two weeks!" Mr. Blankenship added.

I clamped my hand over my mouth to keep myself from getting in even worse trouble. But I was so angry, I could have let *all* the mice out of their cages!

Which gave me a great idea. "Benjy," I whispered when Mr. Blankenship had turned away. "After school. My house. Get ready for Operation Mouse Rescue."

Later, after school, Benjy and I worked out all of the details. Operation Mouse Rescue would take place on Thursday night, after our parents went to play bridge.

The plan was simple. Simple, but excellent. Benjy and I were going to sneak into school and set all of the white mice free. We could just picture Mr. Blankenship's face when he arrived Friday morning and found the mice scampering all over the room.

Thursday seemed to stretch on forever. I barely heard a word Mr. Blankenship said. I was too busy watching the clock, waiting for the bell to ring.

22

I know I ate dinner with my family — but don't ask me what we had. All I could think about was Operation Mouse Rescue.

Finally, my parents said good-bye, left all the right phone numbers, and drove off to their bridge tournament. It didn't take long before Benjy gave me our secret signal — a single ring of the telephone.

My heart pounding, I pulled on my black jeans and dark jacket and raced up the block to Benjy's house. He was waiting for me at the bottom of the driveway.

"What took you so long?" he demanded. "You're not wimping out — are you?"

"No way!" I replied, although I suddenly felt as if *I* had white mice fluttering around in my stomach. "Let's go."

Half walking, half jogging, we made our way to school. It was a cool, breezy night. The trees shivered, shedding fat brown leaves. Shadows twisted and bent over our path as we crept up to the dark school building.

"Around the back," I whispered.

The school seemed so much larger, so much scarier at night, bathed in total blackness.

We found our classroom. Benjy clicked on his flashlight.

"No — turn it off!" I instructed. "Someone may see us."

He obediently clicked off the light. We spotted

23

the open window, the window in the corner that Mr. Blankenship always leaves open.

My hands felt cold and wet as I grabbed the stone window ledge and pulled myself up. Inside the room, I turned and helped pull Benjy in.

"It — it's so dark," he whispered, huddling close to me. "Can't we turn on the flashlights?"

"Okay," I whispered back. "But keep the light down on the floor."

Our circles of yellow light swept over the floor. Slowly, we made our way to the table that held the mice cages. The floorboards creaked under our sneakers.

I glanced nervously around the room. Tiny lights flickered in the blackness. It took me a long moment to realize they weren't lights. They were glowing snake eyes.

"They — they're all watching us," I whispered to Benjy. "The snakes — they're — "

So many glowing eyes. So many snakes! All around us. Staring. Staring.

I forgot to watch where I was going. I stumbled over a chair.

"Ow!" I cried out. I tried to catch my balance, but fell against a table.

A glass tank toppled to the floor with a shattering *crash*. I glanced down in time to see two snakes slither onto the floor. They uncurled in the trembling light of my flashlight. Then moved quickly toward my legs.

"Benjy — help!" I thrashed out my arms. I turned to run. And knocked over another snake cage.

A long black snake rolled silently onto the floor, arched itself up, opened its jaws, and shot its head toward me.

"Run!" I shrieked. "Benjy — the snakes are out!"

"How — ?" Benjy started.

I jumped as a snake slithered between my feet.

We turned to run — but stopped as our lights played over the enormous, empty glass case.

Which wasn't empty anymore.

A giant gray-and-black cobra glared into the shaking lights. The cobra arched its head up, opened its jaws, and hissed at us, its red eyes gleaming excitedly.

When did that snake get in there? I asked myself. The cage was empty this afternoon!

"R-run!" I stammered, grabbing Benjy's shoulder.

But neither of us could move. We stood staring in frozen horror as the enormous cobra rose up. Lifted itself up. Out of the cage.

It stood over us, at least six feet tall. Its eyes glowing. Its thick tongue flicking across its open jaws.

And as it rose up, its skin shifted and stretched. Its head tilted up. Its body grew wide. Grew arms. Legs.

25

And we recognized him. We saw him. We knew him.

We knew we were staring at Mr. Blankenship. The snake was Mr. Blankenship!

"Nooooooooo!" Did that terrified howl escape *my* throat? Or was Benjy howling like some unearthly creature?

I only knew that we turned and ran. Dived out through the open window. Into the dark night. And kept running. Running till we were safe at home. Safe. Safe from snakes. Safe from the biggest snake — Mr. Blankenship.

But safe for how long? Safe till we had to return to school the next morning?

Trembling with fright, Benjy and I hesitated at the classroom door on Friday morning. What would Mr. Blankenship do to us now that we knew his horrible secret? What would he say?

He smiled as Benjy and I entered, and didn't say a word. The day went by like any other day. He didn't say a word about what had happened the night before.

Until the final bell rang that afternoon. He dismissed the rest of the class, then turned to Benjy and me. "I want you two to stay," he said sternly. He moved quickly to block the doorway.

We were alone with him now. He closed the door and moved toward us, rubbing his slender hands together, his dark eyes glowing excitedly.

*   *   *

Mr. Blankenship isn't such a bad guy. He made us a deal. He said he wouldn't tell anyone we broke into the school. And he promised not to harm us as long as we didn't tell anyone his secret.

Of course Benjy and I quickly agreed.

There's just one part of the deal that I hate.

We have to bring in white mice and feed him every afternoon.

I really hate the way the mice wriggle and squirm as I hold them up by their pink tails.

But what choice do I have?

A deal's a deal.

"Here you go, Mr. Blankenship. Open wide."

STRAINED PEAS

My life changed forever the day Mom brought the new baby home from the hospital. My little sister is no ordinary baby.

If only she were.

I sat on the front steps with Mrs. Morgan, waiting for Mom and Dad to bring the baby home. Mrs. Morgan had stayed with me and Dad while Mom was in the hospital.

I thought about the new baby. Hannah. A little sister.

Yuck.

I sighed and tapped a stick against the brick steps.

"Stop fidgeting, Nicholas," Mrs. Morgan scolded. "Why don't you read your comic book until your parents get home?"

I opened my *Iron Man* comic book and picked up where I'd left off. Iron Man has cornered a bad guy disguised as a kindly doctor. "Unmask yourself!" says Iron Man.

Iron Man rips the mask off the doctor's head, revealing the hideous face of a mad scientist. Iron Man gasps. "The Mark of Evil!" he cries. "Dr. Destro!"

Iron Man has never seen Dr. Destro before, but he recognizes the bad guy by the birthmark on his face — the Mark of Evil.

I heard a car coming and glanced up. Dad's dark green Volvo chugged down the street and pulled into our driveway. Mom sat in the passenger seat, waving to me and smiling brightly.

Mrs. Morgan gave me a little shove. "Go on," she said. "Go meet your new sister!"

Ugh, I thought. I *was* glad to see Mom, though. I dragged myself over to the car.

Dad opened the car door. Mom stepped out, carrying a little bundle in her arms. She bent down and said, "Look, Nicholas. Isn't she adorable?"

I looked at the crumpled red face in my mother's arms. A thin fuzz of dark hair covered her head. She had blue eyes and tiny, wet red lips. No teeth. She waved a wrinkled fist in the air, then stuffed it into her mouth.

I didn't think she was so adorable. I thought she was kind of ugly.

But then I nearly choked. On Hannah's cheek was a tiny, brown, heart-shaped birthmark.

I pointed to the birthmark and gasped, "The Mark of Evil! Just like Dr. Destro!"

"Cut it out, Nicholas," Dad said sternly. "This is no time for your crazy comic book talk."

He turned his back on me to gawk at Hannah.

"She's perfect," Dad said, giving Mom's shoulders a squeeze.

How could he be so stupid? I picked up my comic book and pointed to the mark on Dr. Destro's face.

"Look!" I cried. "Hannah has a birthmark like Dr. Destro's! It's a sign of evil!"

Mom smiled vaguely at me. "Don't be silly," she said. She carried the baby inside, and the rest of us followed her.

Soon Grandma and Grandpa came over, and Aunt Julie and Uncle Hal. They oohed and ahhed every time Hannah burped, or hiccupped, or cooed. It was disgusting.

"Look at that — she blew a bubble!"

"She's a genius!"

"Dori, darling, let me hold her for a few minutes," Grandma begged Mom.

But Mom said, "Let Nicholas hold her. He's her big brother, after all."

"No," I said, backing away. "That's okay."

"Oh, come on, Nick. You'll like it." Mom smiled and put Hannah in my arms. She showed me how to hold her. Hannah burped. Everyone laughed.

As I held her, I thought, she's sort of cute, I guess. Maybe I got a little carried away with that Mark of Evil stuff. After all, comic books don't come true. And Hannah's just a baby.

But like I said, she was no ordinary baby.

I swear I saw something glint in her dark blue eyes.

That little heart-shaped birthmark on her cheek seemed to darken.

Then Hannah opened her mouth wide — and threw up all over me.

"Ugh!" I cried. I was covered with milky white glop.

Mom quickly took the baby.

Hannah started crying. "Poor little Hannah," Mom said.

Poor little Hannah! *I* was the one she threw up on!

And she did it on purpose. I knew she did.

That night, the howling began.

A horrible sound woke me up. A loud, screeching wail.

I sat up in bed, shaking. My eardrums rattled in my ears.

What was that noise?

I got out of bed to see what was going on. Mom was walking Hannah up and down the hallway, patting and shushing her. But Hannah didn't stop screaming. She sounded like some kind of wild animal in pain.

"Mom — what's wrong with her?" I asked.

"Nothing," Mom replied. "It's just a normal baby sound. Go back to sleep."

I didn't get any sleep. Hannah never stopped crying.

That's no normal baby sound, I thought. No one can tell me that terrifying screech is normal.

Hannah's wailing continued, night after night. Each night was worse than the last. Wild screams that even the neighbors could hear. Monstrous screams. When Hannah started crying, the neighborhood dogs threw their heads back and howled along with her.

I could swear I saw her birthmark grow, just a little.

A few months passed. Hannah learned to crawl early. Mom and Dad thought that meant she was smart. I knew better.

She had a mission. She wanted to be an only child.

She wanted to get rid of me.

The crying didn't get rid of me. The puking didn't get rid of me.

But Hannah had other tricks up her little terry-cloth sleeve.

One morning before school I found Hannah in my room, chewing on something. She held a bit of paper in her hand. When she saw me coming, she tried to stuff it into her mouth. I snatched it away from her.

"Oh, no!" I cried. "My math homework!"

Or what was left of it. Mostly just my name and the date. Covered with drool.

Hannah had eaten my homework.

She swallowed and smiled that evil smile.

Ha-ha, her smile seemed to say. Gotcha.

"Mom!" I called. "Hannah ate my homework!"

Mom swooped in and picked up Hannah. "She *what?* Is she all right?"

"Mom! What about my homework?"

Mom frowned at me as if she just realized what I was telling her.

"Nicholas, you didn't do your homework, did you? And now you're trying to blame it on Hannah!"

"Mom, I'm telling the truth! Give Hannah an X ray. You'll see my homework in her stomach!"

Mom shook her head. "Nicholas, what's wrong with you lately?"

Later that day, when my teacher asked me where my math homework was, I told her my baby sister had eaten it.

She kept me after school.

That's what I got for telling the truth.

"Nicholas! Get in here! I want to talk to you!" Dad called.

I was playing in the backyard when his voice boomed at me from an upstairs window.

I found Dad in my parents' bedroom. At least I *thought* it was their room. It was where their room was supposed to be. Only it didn't look much like their room anymore.

Normally, my parents' room was white. I mean WHITE. White rugs, white walls, white curtains, white bedspread. I wasn't allowed to play in there, or eat, or do anything. They were always worried about all that white stuff.

The room wasn't white anymore. It was multicolored. Paint splashed everywhere.

"Nicholas," Dad said. "You are in big trouble. Huge trouble."

Little jars of paint from my paint set littered the floor. Red, blue, green, yellow, and black paints were splashed all over the white rug, the white curtains, the white bedspread, the white walls. And in the middle of it all, splattered with blood-red paint, Hannah sat laughing her evil laugh.

"You have one minute to give me an explanation for this, Nicholas," Dad said. "Go."

"I didn't do it," I said. "Hannah did it."

Dad laughed sarcastically. "Hannah did it? Hannah took your paint set, brought it all the way to our room, opened the jars, and splattered paint all over everything?"

"Yes," I said.

"Nicholas, go to your room."

"But, Dad — I didn't do anything wrong!"

"Oh, no? Go to your room and think about it until you can see what you did wrong."

"Dad — Hannah did it! She did it on purpose —

35

to get me in trouble! You're playing right into her hands!"

Dad gave me his stony glare. He pointed to my room.

I went. There's no fighting Dad's stony glare.

She's a monster, I thought. She's really a monster.

But she won't get away with this. I'll find a way to convince them, somehow. I'm not leaving this family. *She* is.

The next day, when I came home from school, I heard terrible screams from the kitchen.

I ran in. Hannah sat in her high chair, screaming with laughter. My mother stood beside her. Mom, Hannah, the floor, the walls — all covered with green slime.

Green slime oozed out of the corner of Hannah's mouth.

Hannah had spewed green slime everywhere.

"She's a monster!" I shouted. "This is proof!"

Mom ignored me. "Hannah, you naughty girl!" she said. "Strained peas all over the kitchen!"

Hannah banged her spoon on her high-chair tray. More green stuff splattered on the wall.

All right. It wasn't exactly green slime. But it was close enough. Strained peas. They're green, and they're slimy.

Mom said, "Nicholas, get a sponge and help me clean this up."

"Why do I have to clean it? *She* made the mess!"

36

"Nicholas, I'm tired. Just help me out, please."

I stared at Hannah's pea-covered face. Something was different. Her eyes. Her eyes — were brown!

"Mom!" I cried. "Hannah's eyes changed colors! I told you she had evil powers!"

Mom just laughed. "Most babies are born with blue eyes," she explained. "Sometimes their eyes change after a few — "

"Mom, that's impossible! People's eyes don't change color!"

"Yes, they do, Nicholas. Some babies — "

I grabbed her by the arms and tried to shake some sense into her. "Mom — you're losing it. Hannah's brainwashing you! She's trying to get rid of me! We've got to send her back — before it's too late!"

"Nicholas, that's enough! You've been jealous of Hannah from the beginning. It's time for you to get over all of this and start acting a little more mature!"

I felt like tearing my hair out. Why wouldn't my parents believe me? How could I get them to see what Hannah was doing?

Mom started cleaning the strained peas from Hannah's face. The birthmark seemed to glow like a tiny spark.

The worst was still to come.

I was sitting in the den, watching TV. Minding my own business. Then I heard a creeping sound.

Creep, creep, creep. The sound of little knees scraping against the rug.

Oh, no, I thought. Here she comes.

I turned around to look. Hannah was crawling toward me — clutching a pair of scissors in her tiny fist!

She crawled closer, closer, that evil gleam in her eye, the birthmark pulsing on her face.

She was going to stab me!

"NO!" I yelled. I backed away. She kept crawling toward me, the scissors gleaming.

This is it, I thought. My baby sister is going to kill me.

"Nicholas!" My mom stood in the doorway. Then she ran to Hannah and snatched the scissors away from her.

"Thanks, Mom. You saved my life!" I cried.

"How could you *do* this?" Mom said. "How could you let Hannah carry around such a sharp object! She could have been seriously hurt!"

"*She* could have been hurt! Mom, she was going to kill me!"

"Nicholas, this is ridiculous."

"Mom, she's trying to get rid of me! She wants to be an only child!"

"I think that's what *you* want, Nicholas," Mom said. "I think we need to have a long, long talk."

"I'm not making this up, Mom! Why won't you believe me? You always trusted me before — until Hannah came along!"

The phone rang. Mom picked up Hannah and stormed off to the kitchen to answer it.

A few minutes later, I heard Mom cry out, "Oh, no! No! I don't believe it!"

I hurried to the kitchen to see what was wrong.

Mom was crying. She said, "All right, Dr. Davis. We'll be there this afternoon."

She hung up the phone and cried some more. She gripped the wall as if she thought she'd faint. Then she stopped crying and stared at Hannah with a new, weird look on her face. A look of horror.

At last, I thought. She believes me!

The doctor must have called to warn us that Hannah is a monster!

"That was the hospital," Mom said in a slow, hoarse voice. "They said . . . they said — "

"That Hannah's a monster!" I finished for her.

Mom turned sharply to me. "Nicholas, stop it!" She scooped Hannah up and hugged her tightly, crying.

"I can't believe it," she said. "I love her so much. But she's not really our baby."

"What?" I was afraid I hadn't heard her right. It seemed too good to be true. Had Mom just said Hannah was not really our baby?

"Our real baby and Hannah were switched at birth," Mom said through her tears. "Hannah is someone else's child."

Hannah wasn't my sister at all. Her real parents

39

were probably monsters, too. It explained every-thing.

"Yippee!" I shouted. I was free! Free from Hannah's evil! Everything would be okay now. We'd get my *real* baby sister, and she'd be cute and normal like other babies. She wouldn't try to get rid of me. She wouldn't be a monster.

Mom started crying harder than ever. She carried Hannah upstairs to her room and shut the door.

I felt a little bit sorry. Mom was really upset. I knew Dad would be, too.

But they'll be happier when we get our real baby, I thought. And so will I.

Dad came home from work early. We bundled Hannah up and took her to the hospital. A nurse introduced us to a woman who held a baby Hannah's age. Hannah's real mother. She had a tiny heart-shaped birthmark on her cheek, just like Hannah's.

Monster Mom, I thought, even though she didn't look like a monster at all.

The nurse gave my mother the new baby. It seemed "weird to call the new baby Hannah, so Mom decided to name her Grace.

When we got home, the first thing I did was check Gracie for birthmarks. She was clean. No birthmarks anywhere.

She was a sweet baby, blond, blue-eyed, smiling, and rosy-cheeked. She looked like an angel. She smiled and cooed at me.

I watched Gracie carefully the first day. Just to be sure.

She didn't cry like an animal. She didn't spew peas or try to stab me. She did nothing but gurgle and coo.

By the end of the day, I thought, she's normal! She's not a monster. She's not out to get me. She's even cute!

Everything is going to be okay now.

Mom put Gracie to bed. I sneaked into her room to play with her for a few minutes.

I tickled her. She giggled. I tickled her again. This time she didn't giggle so much. So I tickled her one more time.

She opened her mouth and croaked, "If you tickle me again, kid, I'll rip your arm off!"

Her eyes bulged as she uttered a deep growl.

"Aaaauuugh!" I wailed. "A monster!"

I ran from the room, screaming my head off. And as I was leaving, I heard the baby cackle, "I'll get rid of you, creep. Just wait till I can walk!"

STRANGERS IN
THE WOODS

"This ruins everything, Lucy," wailed Jessica when I called her to deliver the bad news. "I can't believe you're getting shipped off to . . . what's the name of that town, anyway?"

"Fairview," I said, with a long, very sad sigh. I twisted the phone cord around and around my finger. "I could just *cry*."

I'm not usually so depressed. Actually, Jessica says I'm annoyingly happy most of the time.

But finding out that I'd be spending six weeks this summer with Great-Aunt Abigail in her boring farm town was enough to put me in a bad mood forever. I mean, there's *nothing* in Fairview but tractors and cows and cornfields.

I hoped that something exciting had happened to Fairview since my last visit to Great-Aunt Abigail's two summers before. But when Dad pulled the car into town, the place looked even duller and drabber than I remembered. One grocery, a hardware store, a gas station, and a tiny library.

We bumped our way down Great-Aunt Abigail's long dirt road and pulled up in front of 25 Butterfly Lane, her small, redbrick house. I climbed out of the car and looked around. Fiélds and forests as far as I could see.

Great-Aunt Abigail came running out, dressed in her usual flowered housedress and sneakers. She looked a little different than I remembered, a little older, a little more wrinkled, a little skinnier.

We all greeted one another. Then Mom and Dad followed Great-Aunt Abigail into the house to have tea.

I started to let my dog Muttster out of the car so that he could explore the yard. But the big brown mutt pulled back, his tail between his legs.

"Muttster — what's your problem?" I asked. He acted like a big scaredy-cat, whimpering and huddling in the backseat.

When I finally coaxed him out with a doggie pretzel, he started barking really loud, and running around and around in circles.

The thing you have to know about Muttster is that he *never* barks. He's really well-behaved. That's why he was being allowed to stay in Fairview with me while Mom and Dad went off on their big trip to Asia.

I should have known that something was terribly wrong as soon as Muttster started barking.

But I didn't guess. I just figured the big dog was excited.

Then when Great-Aunt Abigail came outside to see what all the fuss was about, Muttster really went crazy — growling and snapping like a mean old junkyard hound.

"Oh, dear, Lucy," she said nervously. "Why is he doing that? Maybe you should put him in the yard."

I didn't want to tie him up. But Muttster was just going ballistic! So I tied him to a huge oak tree and ran back to the porch to say good-bye to my parents.

"Honey, I'll miss you," Mom said. "You won't be able to call us because we'll be moving around so much. But we'll call when we can and send lots of postcards."

After a lot of hugs and kisses, my parents were off on their trip. I waved sadly, until their car disappeared down the long driveway.

What a boring summer this is going to be, I thought glumly.

I had no idea how *wrong* I was.

Great-Aunt Abigail did her best to cheer me up. "I have a surprise for you, dear," she said. "Your favorite cookies."

Cookies? I'd almost forgotten that Great-Aunt Abigail made the best peanut-butter fudgies in the world.

I took a cookie off the tray she offered. Still warm and soft from the oven. I bit into it eagerly. It was chewy and fudgey and peanut buttery — but something was wrong. Something didn't taste right.

Was it too salty? Were the ingredients different?

How weird, I thought. Great-Aunt Abigail's cookies are always perfect.

I could see her watching me eagerly, so I finished the cookie and pretended to love it. Then I jammed a few cookies in my pocket and threw on my denim jacket. "I'm taking Muttster for a walk," I called out. "Just to relax him."

"Have fun, dear," she said. "But stay out of the woods, okay?"

That's weird, I thought. She never warned me away from the woods during my other visits.

Muttster and I had a nice walk in the sloping, green fields. At times, the dog seemed as calm and playful as always. But then he would start barking excitedly again — for no reason at all.

I couldn't get to sleep that night. Maybe it was because Muttster had to spend the night outside as punishment for his constant barking. At home, he *always* slept at the foot of my bed.

I tried reading a book, but that only made me feel more awake. So I gazed out the window and counted the stars.

And that's when I saw the frightening lights.

In the purple night sky. Six lights, forming a circle.

At first, I thought they were super-bright stars because they were up in the sky. But then I realized they were moving, lowering slowly to the ground.

As I stared with my mouth hanging open in amazement, the lights hovered over the woods on the other side of Great-Aunt Abigail's cornfield. I felt their light washing over me — brightening my whole room, bright as daylight.

Then, slowly, the circle of lights lowered into the woods. And it became dark again.

A cold shudder shook my body. What had I just seen?

I crept down the hall to Great-Aunt Abigail's room and called softly outside her closed door. But she has always been a sound sleeper. She didn't wake up.

Back in my room, I could hear Muttster down in the yard, barking furiously. I shut the window tight. How would I ever get to sleep?

"Do you know what those lights are out in the woods?" I asked Great-Aunt Abigail as I sat down to breakfast.

She narrowed her eyes at me. I thought I saw her cheeks go pink. "Lights? What lights, dear? How do you want your eggs?"

47

"Scrambled, please. There were about six lights, all in a circle. They were so weird."

"Don't worry, dear. I'm sure it's just reflections or something. Have you fed Muttster?"

Why is she so eager to change the subject? I wondered. Why does she seem so nervous?

Her scrambled eggs tasted different, too. Not as fluffy and fresh-tasting as in the past.

After I ate, I took Muttster his breakfast, a bowl of dry dog food. Then I sat on the lawn, talking to the dog, and staring at the woods — hoping to see something, *anything*, that might explain those lights.

Thinking about those lights made me feel strange. You know how your stomach feels after you've eaten five slices of pizza? That was it, only more nervous and fluttery.

My stomach felt even funnier after Great-Aunt Abigail and I took a drive to the hardware store. Did I say "drive"? It was more like a roller coaster ride!

To my shock, my usually careful great-aunt drove like a maniac! We almost clipped the mailbox on the way out of the driveway. Then she kept weaving from lane to lane and whizzing right through stop signs. I held on to the dashboard, too terrified to scream.

I got my voice back when we finally pulled over on Main Street. "Aunt Abigail!" I cried breathlessly. "Is there something wrong with the car? Why are you driving like this?"

"Like what?" she replied innocently.

The only thing more frightening than the drive to town was the drive back to the house! By the time we returned, we'd gone through two red lights, terrorized a farmer on his tractor, and missed a parked car by an inch!

Great-Aunt Abigail didn't seem to notice that anything was wrong.

My heart still in my mouth, I leaped out of the car and staggered over to Muttster. He wagged his bushy brown tail and licked my face, as if I'd been gone for ten years!

But he stopped in mid-lick when Great-Aunt Abigail climbed out of the car. "GRRRRRRRR," he growled ferociously, straining at his leash.

What is going *on* here? I asked myself.

Why does everything seem so different — so *wrong*?

I saw the eerie lights again that night. And the next night, too. Bigger and brighter than ever. Hovering in a circle over the woods.

As I pressed my face up against the window to watch them, I suddenly had a frightening thought. They looked just like the lights of the alien space-ship in my favorite movie, *Attack of the Pod People*.

I tried desperately to come up with another explanation for the lights. Streetlights? Not in Fairview. A plane? A plane couldn't hover like that. And I'd *never* seen a plane with lights that bright.

I felt a chill down my back as I realized there was no other explanation. Aliens had invaded Fairview. And they were landing in the woods near my great-aunt's house!

Wrapping my arms around myself to stop the chills, I found myself thinking about Great-Aunt Abigail. She seemed so different, so changed.

Had the aliens taken over Great-Aunt Abigail's mind? Just like in the *Pod People* movie?

I could hear Muttster start to bark down in the yard. Dogs have a sixth sense, I knew. Muttster sensed that Great-Aunt Abigail was possessed by an alien. That's why he had been barking and growling at her.

Suddenly gripped with fear, I turned away from the window.

Was I next? Would the aliens come after me next?

I had to get out of there. Run away. But where?

Mom and Dad were thousands of miles away. Should I call my best friend, Jessica, back home? She'd think I was joking. Besides, how could she help?

I needed someone closer. The police!

Trying not to make a sound, I crept down the

50

stairs to the phone in the kitchen. Great-Aunt Abigail — or *whoever* she was — had gotten there first.

She had her back to me. She couldn't see me. But I could hear her: "Don't worry, my niece doesn't know. Yes, yes, I told her to stay away from the woods. And she won't know anything until it's all over tomorrow night."

My palms started sweating, and I got that itchy feeling under my arms I always get when I'm really nervous.

"All over?"

Until *what* was all over? The alien invasion? Until Muttster and I had been taken off to some weird planet where they'd put us in cages?

I had to get back to my room — and fast. I turned back to the stairs. But the floorboards creaked loudly beneath me.

Great-Aunt Abigail whirled around to face me.

I gasped, and my mouth dropped open in horror.

My great-aunt's face was glowing green!

"Lucy — what are you doing up?" Great-Aunt Abigail demanded. She took a few steps toward me. I suddenly realized I was *terrified* of her.

"Uh . . . just going back to b-bed," I stammered, backing away.

I hurried up the stairs, my entire body trembling. I closed the bedroom door tightly and waited. Waited to hear Great-Aunt Abigail pad up the stairs and go into her room.

I knew I couldn't spend another minute in the house. I couldn't stay there with an alien from outer space.

Frantically, I pulled on jeans and a sweatshirt. I had to get to the police. I had to tell them about the aliens.

But would they believe me?

They will if I go to the woods and see the aliens first, I decided.

I know, I know. I wasn't thinking clearly. But I was having a major panic attack. And it seemed like the best idea at the time.

I sneaked silently down the stairs and out the back door. I should have woken up Muttster and brought him with me to the woods. But I was so out of my mind with fear, I didn't even think of him.

I ran across the backyard, heading to the woods. Nothing but darkness ahead. No lights hovering in the sky.

What was waiting for me in that darkness? Were there really aliens there? I needed to get a glimpse of them. Just a glimpse, so I could describe them to the town police.

The woods were dark, steamy, and wet. It was like plunging through a thick jungle. There was no path, so I had to push my way through, stumbling over fallen logs and marshy ground.

As I made my way, I kept hearing rustling noises on both sides of me.

Was I being followed? Was I being watched?

As I stopped to catch my breath, a light appeared up ahead. Swallowing hard, I moved toward it. The trees thinned out, and I found myself in a large clearing.

What were those sounds? Voices? Human voices?

Or alien voices?

I gasped as the bright lights washed over me. The white beam blinded me, captured me in a harsh spotlight.

I shielded my eyes as the light hovered over me, closing in, covering me, holding me helpless.

"Bring her here," I heard a deep voice order.

I felt hands tugging me.

I tried to pull away. But my captor was too strong.

"You can't take over my brain!" I shrieked. "I won't let you!"

"Cut the lights," another voice ordered.

The harsh lights dimmed to black. I could see smaller lights all around.

As my eyes adjusted to the darkness, I saw a man walk toward me. He wore a baseball cap and a long-sleeved Polo shirt over jeans.

"Young lady, I don't know what you're screaming about," he said. "But you can't just wander on to a film set. You just ruined a shot that took three hours to set up."

Film set? I opened my mouth to reply. But no sound came out.

"We asked the people in town to stay out of the woods," the man said sternly. "We're finishing our movie tomorrow. Then we'll be out of here."

"M-movie?" I took a deep breath, trying to get myself together. Suddenly, I heard dogs barking.

"The dogs are ready," a young woman carrying a clipboard announced. She raised a dog whistle to her lips. She blew into it. It made no sound that I could hear. But the dogs immediately barked louder.

That explains why Muttster has been barking all the time, I told myself. He keeps hearing the dog whistle from the woods.

Everything made sense now. Great-Aunt Abigail warning me to stay out of the woods. The bright lights. My great-aunt saying on the phone that it would all be over tomorrow night.

"I-I'm sorry," I told the man. "Really. I'm so sorry."

I felt like a total jerk.

I ran all the way home. Great-Aunt Abigail was waiting for me at the back door, her face tight with worry. "Lucy, where did you go? Where have you been? I was about to call the police."

I told her how sorry I was. And then the words just burst out of me. "I saw the lights. And Muttster was acting so strange. And your skin was green. And you drove so wildly. And the cookies were wrong. And — and — "

Great-Aunt Abigail wrapped me in a hug and held me till I stopped trembling. When I finally backed away, she was chuckling. "I guess my green mint julep facial mask would give *anyone* the creeps!" she declared.

I laughed, too.

"I should have told you about the movie folks," Great-Aunt Abigail said, shaking her head. "But I figured they'd be gone by tomorrow."

I started to say something. But she raised a hand to stop me. "I have more to explain," she said, frowning. "I have a confession to make, Lucy. I lost my glasses just before you arrived. And I've been trying to get along without them."

"That's why your driving was so wild?" I cried.

She nodded. "And that's why my cooking may have been a little off. It's so hard to see the ingredients."

We hugged each other again and shared a good laugh. "I can't believe you thought I was an alien from outer space!" Great-Aunt Abigail said. "You've seen too many movies!"

She was right. I felt like such a fool.

We had some hot chocolate. It didn't taste quite right, but I didn't complain. Then I made my way upstairs to go to sleep.

The night had grown cool, and I love sleeping

with the windows open. So I went to the linen closet to get an extra blanket.

As I pulled open the door, Great-Aunt Abigail's glasses tumbled out.

Terrific! I thought. Now she won't have to buy new ones.

I picked them up and carried them down the hall to her room. "Aunt Abigail?" I called.

The door was open a crack. I pushed it open and stepped inside. She stood with her back to me. "Aunt Abigail — look. I found your — "

My words choked in my throat as she turned to face me.

And I saw the four slimy tentacles waving at her sides. Her skin glowed bright green in the light from the dresser top. And her three fat, black lips made sucking sounds as she unrolled a long blue tongue.

"You found my glasses!" she croaked, reaching out all four tentacles toward me. "Thanks, Lucy."

GOOD FRIENDS

Jordan and his best friend, Dylan, hopped off the school bus and walked up Oak Street. "Want to ride bikes?" Jordan suggested.

"Yeah, okay," Dylan replied. "But I have to do my homework first."

Jordan rolled his eyes. Dylan was the only sixth-grader he knew who always did his homework the second he got home from school.

Jordan dropped his backpack on the front lawn and crossed the street. "Can't you do it later?" he asked.

Dylan kicked a pebble across the sidewalk. "No way. My mom will have a cow," he muttered.

Jordan sighed and pushed his bangs out of his eyes. "Then just tell her you did your homework in school, Dylan. She won't be home for hours. She won't know if you did it or not."

Dylan bit his bottom lip. "I don't know, Jordan," he said, lowering his voice. "What about — ?" He pointed toward his house.

57

"Who? Richard?" Jordan asked, making a face. "Will you forget about him already? Your older brother is a total jerk!"

Dylan shot a nervous glance toward the house. "Sshh! He'll hear you!"

Jordan folded his arms across his chest. "So what?" he demanded loudly. "Everyone knows Richard is a total jerk!"

Dylan gasped. "Come on, Jordan," he pleaded. "Be quiet! He'll *pound* me!"

Jordan shook his head. He couldn't believe Dylan was so scared of his brother. Richard was fourteen, and big and strong. But so what?

"Just forget about him, will you?" Jordan said. "Come on. Let's ride."

They rode their bikes around the neighborhood for a while. Then they stopped in Dylan's driveway to shoot some hoops. Dylan kept staring up nervously at his brother's bedroom window.

"I hope he leaves us alone today," he said to Jordan. "Ever since my mom put him in charge after school, Richard has been worse than ever. He acts like he's the king of the house."

"Oh, he's King all right," Jordan snickered. "King of the Jerks!"

Dylan laughed nervously and glanced back up to the window.

"Would you forget about him already?" Jordan said. "Come on, let's play. Show me your best slam dunk!"

Dylan dribbled the ball on the driveway. He was just about to shoot — when The Pest came skipping across the street.

The Pest was Ashley, Jordan's seven-year-old sister. Ashley plopped down on the sidewalk in front of Dylan's house and began playing with her Barbie dolls and talking to herself.

"Jaclyn, your hair is long and pretty like Barbie's!" Ashley said.

Jordan and Dylan exchanged glances, then cracked up. "Your sister is talking to her imaginary friend again," Dylan said, rolling his eyes.

"You're *sad!*" Jordan called out to his sister. "You're really *sad!*"

Ashley shot Jordan an angry look. "Shut up, dummy!" she screamed at him. "Jaclyn and I think that *you're* sad!"

"Where *is* Jaclyn?" Jordan demanded. "How come Dylan and I can't *see* Jaclyn? How come it looks like you're talking to yourself again?"

Ashley ignored her brother. "Don't pay any attention to them, Jaclyn," she said. "They're just acting dumb."

Dylan shook his head. "Come on, Jordo," he said softly. "Let's just play."

Jordan made a face at his sister, then grabbed the ball and took a jump shot. The ball hit the rim and bounced off.

"Hahaha!" Ashley burst out laughing. "Did you

59

see that, Jaclyn?" she cried. "Jordan missed an easy one."

"Ashley — get lost!" Jordan cried angrily. "And take your imaginary friend with you!"

Ashley dropped her dolls and ran up to him. "I told you, Jaclyn isn't imaginary!" she screamed. "She's real!"

"Oh, yeah?" Jordan shot back. "Then if Jaclyn is real, where is she standing?"

"Right here," Ashley replied, pointing to her left.

Jordan lobbed the ball at high speed in that direction. "Think fast, Jaclyn!" he shouted.

Ashley gasped. "No! Stop it! You'll hurt her!"

Jordan laughed and moved closer to his sister. "How come Jaclyn didn't catch the ball?" he teased.

"Because . . . because . . . you threw it too fast!" Ashley stammered.

"Where is she now?" Jordan demanded. "Let me try it again. This time, I'll aim for her head!" He and Dylan both laughed.

"You leave us alone! I'm telling!" Ashley whined. "Come on, Jaclyn. Let's go." She turned to leave.

"Come on, Jaclyn!" Jordan mocked in a whiny voice, trying to imitate his sister.

"Shut up, Jordan!" Ashley cried.

"Shut up, Jordan!" Jordan repeated.

"Cut it out!"

"Cut it out!" Jordan grabbed the air and pretended to hold somebody. "Hey, look, Ashley — I've got Jaclyn! She's my prisoner!"

Ashley balled her hands into fists. "Let her go! Let her go!"

"Hey, Dylan, bring me that rope from the garage. Let's tie Jaclyn to that tree!" Jordan cried, grinning.

Ashley screamed. "No! Stop! Jordan, let her go!"

Jordan kept laughing. "Wait! Maybe Jaclyn would like to help us practice our jump shots! We can hang a net on her head and use her face as a backboard!"

"I'm telling! I really am!" Ashley declared. She picked up her dolls and angrily ran down the driveway and across the street.

"Do you see what I have to put up with?" Jordan said, shaking his head.

Dylan started to answer. But an angry voice interrupted, shouting from the window above them. "Hey — loser!"

Jordan and Dylan raised their eyes to the upstairs window.

Dylan's brother, Richard, stuck his head out. "Dylan, did you do your homework yet?" he called down. "You'd better have it finished — or I'm telling Mom!"

Dylan nervously rolled the ball between his hands. "Just ignore him," Jordan whispered.

Dylan lifted the ball and tossed it up to the net. The ball missed the backboard completely.

Richard burst out laughing. "You really *are* a loser, Dylan! I could make that shot blindfolded. Who taught you how to play? Did your best friend, Jordan, teach you how to shoot like that?"

Jordan's face grew red. He opened his mouth to say something nasty. But Dylan's eyes pleaded with him not to.

"Please, Jordan," Dylan begged in a whisper. "Just ignore him! Please!"

"What did you say?" Richard shouted down from the window. "Are you talking to me, loser?"

Dylan cleared his throat. "No. Just leave me alone. I did my homework already. So just leave me alone."

Richard shook his head. "Try shooting with *both* hands!" he called down. Then he slammed the window shut with a loud thud.

Dylan hugged the ball tightly to his chest. His face was white. "He thinks he's so great," he muttered, his voice trembling.

"What a jerk!" Jordan exclaimed. "Why do you let him boss you around like that?"

Dylan shrugged. "Because he can beat me up," he admitted.

"Well, if he were my brother, I'd tie him to his

bed at night and tape his mouth shut!" Jordan said seriously.

Dylan laughed. "You always have the *best* ideas, Jordan!"

"What are good friends for?" Jordan replied.

Later, Dylan sat at his desk, slumped over his math book.

"I've got it!" Jordan cried suddenly, startling him.

"You've got what?" Dylan asked.

"The perfect trick to play on Ashley!" Jordan announced with a mischievous grin.

Dylan smiled and lowered his pencil. "What is it?" he asked eagerly. "Your tricks are always the coolest!"

"Thanks!" Jordan replied proudly. "Okay, here it is. You know how scared Ashley is of Axel and Foley, right?"

Dylan nodded. "Yeah. I don't like Richard's pet tarantulas much, either."

"Well," Jordan continued, grinning, "what if Axel and Foley somehow got loose?"

Dylan's eyes widened. "I don't know — "

"Oh, come on!" Jordan insisted. "Ashley would freak! I'll run up to her and scream, 'The spiders are loose! The spiders are loose! Run for your life!' Then, when Ashley runs out screaming, I'll tell her that I saw Axel swallow Jaclyn up whole!"

"Well . . ." Dylan hesitated. His friend's plans always scared him a little.

"Dylan, come on! It's perfect! Look at her!" Jordan pointed out the bedroom window. "My dopey sister is playing catch with her invisible friend right there in the front yard for everyone to see!"

Dylan peered out the window. "She does look pretty stupid," he admitted.

"Okay, so let's sneak into Richard's room, and — "

"Jordan, I don't know if this is such a good idea," Dylan said. "Richard will pound me for sure if we touch his spiders."

"Oh, stop worrying so much!" Jordan replied impatiently. "He'll never know! He's down in the den right now watching television. We'll be real quiet. No problem!"

Dylan peered out the window again and watched Ashley playing catch with her imaginary friend. "Okay. Let's do it," he agreed.

Jordan led the way to Richard's room. They crept inside and made their way to the tarantula tank.

"Go ahead," Jordan urged, whispering. "Pick them up. Hurry."

Dylan picked up the two tarantulas, one in each hand. They felt warm and hairy. They kind of tickled.

Tiptoeing silently, they made their way downstairs, sneaking past Richard in the den. Jordan pushed open the front door. They crept down the front steps and onto the driveway.

"This is going to be awesome!" Jordan whispered as they crept up behind Ashley.

Dylan held the tarantulas high above his head.

Ashley didn't hear them coming. She was laughing, calling out to her invisible friend, "Nice throw, Jaclyn!"

They tiptoed closer, until they were right behind her. One more step, and . . .

"DYLAN!" a voice roared from the porch.

Jordan and Dylan whirled around.

"It's Richard!" Dylan gasped in horror. Jordan saw his friend's face go white.

Richard moved toward them quickly, glaring furiously at Dylan.

"What are you doing out here with my tarantulas?" Richard demanded.

"I . . . uh . . . well . . ." Dylan stammered.

"I *know* what you're doing!" Richard accused angrily. "You're playing with Jordan and Ashley again, aren't you?"

Dylan stumbled backward as Richard moved closer. "Well . . ."

"Do you know what an *embarrassment* you are?" Richard cried. "You're just such a weird kid! Always playing by yourself and talking to yourself!"

"But — but . . . " Dylan sputtered.

Richard took the tarantulas from Dylan's hands. "Dylan, you're too old for imaginary friends," Richard said. "Forget about Jordan and Ashley. Okay? They don't exist. They're just in your mind. Imaginary friends are for babies!"

HOW I WON MY BAT

I guess you're admiring my swing, right? And you're admiring the baseball bat I'm holding.

Maybe you're wondering how I got this bat.

There's a story behind it. That's for sure.

I was the power hitter on my junior high's baseball team. Our team went to the state finals every year, and I was the star.

You could read about me in the local paper all the time: "Michael Burns: He's Got the Power." "Michael Burns Wins It for Lynnfield . . . Again!"

That's me, Michael Burns. But now I wish I'd never even touched a baseball bat. Things are diferent now. I'm different.

How much time has gone by since the afternoon that changed my life? I'm not sure. But I can remember everything that happened as if it were yesterday. . . .

Baseball practice. We had just finished doing our warm-up exercises on the field. Coach Manning called out, "Hey, Mike! You're up at bat."

At the games, I always batted cleanup. Fourth in the lineup. That made sense. I was the best.

But this was only practice. And the coach liked to shuffle us around, to keep us on our toes.

I felt all my muscles go tight as I stepped up to the plate. You see, I had a problem. A big problem. I was in a real batting slump.

The last game we played, I struck out four times!

And the past few batting practices? Jimmy, the pitcher, would lob me the ball and I'd choke — swinging with everything I had as if they were fastballs.

Some power hitter, huh? I couldn't even connect. And everyone knew it. I was afraid my new nickname was going to be "Swing-and-Miss Mike!"

"Come on, Mike," Coach Manning called as I took a few practice swings. "Concentrate now. You know tomorrow's game with Lakeland is for first place."

"Yeah, Mike, don't mess up," Jimmy muttered from the pitcher's mound.

I hunched over the plate. The bat just didn't feel right. It felt heavy. Too heavy. "Relax," I told myself. "Just relax, and everything will be fine."

The pitch came. High. I let it go. "Strike!" Ron called from behind me.

I turned to him. "Since when does the catcher make calls?"

"Since when does the power hitter strike out every time?" he shot back.

Well, that did it. No way could I relax after that crack.

I tried to get my old swing back. But the bat felt even heavier. And I could see my teammates shaking their heads.

After about ten minutes of batting practice — where the best I could do was a little dribble right to the pitcher — the coach called in somebody else.

"Listen, Mike," he said, putting his heavy arm around my shoulder. "Why don't you go home and get some rest for tomorrow's game."

I thought he was being nice. But then he added in a sharp voice, "You'd better shape up, kid. This game is for all the marbles."

I trudged off the field feeling lower than a grounder to third.

"Hey, Mike. Hold up a second." I recognized the guy jogging toward me. It was Tom Scott, a local TV reporter.

School sports are a big deal in Lynnfield. But a TV reporter covering a practice? Wow!

"You feeling okay, Mike?" he asked me. "Are you doing anything to shake this slump?"

"I'm trying," I mumbled, feeling my face turn

red. "Really." I hurried into the locker room, feeling really embarrassed.

I showered and dressed in a hurry. I wanted to get out of there before the team finished practice. I knew I couldn't stand all the teasing I'd get.

A few minutes later, I stepped back outside and started toward the bike rack. I had my eyes on the ground, and I was deep in my unhappy thoughts. "I'd give *anything* to get out of this slump," I muttered to myself.

I didn't even see the strange-looking little man until I nearly tripped over him. "Oops. Sorry," I muttered.

He smiled at me. "I heard what you said. You just need a lighter bat," he said.

"Huh?" I squinted at him, startled.

The man wore a heavy, black wool suit. He had a tiny, round head, completely bald. His skin was so pale, he looked like a lightbulb!

Had this guy ever been outdoors?

"What did you say?" I asked him.

"You need a lighter bat," he repeated. His eyes were silvery. They crinkled as his grin grew wider.

I saw for the first time that he held a baseball bat in one hand. He raised it so that I could see it better.

It was shiny black wood. It had tape wrapped around the end. It looked as if it had been used before.

"It's very light — and very powerful," the man said. He let out a strange cackle, as if he had just told a joke.

"Wh-who are you?" I stammered, staring at the bat.

"I'm a sports fan," he said. With his free hand, he reached into his suit jacket pocket. He pulled out a business card and handed it to me.

It read: MR. SMITH, DIRECTOR. LYNNFIELD SPORTS MUSEUM.

I handed the card back to him. I stared at the bat. "You want to sell me this bat?"

He let out another cackle. He shook his shiny bald head. "I'll give it to you, Mike." His strange, silver eyes glowed excitedly.

Had I told him my name?

"It's a very good bat. You'll like it," he said. "Very powerful."

The bat didn't look very special to me. "You want to *give* it to me?"

He nodded. "Take it. Now. You just have to make one promise."

I knew there had to be a catch! "What promise?" I asked. Clouds rolled over the sun. The air turned cold. I felt a chill at the back of my neck.

"You have to promise you will return the bat to the museum — right after the game. You will not change clothes. You will not go home first. You will return it to me at the museum. Understood?"

71

He pushed the bat into my hands.

He's crazy! I thought. Why am I taking this bat? Am I *that* desperate to get over my batting slump?

Yes!

My hands wrapped around the bat. It didn't feel any different from the bat I had used that afternoon.

Then a chill passed through my body. Mr. Smith's ice-cold hand gripped my shoulder. "Remember," he said, "return the bat right after the game."

I nodded and slung the bat over my shoulder. Then I made my way to my bike and pedaled away as quickly as I could.

The next day was sunny and cool. A perfect day for baseball.

The locker room was noisy before the game. All the guys were talking and laughing. But I was sitting quietly, trying to psych myself up.

"Hey, Mike," Jimmy called, tossing me a water bottle. "We're behind you all the way. We're counting on you, man."

"Yeah." Ron gave me the thumbs-up. "We know you won't let us down."

I felt so nervous, the water bottle nearly slipped out of my hand. I took a long swig of water. "I can't strike out," I told myself. "I won't strike out."

And then it was time. We were up at bat.

In the dugout, Coach Manning called everyone to gather around for the new batting order. "I've made some changes," he began, staring right at me.

I knew what the coach meant, and so did everyone else. He was moving me from the cleanup spot. "Ron will bat fourth," he said, "and Mike will bat second."

Second? I could deal with that. I'd be able to show everybody that much sooner that I was still a winner.

Rick, the first guy at bat, hit a single.

My turn at the plate.

"I can't watch this," I heard Jimmy groan to Ron.

I picked up my new bat. All of a sudden it felt really light, just as the strange little man had said.

I carried it to home plate and took my stance.

This is weird! I thought. The bat started to tingle. Suddenly, I felt tiny vibrations all the way to my toes.

The pitch came — low and outside. "Strike!" called the umpire.

I let the second pitch go, too. Strike again.

I had to swing at the next one, no matter what. The bat tingled and vibrated in my hands.

The pitch was a fastball. I sucked in my breath and swung, trying to stay in control.

Crack!

The ball sailed high into the air. I shaded my eyes as I ran to first. But the ball flew so high, I couldn't see it. Was it going over the fence for a home run?

It was!

"It worked!" I shouted gleefully. "The bat worked!"

I jogged to second, my arms held high above my head in a victory sign. The third-base coach was grinning, waving me along.

My teammates charged over as I rounded third, cheering and thumping me on the back. Then I came home.

Lynnfield: 2. Two runs batted in for me.

The next inning, I hit an even higher home run.

Two innings later, I came to bat twice — and hit *two more* home runs!

That's the way it went every time I went to bat. I pounded out homer after homer. By the time I hit my seventh, the crowd was going *ballistic!*

Seven home runs broke the school record. And when I hit my ninth? That broke the state record!

The final score: Lynnfield: 19, Lakeland: 3. Not shabby. Not shabby at all.

Afterward, a crowd of people swarmed around me. Jimmy and Ron hoisted me on their shoulders, and Tom Scott, the TV guy, asked me questions while camera crews and photographers took pictures.

"Hey, Mike!" Ron waved me over after everything settled down. "We're all going to Pat's Pizza Place. You know, to celebrate. So come on, man — you're the star!"

I hopped on my bike. "Lead the way!" I cried, so excited about the game, I thought I might burst.

We rode off, still in our uniforms. The whole team was chanting, "Mike! Mike! Mike!"

It was a great feeling. But, suddenly, my heart sank. The bat! I had promised to return it right after the game. I had promised to deliver it back to Mr. Smith at the sports museum.

I slowed down, letting the other guys pass me by. They were still chanting my name as they disappeared around the corner. "Catch up with you later!" I called. I don't know if they heard me or not.

But I knew one thing for sure. I couldn't return the bat.

No way.

I had to keep it.

It was the greatest bat in the world. The bat had hit nine home runs in one game. I couldn't part with it. Promise or no promise — I had to keep it.

Standing over my bike, I gripped the bat in my hands, trying to decide what to do. My first thought was to ride home and hide the bat in my room. Mr. Smith didn't know where I lived. Chances are, he would never find me.

No. I decided that wasn't right.

I decided to go to the museum. To tell Mr. Smith the truth. That I *had* to have that bat. I'll offer to pay him for it, I decided. Any amount he wants. It's worth it.

I remembered the address from the business card. It took a long time to ride my bike there. The museum was in a strange part of town. Nobody on the streets. No cars. Nothing.

The museum was a low, gray building. Not too inviting. I parked my bike beside the entrance. Carrying the bat, I stepped inside.

What a cool place! I couldn't believe I'd never been there before. The enormous, bright room was filled with life-size sports displays.

Two players elbowed each other fiercely in a hockey display. The figures were made of wax or something. I couldn't *believe* their scary expressions.

I walked past a tennis display. A young man in tennis whites had his racket up, about to serve to another player. They looked so real, I expected to see the ball fly over the net!

I passed two high school basketball players going up for a rebound. Their muscles were straining. I could actually see beads of sweat running down their faces.

Cool, I thought, leaning on the bat as I studied the display. So cool!

The baseball display was under construction. Part of a diamond had been built, but there were no wax figures playing ball.

As I stared at the real-looking scene, Mr. Smith appeared from behind it. "Hello, Mike," he said, smiling. His bald head shone under the bright display lights. "Thanks for returning the bat."

I hesitated. "I . . . uh . . . can't return it," I stammered.

His silver eyes narrowed in surprise. "What?"

"I have to keep it," I told him. "It's the greatest bat in the world. I'll do anything to keep it, Mr. Smith," I pleaded.

He rubbed his pale chin. "Well . . ."

"Really," I insisted. "I really need this bat. I want to keep it forever!"

"Okay," he agreed. "You can keep it forever."

My mouth fell open. I was stunned. "You mean it? I can keep it?"

He nodded, smiling. "If that's what you want," he murmured. "Let me see your swing, Mike. Take a good swing, okay?"

I was so happy and grateful. I lifted the bat, started to show off my swing — and froze in a blinding flash of silver light.

And I've been standing here ever since. Frozen in place. The bat gripped tightly in my hands. About to take my best swing.

A lot of time has passed. I don't really know how much. I stare out at the cardboard backdrop, and I prepare to take my swing.

People visit the sports museum. They come over to the baseball display. And they stare at me.

They talk about how real I look. And what a great swing I have.

It makes me happy that they like my swing.

And, I guess I have one other thing to be happy about.

I get to keep the bat. Forever.

MR. TEDDY

"Mom, can I *please* get this teddy bear! Please? I'll never ask for another thing."

Willa clasped her hands together and gazed longingly at the stuffed teddy bear staring at her from the department store shelf.

Willa was a collector. She collected stuffed animals, dolls, posters, porcelain eggs — you name it. Every inch of her room was crammed with her collections.

"Mom, look at him!" Willa gushed. "Have you ever seen such cute little brown paws? And look at his big, round eyes. They're practically glowing."

Leaning on the counter, Gina, Willa's eleven-year-old sister, started to whine. "Mom! No fair! Willa already has enough stuffed animals to fill this whole store."

"So?" Willa shot back. "I can't help it if *your* room is bare, Gina."

Gina made a face at her older sister. "That's

because every chance you get, you beg Mom to buy you something else. 'Mom, get me this. Mom, buy me that,' " Gina mimicked.

"Girls! That's enough!" Mrs. Stewart cut them off. Willa and Gina glared at each other. "Willa, you're twelve. Aren't you getting too old for teddy bears?" her mother asked.

"I can't help it, Mom," Willa replied. "I want him. He's . . . not like any other stuffed animal I've ever seen."

"His eyes are weird," Gina commented.

"They are not!" Willa protested. But she knew Gina was right. She could almost feel the bear studying her with those huge eyes of his.

"Willa," her mother said. "There isn't any space left in your room. Where will you put it?"

"I'll put Old Bear on the shelf and sleep with this one," Willa replied.

Gina folded her arms. "What's wrong with Old Bear?"

"Nothing," Willa told her. "I just love this one." She pressed him against her cheek. "See how cuddly he is? Please, Mom?"

Mrs. Stewart hesitated. "Well . . ."

"Mom, that's not fair!" Gina wailed. "Willa's always getting stuff. What about my CD player?"

"Gina, a CD player costs a lot more than a teddy bear," her mother answered sharply. "That's something you can ask for on your birthday."

"Mom, please?" Willa said, still clutching the bear.

"Oh, all right," her mother said, sighing. "But this is *it*, understand, Willa?"

Willa threw her arms around her mother. "Oh, thank you, thank you, thank you, Mom."

On the other side of the counter, Willa could see Gina scowling at her.

"Sometimes I really hate you, Willa," Gina muttered.

Willa waved the teddy in Gina's face. "His name is Mr. Teddy, Gina," she announced. "And you'd better be nice to him."

As soon as Willa got home, she took Mr. Teddy up to her room to show him around. "Here we are," she announced, opening the door. Her room was done all in peach, her favorite color.

To the right of the door stood her dresser. On top of the dresser was her porcelain egg collection. Willa gently picked up each egg and told Mr. Teddy where it had come from. Next, she showed him all the rock star posters that covered her walls. Then she went through the two long shelves above the dresser crammed with stuffed animals.

When she finished with the animals, Willa took Mr. Teddy over to the doll collection in the other corner. Willa had been collecting dolls the longest, and had the biggest collection of anyone she knew.

Still clutching Mr. Teddy, Willa crossed the room to her bed. "Hello, Old Bear," she said. She reached onto the pillow and picked up her ragged old teddy bear — the one she'd slept with since she was a baby — and kissed him on top of his head. "You're going to sleep over here now," she said, crossing back over to the shelves. She pushed aside a stuffed unicorn to make room for Old Bear. "Sleep tight," she told him.

Gina poked her head into the room. "Who's in here?" she asked.

"No one," Willa replied.

"Then who were you talking to?"

"Nobody."

Gina's eyes lit up. "You were talking to your stuffed animals again, weren't you?" She started laughing at Willa.

"Shut up, Gina!" Willa snapped. "You're mad because you didn't get a CD player."

"I am not," Gina answered. "I'm mad because you have Mom wrapped around your little finger. Every time you ask for something, she buys it." She stormed out, slamming the door behind her.

Willa glanced down at Mr. Teddy. "Don't worry about Gina," she whispered, carefully placing him on her pillow. "I bet she wishes she had a special bear, too. But she doesn't. You're all mine, Mr. Teddy. All mine."

*   *   *

That night, Willa slept with Mr. Teddy hooked in her arm. At first it felt funny to sleep with something so soft and fluffy. All the fur on Old Bear had worn off a long time ago.

But Mr. Teddy seemed to be staring at her. Every time she turned or moved, she felt his big eyes watching her.

Willa woke up early the next morning. The sun had barely begun to rise. Outside, she could hear birds chirping.

Something didn't feel right. She lifted her head and stared down at her bed.

Where was Mr. Teddy?

She groped around her covers, but couldn't feel him anywhere. Where was he?

Willa pulled herself up, squinting in the dim light. Had Mr. Teddy fallen out of bed?

She peered down at the floor. Not there.

She shook her covers again, then leaned over to check underneath the bed. "Are you there, Mr. Teddy?" she called softly.

A sock and some dust balls stared back at her. Where could Mr. Teddy be?

Willa's eyes moved up her dresser, then over to the windowsill above the doll corner.

She caught her breath. Mr. Teddy sat propped up on the windowsill, staring back at her. His eyes seemed to be shining.

"Huh?" Willa murmured. "How did you get over there?"

She climbed out of bed and lifted him off the windowsill. "Mr. Teddy," she scolded. "What are you doing? Did you get up and move during the night?"

The bear's dark eyes glowed back at her.

"Stop staring at me like that!" Willa laughed. "You're giving me the creeps." She kissed the top of his head, then popped him back on her pillow.

"Maybe I woke up and put him there myself and don't remember," Willa said to herself.

At breakfast, she caught Gina staring at her. "What are *you* looking at?" she asked sharply.

"Nothing," Gina smirked.

"Did you come into my room last night?" Willa demanded.

"No," Gina replied, still smiling. "Why would I?"

The next night, before she fell asleep, Willa made sure Mr. Teddy was hooked firmly in the crook of her arm. It took her a long time to fall into a restless sleep.

She kept waking up and checking on Mr. Teddy. But he was always right where she left him, in the bend of her arm, watching everything with those big, dark eyes of his. In a funny way, Willa felt as if he were guarding her.

She woke up the next morning with a start. Immediately, she felt around for Mr. Teddy.

Gone again!

Willa glanced suspiciously at the windowsill. Not there, either.

She sat up in bed and began to search the room. Her eyes swept over the doll corner, the floor, then moved up the dresser.

"Hey, you!" Willa cried out when she spotted Mr. Teddy on top of the dresser.

"What's going on, bear? What are you doing over there?" She jumped out of bed and hurried over.

She gasped when she saw the two porcelain eggs. They lay smashed under the big teddy bear.

Mr. Teddy's eyes had an evil glow.

"Who did this?" Willa demanded. "Who broke these eggs?"

Willa tried to think. It couldn't be Mr. Teddy. He didn't climb the dresser and plop down on the eggs. No way.

So who *could* it be? The one person who was jealous of all her stuff.

"Gina!" Willa shouted furiously. "How could you *do* this?"

Willa stormed into Gina's room. Empty. Where was she?

Willa stomped back into the hall and stood at

the top of the stairs. "Gina! I'm going to get you for this!"

Her mother appeared at the bottom of the stairs. "Why are you shouting, Willa?"

"Where's Gina?"

"She left early for school," her mother said. "Remember? She has chorus practice."

Willa clenched her fists. "Wait till she gets home tonight," she growled. "She'll be singing a sad song when I get through with her!"

That afternoon Willa paced the front hall, waiting for Gina to return home. She paced back and forth, back and forth, checking out the window every time she passed it.

Finally she saw Gina coming up the front walk. She angrily pulled open the front door to greet her.

"I know it was you who smashed my porcelain eggs last night!" Willa uttered in a shaky voice. She blocked Gina's path.

Gina pushed her aside. "What are you talking about, Willa? Are you totally losing it?"

"You know what I mean," Willa insisted. She followed her sister to the stairs. "You broke my best eggs for no reason. Then you moved Mr. Teddy onto the dresser to make it look like *he* did it. What a sick, stupid joke."

Gina stopped. "I really don't know what you're talking about."

"Do too," Willa snapped.

It *had* to be Gina. Who else could it be?

"You're just trying to get me in trouble with Mom," said Gina. "Leave me alone, Willa. I'm warning you."

Later, when Willa went to bed, she shoved Mr. Teddy all the way under the covers. "I want you to stay down there tonight, okay?" she told him. She curled her body around his, then pulled her covers up to her neck.

Nobody could get Mr. Teddy out now, Willa thought. At least not without waking her up.

But Willa was wrong.

The moment she woke up the next morning, Willa reached under the covers for Mr. Teddy.

Gone again.

"Huh?" Willa sat up, wide awake. "What's going on?"

She let out a shriek when she saw her dresser. The drawers had all been pulled out and turned upside down. Her clothing had all been strewn in clumps and piles over the floor.

Angrily hurling herself out of bed, Willa kicked aside a pile of T-shirts. "Gina!" she shrieked. "I'm going to *murder* you for this!"

Glancing up, she saw Mr. Teddy. He grinned at her from the dresser top.

Willa grabbed him. "Why is this happening to me?" she screamed. "Tell me this is a dream!"

Mr. Teddy's eyes glowed brighter. Willa heaved him onto the bed.

She flew down the stairs and burst into the kitchen. Gina was eating a bowl of cereal. "Why did you do it, Gina?" Willa demanded, clenching her hands into tight fists. "Why? Why? Why did you sneak into my room, and mess it all up, and — "

Gina gazed up from her breakfast. "I haven't been near your room. Honest." A grin broke out on her face.

Willa let out a furious cry. "See, Mom? See? She's smiling."

Mrs. Stewart narrowed her eyes at Gina. "Have you been playing mean jokes on your sister?" she demanded.

"No! No way!" Gina screamed. "Why are you blaming me for something I didn't do? I just smiled because it's funny. But I didn't do anything! Really!"

Willa stared hard at Gina. "I know you're lying," she said softly. "You're a liar, Gina. A total liar."

"I am not!" Gina shouted. She scraped her chair back from the table and jumped up. "You're the liar!" she told Willa. "You're just trying to get me in trouble for no reason!" She turned and stormed out of the kitchen.

"Stay out of my room, Gina!" Willa called after her. "You'll be sorry! I mean it! I really do!"

That night before climbing into bed, Willa shoved her dresser up against her door. "There," she said, pressing Mr. Teddy's soft body against her arm. "That should keep Gina out of here. What do you think, Mr. Teddy?"

Mr. Teddy's round, black eyes glowed back at her.

She slept restlessly again that night. Feeling hot, she kicked off her covers. She turned onto one side, then the other. She had strange nightmares.

When she woke up the next morning, before she opened her eyes, she reached out for Mr. Teddy.

Gone.

Willa's eyes shot open.

She screamed.

The dresser had been pushed to the middle of the room.

She sat up, her heart pounding. "My — my room!" she murmured.

Swallowing hard, she stood up. And gazed around her room.

Her posters — they had all been ripped from the walls and crumpled onto the floor.

Willa's eyes moved to the shelves. To her stuffed animals. A cold, sick feeling spread through her stomach.

Nearly all of the animals had been pulled apart.

Shredded. Bits of them lay strewn across the room. A tail here. A piece of stuffing there.

Their eyes had been torn out of their heads. Their arms and legs ripped from their bodies.

Willa staggered to her doll corner. Every doll had been broken and torn apart. They lay in a heap of arms, scraps of clothing, broken heads, patches of hair.

"Hey!" Willa raised her eyes to the top of the shelf. Mr. Teddy stood there triumphantly, his eyes glowing happily. In one raised paw, he held an arm from one of her dolls.

"No!" Willa murmured. "No. Please — no!"

Mr. Teddy suddenly toppled forward. His outstretched arms reached for Willa's throat.

Willa let out a shriek and dived out of his way.

The bear landed on the floor with a soft thud.

Willa spun around. Tripping over parts of dolls and stuffed animals, she plunged out of her room. Down the stairs. Into the kitchen.

"Willa! What is it? What's wrong?" demanded her mother.

"Mom! Come up to my room!" she sobbed. "Everything I own! All my dolls, my animals. Gina wrecked it all!" she cried furiously.

"Huh?" Mrs. Stewart's face twisted in surprise. "Gina?"

"Yes! Gina!" Willa declared. "She broke into my room last night, Mom. She wrecked everything! Everything!"

"But that's impossible!" Willa's mother cried. "Gina wasn't home last night, Willa. Don't you remember? She had a sleep-over at Maggie's house."

Willa pressed her hands against her face. The room began to spin wildly.

That's right, she remembered. Gina wasn't home last night.

"Nooooo!" She backed out of the kitchen, hands against her cheeks, shaking her head.

She didn't want to believe it. It couldn't be. But there was no other explanation.

She ran blindly up the stairs. She grabbed Mr. Teddy off the floor. His eyes glowed up at her as Willa frantically ripped him to pieces.

"It *was* you, after all, wasn't it?" she cried, tearing off his arms, pulling out his white stuffing, letting it fly over the room. "It was you! You! You!"

With a cry of fury, Willa tore off Mr. Teddy's head. "I hate you!" she shrieked. She tossed the head out the open window. "Evil thing! Now you're gone! You can do no more evil!"

Gasping for breath, her heart thudding, Willa stumbled across the room and pulled raggedy Old Bear off the shelf. She hugged him tightly. "You're all I've got left, Old Bear. Everything else was destroyed by that evil thing."

She clutched Old Bear gratefully. "From now on, it's just you and me."

Willa didn't see the pleased smile form on Old Bear's mouth. She didn't see his eyes begin to twinkle merrily.

Next time, Old Bear thought to himself, *maybe you won't be so quick to get rid of me, Willa. Maybe you've learned your lesson. You can't put me away on a shelf. Not me. I'm your bear. And I'm going to be with you for the rest of your life.*

CLICK

My name is Seth Gold, and I'm twelve. My hobby is channel-surfing on the TV. At least, that *used* to be my hobby.

Why did I sit for hours, clicking from channel to channel with the remote control? I guess I loved the feeling of power it gave me.

A boring show? *Click* — on to the next. A loud commercial about sinus headaches? *Click* — on to something better.

Sometimes I tried to imagine what life was like when people had to get up and walk over to the TV every time they wanted to change the channel. But it was just too *awful* to think about.

One day, my dad came home from work carrying a package about the size of a shoebox. He plunked it down on the kitchen table. "Wait till you see this!" he exclaimed, removing the wrapping.

My four-year-old sister, Megan, shoved past

me. "What is it? What is it? Let me see!" she begged.

I read the big black letters on the box:

UNIVERSAL REMOTE

"I got a great deal on this," Dad explained. "I was on my way home from work, and I passed a little store I'd never seen before. It was going out of business. This thing was only six dollars. Great, huh?"

"What does it do?" I asked, pulling it carefully out of the box.

"It's just like our regular remote control, except it works everything," Dad explained. "It will work the TV, the VCR, the CD player. If we had a laser disc player, it would work that, too."

"Wow!" I exclaimed, excited. "Can I try it?"

"Sure, Seth," Dad replied. "Just put some batteries in it."

I took some AA batteries out of the kitchen junk drawer and loaded them into the chamber. Then I examined the remote. It was slender and black. It fit nicely into my hand. And it had a million buttons on it. This was going to be *awesome*!

I ran up the stairs to the den.

"Don't watch TV for too long!" my mother shouted after me. "You have homework — remember?" But I was already gone.

For the next hour, I fooled around with the new remote. It was really excellent. I could go back and forth between a videotape and the TV. I could play a CD while watching the Weather Channel with the sound turned off. It looked as if the weatherman were singing!

Megan wandered in. "I want to watch a cartoon tape," she said.

"Not now," I told her. "I'm busy."

"But I *want* to!" she insisted.

"Not now, Megan! Beat it!"

"I'm telling!" she whined.

"You are not!" I cried, reaching to stop her.

To my surprise, she grabbed the remote control out of my hand. Then she pulled back her arm and flung the new remote across the room. It crashed into the radiator and fell to the floor.

"Now look what you did!" I shrieked angrily.

I picked up the remote from the floor and shook it. It rattled. It hadn't rattled before. I clicked it at the TV.

Nothing happened.

"You jerk!" I cried. "Now we can't watch anything!"

"Sorry," Megan replied softly. She stuck her thumb into her mouth and backed slowly out of the room.

I sat down on the sofa and went to work on the remote. Using a quarter, I pried off the back and studied the insides. Not much in there except for a few chips and wires. I wiggled things as much as I dared, and then closed it up.

Holding it up to my ear, I shook it.

No rattle.

I pointed it at the TV. *Click.* It worked again!

Ten minutes later, I was busily channel-surfing when my mother stormed into the room. "Seth — I am very disappointed in you! I *told* you not to watch for long, and there are chores to be done in this house, and your sister tells me you won't let her have a turn, and — "

On and on she yelled, shaking her head. I tried to tune her out. But she was yelling louder and louder.

So I pointed the remote at her and pushed MUTE. It was a joke. Just a dumb joke.

But the most amazing thing happened. Mom was still yelling — but no sound came out. *I had really muted her!*

I pushed the button again. " — And your room is a mess, and your homework isn't getting done, and — "

Click. I muted her again. She continued yelling silently.

Awesome! This was really awesome! I could mute my own mother with the new remote control!

" — So you'd better start shaping up, mister," she finished. She turned and stormed out of the room.

"Wow!" I cried out loud. Sitting on the edge of the sofa, I stared at the buttons on the remote.

A few seconds later, our beagle, Sparky,

walked into the room. "Here, boy," I said. Sparky trotted over and started scratching himself behind the ear with his back leg.

I stared down at the remote again. I had to try it once more.

I saw a button labeled SLOW MOTION. I pointed the remote at Sparky, pressed the button, and held it.

Sparky started scratching himself very, very slowly. I could see his lips flapping as his head twisted slowly back and forth. His ears floated around in the air.

"Unbelievable!" I whooped. I let go of the button, and Sparky started scratching himself at normal speed again.

I can control the *world* with this remote! I told myself. I was so excited, I nearly dropped it again!

"Dinner!" Mom called from downstairs.

"Be right down," I shouted. I tucked the remote in my jeans pocket. I wasn't going to let it out of my sight. Then I charged down the stairs.

I was too excited to focus on eating my tuna casserole. I picked at my dinner, thinking about the remote, feeling it in my pocket.

My mother frowned as she cleared the plates. "Well, Seth," she said, "maybe you'll be more interested in dessert."

I glanced at the bowl. Chocolate pudding. My favorite.

Mom spooned it into plates, and I gobbled down my portion.

Then I had a *brilliant* idea. I quietly pulled out the remote and studied the buttons under the table. Ah — there it was: REWIND. I pushed the button and held it.

In rapid motion, Mom, Dad, and Megan *un*-ate their pudding!

I kept rewinding until Mom appeared with the bowl of pudding. Then I let the button go. "Well, Seth," she said again, "maybe you'll be more interested in dessert."

Then we all had pudding again!

"You bet," I said, gobbling down my second portion.

Ha! This was excellent! When I was done, I pushed REWIND again, and then one more time — until I'd had four dishes of chocolate pudding. I was stuffed!

The next morning, I carried the remote to school with me. I knew I shouldn't be messing around with it. But I couldn't help myself. It was too much fun.

After the first bell rang, it was time for the flag salute. I decided I had heard it enough times. So I muted it.

Everyone sat down. "And, now," said Ms. Gifford, "you're going to have a pop quiz in geography, you lucky people." She started passing out papers.

Oh, no! A pop quiz! I had been so busy with the new remote, I hadn't done the homework! I didn't know *anything* about South America!

I swallowed several times, thinking hard. Then I remembered the remote, and I relaxed. I had a plan.

Ms. Gifford finished passing out the papers. "Okay, everyone," she said. "You'll have twenty minutes. Good luck."

I took a quick glance at my test paper. It was full of questions I knew nothing about. The capital of Brazil? Not a clue.

But I wasn't worried. I doodled on my notebook while everyone else got busy answering the questions.

Nearly all the time had passed. "Thirty seconds left," announced Ms. Gifford.

I waited another fifteen seconds. Then I took the remote out of my pocket. I hit FREEZE-FRAME.

Everybody froze. Ms. Gifford stopped in the middle of a yawn, glancing out the window. Mickey Delaney froze in the middle of scratching his nose. Annie Schwartz, the best student in the class, froze in the middle of putting her pencil neatly down on the desk.

I stood up and strolled over to Annie's desk. I took my test paper with me. I peered over Annie's shoulder at her answers.

"San Salvador . . . okay. Andes Mountains . . .

okay . . ." I wrote all of Annie's answers onto my test sheet. Then I strolled back to my desk, sat down, and hit the FREEZE-FRAME button again.

Everybody snapped back into motion. "Okay, everyone," said Ms. Gifford. "Pencils down."

I set my pencil down, making a great show of looking exhausted. Then I passed my paper up to the front. This was really cool!

After the test, I looked for more ways to have fun. I fast-forwarded the teacher and the entire class for a while. I slow-motioned the principal when she came to talk to the teacher. Then I froze the whole class again.

When the teacher squeaked her chalk on the blackboard, I turned the volume way up. Finally, the bell rang for lunch. I couldn't wait to go down to the lunchroom — a whole new place to have fun.

The lunchroom was the usual zoo — everyone yelling and laughing, straw wrappers and juice boxes flying everywhere, kids falling off their chairs, dropping their lunch trays.

Mr. Pinkus, the lunchroom monitor, ran around yelling at everyone to sit down. I pointed the remote at him and froze him in his tracks.

Then I stepped into the food line. I took a cheeseburger, a salad, and two desserts.

"You can't have two desserts," said the lunchroom lady. "You know that."

I didn't even think twice. I pointed the remote

at her and punched the MUTE button. She continued to lecture me silently.

Quite pleased with myself, I continued down the line and picked up a carton of milk. Before I went to sit down, I pointed the remote at the lunchroom lady again and pressed MUTE to turn her voice back on.

Nothing happened.

I pressed the button again. She was still talking without making a sound. I banged the remote against my tray and tried again. But she still didn't get her voice back.

Well, it really isn't a tragedy if that lunchroom lady is muted for a while, I thought to myself. I never liked her anyway.

I figured the remote must need a little jiggling. I'd get it to work. I reached over to take another dessert.

But as I set the plate of pie down on my tray, my blood turned to ice. The remote wasn't there!

Breathing hard, I tried to think. Where was it? I had set it on the tray, hadn't I? I swallowed hard, feeling my panic rise.

"Freeze, Seth!"

I glanced up to see Danny Wexler, a big, freckle-faced, redheaded eighth-grader, standing a few feet away, pointing the remote at me!

"Danny — don't touch that!" I pleaded. "Don't press any buttons!"

Danny grinned at me. "Why not? Hey, why do

you have a remote control in school, anyway?" He moved his finger over the buttons, deciding which one to push.

"Don't touch it!" I begged. I dove for him and snatched it out of his hand.

"Hand it back, Seth," Danny growled. His eyes narrowed. His expression turned mean. He moved toward me with his hand outstretched.

In a panic, I hit the FREEZE-FRAME button. And froze him.

I started to back away. But a girl's startled cry made me stop. "Hey, what's going on? Why is Danny frozen like that?"

Melissa Fink stood staring at us. I realized in horror that she could see Danny, could see what was going on. Other kids were starting to crowd around.

"What is that?" Melissa demanded. She tried to pull the remote out of my hand.

"Don't touch it!" I warned. "Please!"

"What is going on here?" A woman's voice burst in. I glanced up to see the principal. "What's all this commotion?"

She saw the remote in my hand. "Seth, let me see that."

In a total panic, I pushed FREEZE-FRAME and froze her.

The lunchroom filled with frightened shouts. "Seth froze the principal! Somebody — help! Seth froze the principal!"

A big crowd moved around me. I started to back away.

I pressed the FREEZE-FRAME button again to unfreeze the principal.

But it didn't work. She stayed still as a statue.

My brain was whirling. The whole room started to spin. The shouts and cries of the other kids made it hard to think straight.

What had I done?

What if I can't unfreeze her? I thought, my entire body trembling. What if I can't unfreeze Danny or Mr. Pinkus?

Would they stay like that forever?

I knew I was in trouble now. *Major* trouble.

"Get Seth!" someone shouted. "Get that thing away from him!"

I turned and ran for the lunchroom door. Kids came running after me. "Stop him! Stop him!" they shouted.

I turned back and pointed the remote at them. I started pushing buttons frantically.

I didn't know what I was doing. I was so frightened. So totally panicked.

My heart pounded. My stomach was doing wild flip-flops.

I pushed button after button.

None of them worked. None of them did anything.

"Stop Seth! Stop him!" The crowd continued to chase me.

I pushed another button. Another button.

Not working. Nothing worked. And then I pushed the button marked OFF.

"Hey — !" I cried out as the world went black.

I blinked several times. But the darkness didn't lift.

It was silent now. Silent and black.

I'm all alone, I realized.

No shouting kids. No kids at all. No school. No light.

No picture. No sound.

A faint glow in my hand made me raise the remote control. I brought it close to my face. A small red light blinked steadily.

Squinting into the blinking light, I read the words beneath it: BATTERY DEAD.

BROKEN DOLLS

"You broke my doll!" Tamara Baker screamed.

"I did not!" Neal, her seven-year-old brother, protested. "The arm fell off. It wasn't my fault!"

Tamara grabbed the doll from his hand. The slender pink arm fell to the floor. "That's the third doll you broke, Neal!" she cried. "Why can't you keep your paws off my doll collection?"

"Aw, you've got plenty more," her brother muttered, pointing to Tamara's shelves and shelves of dolls.

"You could at least say you're sorry," Tamara scolded.

"Sorry," Neal said softly. And then a grin spread across his face as he added, "NOT!" He turned and ran out of Tamara's room.

She angrily slammed her door. She replaced the broken doll on its shelf, shaking her head. Then she walked to the mirror to brush her hair.

Tamara studied her reflection. She was twelve, and her face was longer and thinner than ever before. That was fine with Tamara, who wanted to look older.

She had large brown eyes. They were her best feature. Her skin was tanned, her nose was small and straight and, best of all this year — no braces! Tamara smiled. She was satisfied, except for her hair!

Tamara's hair was a long, dark, wavy mass that had always refused to be put in any normal style. Tamara frowned and tugged at it. I have a bad-hair day *every* day! she thought glumly. She brushed it back and jammed a couple of barrettes in it.

"Tamara, are you coming?"

She heard her dad calling impatiently from downstairs. He hated waiting. He was taking the family to the crafts fair at the fairgrounds. And he insisted on getting there when the fairgrounds opened at ten A.M.

Tamara opened her door and stepped on something squishy. It made a squeaking sound, and Tamara jumped a mile. Then she spotted Neal peeking out his door, laughing his head off.

"I scared you! I scared you!" he crowed.

Tamara picked up the object. It was a bath toy inside a sock, placed just where Tamara would have to step. She aimed and threw it at Neal's laughing face. He bolted for the stairs, and she chased after him.

"Children! Children!" Mrs. Baker cried as the two circled around her. "Stop this right now!"

"She started it!" Neal claimed in his whiniest voice.

"Mom — he broke another one of my dolls!" Tamara said.

"Stop it! Just stop it!" their mother ordered. "Get in the car, both of you."

The car ride seemed to take forever. Tamara sat in the backseat with Neal. Neal had never been able to sit still for more than ten seconds. He squirmed and bounced and stretched his neck to see out all the windows at once. It drove Tamara crazy.

Once they were at the fairgrounds, Neal went wild. He wanted to see everything and be everywhere at once.

"Tamara," Mrs. Baker said, "your dad and I want to see the ceramics. But I don't want Neal around things that can break."

"Good thinking, Mom," Tamara replied, rolling her eyes.

"So why don't you take him for a half hour, and then meet your father and me at the information booth after that?" Mrs. Baker suggested.

"ME take Neal?" Tamara howled in horror. "What do I look like? A wild-animal trainer?"

"No," Neal giggled. "You look like the wild animal! Hahahaha!"

Tamara could see that she was trapped. "Okay, I'll do it," she grumbled. "Come on, you little monster."

Tamara held Neal's hand in a "grip of death" so he couldn't get away. She wished she had a pair of handcuffs. She strolled around looking at exhibits, ignoring Neal's nonstop chatter.

Tamara wasn't much of a crafts person. Her mom was the "craftsy" one. Mrs. Baker couldn't look at a simple T-shirt without wanting to put rhinestone studs on it.

Still, Tamara enjoyed walking through the booths. There were quilts, clay pots, lots of handmade jewelry, and carved wooden toys that got even Neal's attention.

"Wow! How does this wooden popgun work?" Neal asked.

Tamara wasn't too interested in popguns. She turned to the booth across the aisle.

And saw the dolls.

There were at least fifteen or twenty of them. And they were strikingly human looking.

The dolls all had different faces, different expressions. One looked sweet, another pouting. The next was crying. Another was asleep. On and on, like a quiet nursery.

Tamara stared from doll to doll. They were so real looking. She thought if she touched one, the doll would feel warm, not cold like a regular doll. She reached out . . .

"Do you like them?" a raspy voice called from right behind her.

Tamara jumped. She turned and faced the oldest woman that she had ever seen. Her withered face was lined with deep crags. Her white hair hung down stiff as straw. Her eyes were narrowed slits.

"Did you make these dolls?" Tamara asked.

"Every one, dearie."

"I've never seen dolls like these before. They're so *real*!"

"No two are the same," the old woman replied. "and they're perfect in every detail. Go ahead, take a closer look."

Neal padded over to Tamara. "I'm hungry," he whined.

"I'll get you something in a minute," Tamara snapped.

"Aren't you *precious*!" the old lady crooned at Neal. "Quite the little man. I think there may be a cookie around here for such a nice boy."

Neal perked up at the mention of a cookie. Tamara turned back to the doll she'd been studying. It was wearing a dark purple dress with white trim.

She picked it up. "Wow. It weighs as much as a real baby, too," she said. "That's incredible."

Tamara set the doll down and turned around. As she did, she thought she saw the old lady put

109

her hand on Neal's head. The gesture was odd and formal, almost like a blessing.

Strangest of all was the look on Neal's face. He stood still. And quiet.

Tamara grabbed Neal's hand, harder than she intended, and pulled him away from the doll booth. "Come on. We've got to go," she said. "Thank the lady for the cookie."

"Thank you," Neal mumbled through a mouth full of crumbs.

Tamara and Neal met their parents, and the four of them walked around the exhibits together. They didn't go past the doll booth again.

When Mr. Baker had had enough, and Mrs. Baker had bought enough goodies to keep the entire family in puff-paint heaven through Christmas, they all piled into the family car and headed home.

Neal didn't squirm the way he had on the way to the crafts fair. In fact, he didn't do much of anything. He sat back in his seat, staring straight ahead.

Mrs. Baker noticed Neal's unusual quiet behavior as soon as they got home. She felt his forehead. "Ted, he's running a fever," she told her husband.

"Probably all the excitement today," Mr. Baker replied. "I'll get the baby aspirin. Neal, get into bed."

"I don't want to go to bed. It's daytime," Neal protested. But he went upstairs anyway.

Mrs. Baker got Neal into his pajamas and brushed her hand over his head lovingly. Tamara went upstairs just as Mrs. Baker pulled her hand away, chuckling.

"What have you gotten into, young man?" she asked, wiping something off her hand. "You've got some kind of goop in your hair."

"Dolly jelly," Tamara heard Neal mumble, before he drifted into a feverish sleep.

Later in the afternoon, Neal was covered in a light rash. His face was pale, washed out.

"Looks like an allergy, Marge," Mr. Baker decided. "What did he eat today?"

"Oh, Ted," Mrs. Baker replied, sighing. "What *didn't* he eat!"

Tamara felt bad that her brother was sick. She went to his room to sit with him for a while.

He looked so pale. As if his face were fading away.

She placed her hand on his forehead. It felt really hot. Neal was mumbling something in his sleep. She listened.

"No dollies. Don't want to be a dolly. No dolly jelly. No."

Dollies?

Tamara remembered the doll lady. The cookie.

111

Maybe the cookie had something in it that had made Neal sick.

She remembered watching the old woman place her hand on Neal's head. Dolly jelly . . .

"Mom, I'm going out for a little while, okay?" Tamara said, pulling on her jacket.

"Where are you going?"

"Just for a bike ride." Tamara hurried out the back door.

She jumped on to her bicycle and began pedaling furiously. The fairgrounds were a couple of miles away. And she didn't know how late the crafts fair stayed open.

She arrived at the fairgrounds just as the gates closed. "Well, I'm here," she told herself "*Now* what do I do?"

People were packing up their crafts. Closing their booths.

Tamara saw the doll lady step out from one of the crafts areas. She was carrying a box. Tamara watched carefully as the old woman took the box to a trailer marked EXHIBITORS ONLY.

Staying in the shadows, Tamara crept toward the trailer. She watched. The doll maker stepped out of the trailer. She kept walking back and forth, carrying one box at a time into the trailer.

Tamara waited until the old woman was out of view. Then she took a deep breath, and sneaked into the trailer.

Her heart fluttering in her chest, Tamara

searched the trailer. She kept remembering Neal mumbling about the dollies, and "dolly jelly."

Glancing at the trailer door, she opened several boxes marked "dolls" and peered inside. To her surprise, these were not the dolls she'd seen on display.

The faces on these dolls were completely blank.

Tamara shivered. There was something creepy about a doll without any face at all. The smooth white heads stared up at her like ghosts.

With a shudder, Tamara opened another box. This doll had a pale face, so pale she could barely make out its features. She touched the doll's smooth head and her hand came away smeared with the same goop that was in Neal's hair.

Dolly jelly.

"Ohh!" Tamara cried out as the doll's features darkened. Came clearer. And she recognized Neal's eyes. Neal's pointy nose. Neal's mouth.

"Wh-what's happening?" Tamara stammered out loud. She gaped at the doll in horror.

The features darkened some more. Neal's face was growing clearer on the doll head.

Then she remembered how pale her brother had looked, lying in his bed asleep. How his face had appeared to be fading away.

"What is the old woman doing?" Tamara wondered aloud, frozen in sudden horror. "I've got to stop her!"

"Sssssstop her," a voice said.

113

Tamara gasped and spun around. Was it the old doll maker?

No. No one was at the trailer door. Where did the sound come from?

The closet.

"Sssstop her," a tiny voice repeated.

Swallowing hard, Tamara pulled open the closet door with a trembling hand.

Dolls. Crammed into the shelves.

The dolls from the crafts fair.

But they couldn't be dolls because they were moving! Reaching out their tiny, pink arms to Tamara!

"No!" Tamara shrieked. "You can't be alive. You *can't* be!"

She shrank back from their outstretched arms. "Don't touch me! Don't!" she pleaded.

Neal. She had to help Neal.

Tamara snapped back to her senses. She slammed the closet door shut. Then she grabbed the doll with Neal's features and darted out of the trailer.

"Going somewhere, dearie?" The old doll maker grinned at Tamara.

"Stay away from me!" Tamara cried breathlessly. "I've got the doll. My brother's doll! And I'm going to the police!"

The old woman's eyes sharpened. "Why don't you come inside, and we'll talk about it?" she said softly.

114

"No way!" Tamara exclaimed. "I saw your dolls. I know what you're doing!"

The old lady started toward Tamara, walking slowly but deliberately. Her face was hard and evil. "You don't know what I'm doing," she said through clenched teeth. "Your world has no idea of my ancient arts."

Tamara suddenly felt dizzy. What did she mean "your world"? Just how old *was* this woman?

The doll maker reached into her sweater and pulled out a container. Tamara recognized the goop that Neal had called "dolly jelly."

"I think it's time for you to go away, dearie," the old lady said quietly. "Young people disappear so often in this century. You'll just be one more. . . ."

The doll maker smeared a dab of the greasy goop on her fingers. Then she moved toward Tamara, mumbling some kind of chant.

Tamara struggled to move. But she couldn't.

She felt like a bird being hypnotized by a snake. The old woman looked like a cold, unblinking snake, slithering closer . . . closer . . .

"No!" Tamara shrieked — and dove forward. The sound of her own voice gave her strength.

She grabbed the jar of goop from the old woman's hand. Then she spun around and started to run.

"Give that back!" the doll maker called after her.

Tamara saw a small wading pool at the edge of the fairgrounds. She raised the jar of goop — and heaved it into the pool.

"You fool!" the old woman wailed. "You fool! What have you done?"

Tamara stared in disbelief as the pool water began to bubble and hiss. Choking clouds of black smoke rose up from the pool. The water turned green, then blue, then red. It swirled up in angry waves. Then splashed down hard under the billowing black smoke.

When Tamara turned back, the old woman had vanished.

She heard happy shrieks and cheers from the trailer. Were the dolls celebrating in there?

She didn't have time to find out. She ran to her bicycle and started to jam the Neal doll into her bike pack.

But to Tamara's surprise, the doll no longer looked like Neal. Its face was smooth and blank.

With a shiver that shook her whole body, Tamara tossed the doll as far as she could. Then she furiously pedaled home.

"Tamara, where on earth have you been?" Mrs. Baker scolded. "And just *look* at you! You're a mess!"

"Sorry, Mom," Tamara mumbled. "I'll clean up for supper."

Neal popped into the kitchen. He grinned at

116

Tamara. "You look like you've been playing in the mud!" he exclaimed. "Piggy! Piggy!"

"Neal! You're all right!" Tamara cried joyfully. She dropped to her knees and gave him an enthusiastic hug.

"Do you believe it?" Mrs. Baker said. "All of a sudden, his fever dropped, and he was his old self again."

"His old bratty self," Tamara laughed, ruffling Neal's hair. "Well, that's just fine with me!"

Everything was back to normal. Tamara decided to forget about the old doll maker. And the frightening, living dolls.

She forced the old woman out of her mind — until one night a few weeks later.

Her parents had gone out. Tamara was baby-sitting Neal.

Someone knocked on the front door.

"Who's there?" Tamara called out.

No reply.

"Who's there?" she repeated.

Still no reply.

Tamara peered out through the front window. A dark, moonless night. She didn't see anyone.

Curious, she pulled open the front door. And found a package on the front stoop. "Hey — !" She stared out at the dark street.

Who delivered this?

She carried the box inside and started to unwrap the brown paper.

117

"Is it for me?" Neal came hurrying into the living room. "Is it a present? For me?"

"I don't know," Tamara told him, struggling to tear off the wrapping.

A plain box was inside. She pulled open the lid.

And stared at a doll. An ugly doll. A doll with strawlike white hair. A craggy, wrinkled face. Narrow, squinting eyes.

"Ohh." Tamara recognized the doll instantly. It was the old woman. The doll maker.

She's followed me, Tamara realized.

She's found me.

She's here in my house with all of her evil.

Tamara felt cold all over. Her breath seemed to freeze as she stared in horror at the ugly, frightening doll.

She nearly dropped the box. What am I going to do? What can I do?

The idea popped into her mind.

She handed the doll to Neal. "Bet you can't break this one!" she told him.

"Huh?" He gaped at the doll, then back at Tamara.

"I dare you to break this one!" Tamara said.

"You dare me?"

Tamara nodded. "Bet you five dollars you can't."

"It's a bet!" Neal replied. He went to work on the doll.

A VAMPIRE IN
THE NEIGHBORHOOD

We knew there was something different about Helga the first time we saw her.

For one thing, she had that strange name. Helga. Such an old-fashioned name.

Helga looked old-fashioned, too. She wore the same black skirt to school every day. Old looking, and kind of worn, with no style at all.

My friend Carrie and I were sitting in the back of Miss Wheeling's sixth-grade class the first day Helga came to school. "Check her out, Maddy," Carrie whispered, motioning with her eyes.

I turned to the front of the room and stared at the timid-looking girl talking with Miss Wheeling. With her tight, black ringlets of hair and her pale gray blouse tucked into her black skirt, the girl looked as if she had stepped out of an old movie.

"This is Helga Nuegenstorm," Miss Wheeling announced. "She is new to our school, and I'm sure you will all make her feel at home."

Helga lowered her eyes to the floor. Her skin

was so pale, as if it had never seen the sunlight. And she was wearing lipstick. Black lipstick.

"She's weird," Carrie whispered.

"She's kind of pretty," I replied. "I've never seen anyone who looked like that."

Later, Carrie, Yvonne, Joey, and I took our usual table in the lunchroom. The four of us are really good friends. We have been friends for a long, long time. We sit together in the lunchroom every day.

"Did you see the new girl?" I asked. The four of us were tossing an apple back and forth across the table to each other.

"Isn't she weird?" Carrie asked.

Yvonne and Joey nodded. "She's so pale, but she wears that yucky black lipstick," Yvonne said.

"Maybe she isn't wearing lipstick," Joey joked. "Maybe those are her lips!"

"Do you know where she lives?" I asked, catching the apple and tossing it to Joey.

"She moved into the Dobson house," Yvonne replied. "I was walking by and saw her moving in."

Carrie, Joey, and I gasped in surprise. The apple fell out of Joey's hands and rolled away.

The Dobson house stood all by itself on the edge of Culver's Woods. The house had been empty forever.

"What a creepy old house," Carrie said. "Did you see Helga's parents?"

Yvonne shook her head. "No. It was kind of strange. I saw the moving men carrying in all this heavy, old furniture. And I saw Helga. But I didn't see any grownups."

"Weird," Carrie muttered again. Her favorite word.

I started to say something else. But I glanced up and saw Helga standing awkwardly in the lunchroom doorway. "I'm going to invite her to sit down with us," I announced, jumping up.

"Why, Maddy?" Joey asked.

"Maybe we can find out more about her," I replied. I hurried over to Helga. "I'm Maddy Simon," I told her. "I'm in your class. Want to sit with me and my friends?"

She stared back at me with her pale, gray eyes, the strangest eyes I've ever seen. *Ghost eyes,* I thought.

"No thank you," she replied. Her voice was soft and whispery. "I never eat lunch."

She's a vampire, we decided.

The four of us were always searching for vampires.

"Helga *has* to be a vampire," Carrie declared. "She never eats. She looks so old-fashioned. She keeps totally to herself. And she's as pale as death."

It was three nights later. We were crouched

across the road from the old Dobson house. Helga's house.

A long, low hedge stretched along the dark street. We hid behind the hedge, huddled together, whispering.

We couldn't help ourselves. We had to spy on her. We had to find out the truth.

The creepy old house rose up in front of us, pale in the light of the full moon. Behind the house, the trees of Culver's Woods shook and shivered in the wind.

"Where is Helga?" Yvonne whispered. "The house is totally dark."

"She's in there," I replied, my eyes on the black windows. "She's in there in the dark."

"Weird," Carrie whispered.

"I tried to talk to her in school today," Joey reported. "But she walked right past me. She wears those heavy, black shoes. But her footsteps didn't make a sound."

"Why would anyone move into this horrible old house?" Carrie asked. "It's so far from town. Nothing but woods all around."

"For privacy," I replied. "Vampires crave privacy."

The others giggled.

I thought I saw something move in the window. A gray shadow against the blackness. "Come on, guys," I whispered. "Let's take a closer look."

We crept across the road. The silence was eerie.

The only sound was the soft, steady whisper of the wind through the trees.

The old house seemed to grow darker as we approached it. We pushed through the tall weeds that blanketed the front lawn. Moving silently, we huddled beneath the big front window, pressing ourselves against the damp, moldy shingles.

"Give me a boost," I whispered to Joey. "So I can look in the window."

"Be careful, Maddy," Carrie warned. "Helga might see you."

I ignored her warning. I had to take a look. I was just so curious.

Joey and Yvonne helped lift me. I grabbed the stone windowsill with both hands and hoisted myself up just high enough to see in.

Then I stared in through the dust-smeared glass. Into a vast, dark living room. A pale square of moonlight poured into the room. I could make out a long couch, wooden and stiff looking. Two old-fashioned chairs.

I nearly toppled to the ground when I saw Helga.

"She's in there!" I whispered excitedly to my friends. "I can see her. Standing in the dark, in front of a tall mirror."

"Does she have a reflection?" Joey whispered. "Check it out, Maddy. Does she have a reflection?"

I narrowed my eyes, trying to focus on the darkness.

Vampires don't have reflections, I knew. Did

Helga have a reflection? "It's too dark to see," I told my friends.

Helga turned suddenly toward the window. She seemed to be staring right at me.

"Let me down! Quick!" I demanded. I slid to the ground.

"Did she see you?" Carrie asked, her dark eyes wide with excitement.

"I don't know," I told her. "I hope not."

"Why is she there in the dark?" Joey asked. "Did she have a reflection? Was she walking, or floating?"

Questions I couldn't answer.

"We'll come back tomorrow," I said.

The four of us met there every night. We hid behind the long hedge and spied on Helga's house. We peered into the windows. We crept around back and tried to see in through the kitchen.

Some nights we spotted a dim light in an upstairs window. Most nights, there were no lights on at all.

Some nights we saw Helga inside the house. Always alone. We never saw her parents. We never saw anyone else.

My friends and I became obsessed with Helga, with finding out the truth about her.

We tried to talk to her in school. But she stared back at us with those wintry, gray eyes and never even pretended to be friendly.

I invited her to come with us to the basketball game in the gym on Friday night. But she said she didn't like basketball.

We tried to get invited to her house. One day, Joey asked if he could come to her house and copy her history notes.

Helga said she wouldn't be home that night.

"Then how about tomorrow after school?" Joey insisted.

"It's not a good idea," Helga replied mysteriously.

She wore the same black skirt every day. She never changed her hairstyle. Her black ringlets hung down around that pale, pale face.

One day, on an impulse, I grabbed her hand. We were standing side by side in the hall at school, waiting to get into the auditorium.

I couldn't help myself. I reached out and squeezed her hand. I had to know what it felt like. I had to find out if it felt alive.

I jerked my hand back in shock when I felt how cold Helga's hand was. As cold as a winter day. As cold as . . . death.

She *is* a vampire! I decided.

She clasped her pale hands together and gazed at me with those frightening gray eyes. "It's so cold in here," she whispered. "Don't you think so, Maddy?"

It was the first time she had ever said my name, and it sent a shiver down my back.

*　　*　　*

That night, my friends and I met in front of Helga's house. Once again, pale moonlight washed over us. It was the only light except for a dim, orange glow in an upstairs window.

Crouching low behind the hedge, we stared up at the window. The shade was pulled. But we could see Helga's silhouette moving back and forth on the window shade.

"She's all alone in there," Carrie whispered. "No parents. No one."

"She's probably hundreds of years old," I whispered back.

"She doesn't look it!" Joey joked.

We giggled. But our laughter was cut short when the light in the window went off.

"She went to bed," Yvonne guessed. "Does she sleep in a coffin?"

"She must," I replied, gazing up at the dark window. Something fluttered low over the old house's sloping roof. A bat?

"All vampires sleep in coffins," Joey murmured. "Coffins filled with the ancient dirt from their graves."

"I want to see Helga's coffin," I whispered, standing up. I took a step toward the street, my eyes on the house.

"Maddy — come back," Carrie warned.

"I have to see Helga's coffin," I told her. "I have to know for sure."

We all wanted to know. That's why we spied on Helga every night.

I crept silently across the street and into Helga's front yard. Huddled closely together, the other three followed.

A twisted, gnarled old tree tilted up toward Helga's bedroom window. I grabbed a low branch and started to pull myself up.

The bark felt cold and rough against my hands. The slender branches shook as if trying to toss me off.

I clung tightly to the trunk and reached for a higher branch. Hoisting myself on to it, I peered through the leaves at the house.

Helga's bedroom window was still high above me. I glanced down and saw Carrie, Yvonne, and Joey. They had circled the tree and were peering up at me. Even in the darkness, I could see the tense expressions on their faces.

Up I climbed. Ignoring the scratch of the bark, the trembling of the branches.

Slowly, steadily, I pulled myself up. Until I was high enough to see into the bedroom window.

Holding tightly onto the trunk, I turned slowly. Lowered my head to see through a tangle of dark leaves. Gazed into the window —

— and saw Helga gazing back at me!

Her face gleamed, silvery in the wash of moonlight. Her gray eyes glowed evilly as she stared out at me, her ghostly face pressed against the windowpane.

Too startled to cry out, I started to slip. My hands slid off the trunk, and I lurched backwards.

"No!" I thrust out both hands. Grabbed the hard trunk — and held on.

"She saw me!" I called down to my friends. "Helga saw me!" I scrambled down, moving frantically, sliding and scraping down the rough trunk.

By the time I reached the ground, my three friends were already running around to the front of the house. "Wait up!" I called hoarsely.

Too late.

The front door swung open.

Helga moved quickly. Out the door. Down the front stoop. Across the weed-choked lawn to block our path.

"I know you've been spying on me!" she cried angrily. "You'd better quit it! I'm warning you!"

I stopped. Carrie, Yvonne, and Joey stopped, too. We moved together, watching Helga storm toward us.

She had her hands balled into tight fists. Her eerie eyes were narrowed at us, her face twisted in a frightening scowl.

My friends and I huddled there in the middle of the dark yard. The trees whispered and shook. The tall weeds swayed all around us.

And then the words just burst from my mouth. "Helga — are you a vampire?" I just blurted out the question, without even thinking. "Are you a vampire?"

She moved closer, her gray eyes glowing. "Yes," she whispered.

"Show us your fangs," I demanded.

A strange smile spread slowly over Helga's face. "No," she replied. "You show me *your* fangs."

I hesitated for a second. Then I lowered my fangs.

Then Carrie, Yvonne, and Joey lowered their fangs, too. Our fangs slid easily out over our lips, down to our chins.

We grinned expectantly at Helga. "Your turn," I said.

But to my surprise, Helga stumbled back and let out a frightened squeal. "I was just *joking!*" she cried. "I — I thought you were joking, too!"

"No way," I told her.

We weren't joking. We're vampires. Me, Carrie, Yvonne, and Joey — all four of us are vampires.

We were so disappointed about Helga. We had such high hopes.

But we knew what we had to do.

We formed a tight circle around her. Then we moved in.

The mystery about Helga had been solved. In a few minutes, she would be a vampire, too.

More TALES TO GIVE YOU Goosebumps ®

THE WEREWOLF'S
FIRST NIGHT

"What's the problem, Brian?" my dad asked, peering at me in the rearview mirror. "We've been on the road for four hours, and you haven't said two words. Aren't you excited?"

"Sure, Dad." I scrunched down in the seat of the car. That way, he couldn't see my face. He couldn't see that I was lying.

We were driving to Thunder Lake. We go to Thunder Lake every summer. It's a vacation resort, with cabins, a golf course, a big lake, and some other stuff.

Lots of families go there because they have a camp for the kids. The grown-ups dump their kids in the camp. Then they play golf or hang out in the clubhouse.

"Are you sure you're okay, Brian?" Dad asked.

"Leave him alone, honey," my mom said. "Brian's probably a tiny bit nervous about being in the teen camp this summer."

133

Nervous wasn't the right word. *Terrified* was more like it.

Dad cleared his throat. He always clears his throat before he gives me a pep talk. "Look at it this way, Brian. The teen camp will help you get over your shyness. You'll feel more grown-up being with older kids. Anyway, you belong there. You're twelve years old now. . . ."

That's right, I thought. I'm twelve years old. And I'd like to live to see *thirteen*!

"You're going to have a great time," Dad insisted.

"I know you're scared now," Mom told me. "But the time is coming when you won't be afraid of anything. Just wait and see."

Mom and Dad had it all wrong. Sure, the teen camp made me a little nervous.

But what made me afraid were the stories about Thunder Lake. Stories about creatures in the night. About howls and shrieks, and enormous footprints.

About werewolves living by the lake.

I've been hearing those stories since we started spending our vacations at Thunder Lake six years ago. I've been really scared ever since. And that really annoys my parents.

My parents think I'm a wimp.

So I keep my mouth shut about the stories.

But I'm still scared.

"There's the ten-mile sign!" Dad called out.

I sat up straight and stared out the window. Sure enough, the sign said THUNDER LAKE: TEN MILES.

Next came the five-mile sign.

Time was running out.

Finally I spotted the sign I'd been dreading: WELCOME TO THUNDER LAKE! A FAMILY RESORT. SWIMMING. HIKING. BOATING. GOLF. TENNIS.

And werewolves.

The teen camp had ten kids in it. A guy named Kevin was the only other twelve-year-old. He and I were the youngest.

Kevin had red hair and the whitest skin I've ever seen. The older guys made fun of him because his mother forced him to smear on lots of lotion to keep from getting sunburned.

I have brown hair and eyes, and my skin doesn't burn. So they don't joke about the way I look. But I'm short and sort of klutzy. And that's what they make fun of.

The three oldest guys were the toughest. Jake, Phil, and Don. They were all fifteen.

Jake had dark curly hair and a gold earring in one ear. Phil had beady blue eyes and always wore a red Bulls T-shirt. Don was short, wide, and mean.

"If I had the guts, I'd call him Fatso," Kevin whispered to me one day during a baseball game.

"Yeah," I whispered back. "But he'd sit on you and squash you to death."

When it was my turn to bat, I trotted to the plate. Don was the catcher. When he saw me he called, "Easy out!"

Then he grinned.

And I froze.

I'd never seen Don smile before. So I'd never seen his teeth.

But I could see them now.

They were the longest front teeth I'd ever seen in my life. And they were sharp.

Like fangs.

Like a wolf's fangs.

Then Don did something strange. He shut his mouth real quick and turned his head away.

Like he forgot he wasn't supposed to smile.

I swallowed and licked my lips. Every second I stood at the plate, I expected to feel his fangs stick into my leg.

When I struck out, Don grinned again. I couldn't believe it! His teeth looked normal. His fangs were gone!

But I knew I hadn't imagined them.

Then I remembered the stories about werewolves. They started out as humans. They didn't change into wolves all at once. But on the night of the full moon — total werewolf!

Could Don be a werewolf?

After the game, I told Kevin about Don's teeth. Then I waited for him to laugh. But he didn't.

"Man!" he said. "I heard all the stuff about this lake and families changing into werewolves. But I didn't really believe it. Are you sure it wasn't a trick?"

"I guess it could have been," I admitted. "But if he wanted to scare me, why did he try to hide the fangs?"

"Yeah," Kevin agreed. "We'd better be careful when the full moon comes."

Later, I looked up the dates of the moon on Mom's little pocket calendar.

Only four nights until the next full moon!

I wanted to tell Mom and Dad how afraid I was. Afraid Don would come after me. But I didn't want them to get on my case about being such a wimp.

So I didn't say anything. Not even when they went to play cards at the clubhouse and left me alone in the cabin.

I kept telling myself that there were no such things as werewolves. That Don was just a kid.

Everything was quiet for a while. Then I heard rustling outside the cabin.

My heart started pounding. But I told myself it was a squirrel.

The rustling grew louder.

My knees began to shake. I told myself it was a raccoon.

I heard a low growl right outside the door. Then scratching sounds, and another growl.

I told myself it was Don.

I shut off the lights and peered out the front window. The moon lit up the darkness. In the distance, I saw something red moving through the trees toward the lake.

A red Bulls T-shirt.

Phil! Running through the woods like a wild animal!

As soon as Mom and Dad came back, I told them. I didn't care how wimpy I sounded.

"Oh, Brian, don't you get it?" Dad asked. "The guys are just playing a trick on you. They know you're scared, and they're taking advantage of it!"

"I know it's hard not to be scared, dear," Mom said. "But it will all change soon. Trust me."

"Your mother's right," Dad agreed. "I'm surprised you fell for that trick, Brian. Don't you realize how easy it is for someone to sneak up to a cabin and make a few scary sounds?"

Okay, so it's easy to make scary sounds and growls.

But how easy is it to make wolf tracks?

Because that's what I found the next morning.

Not regular wolf tracks.

These paw prints were at least ten inches long!

I found them in the dirt around the cabin and followed them until they disappeared into the woods — at the exact spot where I'd seen Phil the night before.

Phil was a werewolf, too. No doubt about it.

A couple of nights later, the teen camp had a cookout by the lake. I didn't want to go. But since the moon wasn't full yet, I figured I'd be okay.

After we ate hamburgers and toasted marshmallows, we all sat around the campfire. Jake told a spooky story about some guy with a hook for a hand.

I didn't pay much attention. A guy with a hook for a hand didn't scare me. Werewolves did.

I kept my eyes on Don and Phil. The firelight threw weird shadows on their faces. It turned their eyes blood-red. I expected them to start growing fangs and claws any minute.

But nothing happened.

When the cookout was over, we started along the path toward the cabins. Suddenly, I realized I'd forgotten my new jacket. Mom would kill me if I left it out in the sand all night. So I ran back to get it.

The moon lit up the dark beach. I saw a figure kneeling in the sand. When he lifted his head to the sky, something glinted in the moonlight.

Jake's gold earring.

As I watched, Jake held his arms up toward the moon, opened his mouth, and howled.

139

The bloodcurdling howl of a wolf.

I knew no human could howl like that! I turned and ran up the path as fast as I could.

I caught up to Kevin. "Kevin, did you hear that howl?" I gasped. "It was Jake!"

As I raced up to him, Kevin quickly stuffed something into his mouth.

But he wasn't quick enough, because I caught a glimpse of it — a piece of hamburger meat. *Raw* hamburger meat.

The blood from the meat oozed down his chin.

Kevin was one of *them.*

One more night until the full moon. I was terrified. But I figured if I stayed in the cabin, I'd be safe.

Then I learned about the overnight trip. We'd hike to a campground, pitch our tents, and sleep under the sky.

On the night of the full moon!

No way, I thought. I had to get out of it! But how?

On the day before the overnight, I told Mom I had a sore throat. "I think it's my tonsils," I croaked.

"Brian," Mom said with a sigh. "You had your tonsils out two years ago."

How could I have been so dumb? Now, even if I really got sick, she'd never believe me.

Next I tried making myself sick by swallowing

140

too much water during swimming. All I did was choke a lot.

Then I tried rubbing what looked like poison ivy leaves on my face and arms. Nothing happened.

Finally, I decided to tell the truth. Well, not the whole truth. I knew my parents would never believe that. So I just told part of it.

"The guys are mean," I said. "I know they're going to do something awful to me. Please don't make me go on the overnight. Please?"

Dad crossed his arms. Then he cleared his throat. "Brian," he said, "if I let you stay in the cabin, it would be the worst thing for you. Maybe these guys have been a little rough on you. But if you let them know you're scared, they'll get even rougher."

"Your father's right," Mom told me. "You just have to be patient. Everything will be okay."

"But Mom!"

"That's enough, Brian," Dad said sharply. "I don't want to hear another word. You're going on the overnight — and that's that!"

So there I was stuck in the woods with at least four werewolves.

When it started to get dark and the stars came out, I ducked into my tent.

"Hey, Brian, what are you doing?" Kevin yelled. "Don't you want to eat?"

141

Yeah, right. What was on the menu — raw squirrel?

While the others ate, I stayed in my tent. Pretty soon, the campfire died down. The woods around the lake grew quiet.

Then I spotted a light through my tent. The bright orange light of the rising moon.

The full moon.

I scrunched down in my sleeping bag.

I crossed my fingers and hoped I'd been wrong all along. Maybe nothing would happen.

That's when I heard the first howl.

The hairs on the back of my neck stood up straight. My heart banged away like a hammer. I'd heard that savage howl before.

I had to get out of there! I had to make a run for it.

I wiggled out of my sleeping bag. Then I crawled across the tent and pulled the flap back a little. Peeking out, I saw Phil standing in front of his tent in his red T-shirt.

Except he wasn't Phil anymore.

Thick dark hair covered his face and arms. White fangs poked out of his mouth, gleaming like daggers. He raised his head to the moon and howled again.

Phil had become a werewolf.

As his howl died down, I lifted the flap a little more. Shadowy figures began to emerge from the other tents. Growling, snarling figures, with thick fur and sharp fangs.

My heart beat double time. I recognized them all. Don, Jake, Kevin, and the five other kids in the teen camp. Werewolves! Every one of them!

They huddled around Phil. Formed a pack.

Together they raised their furry heads and howled at the moon.

The sound turned my blood to ice water.

Before I could move, the werewolves turned their wild eyes on me! Their fangs glowed as they began moving toward my tent.

I squeezed my eyes shut. My whole body shook.

Raw squirrel wasn't on the menu. *I* was!

The growls grew louder. My eyes popped open. The werewolves were closing in!

I opened my mouth to scream in terror. But I couldn't make a sound.

I tried to stand, but my legs had turned to jelly. My heartbeat thundered in my ears.

The pack crept closer.

Closer.

Then, Phil's eyes met mine. He put his furry hands under his chin.

And he pulled off his mask.

My mouth fell open in surprise. Phil laughed and laughed. Then Jake, Kevin, Don, and the others took their masks off and began laughing, too.

"Welcome to teen camp, Brian!" Phil shouted

through bursts of laughter. "We pull this trick on a new kid every summer. But you were the best!"

"Yeah, you really fell for it hard!" Jake hooted. He pulled a little tape recorder out of his pocket and turned it on. First I heard a single howl. After a pause, the horrifying howling I'd heard just minutes before.

"A whole pack of wolves," Jake explained. "It's on a sound effects tape!"

Phil held up the old shoes he'd carved up to make wolf tracks. Don showed me the fake fangs he'd worn during the baseball game.

Kevin held out a plastic bag. "Ketchup and chopped-up spaghetti!" he said. "Looks like raw hamburger, doesn't it?"

Dad had been right. It was all a trick.

I sighed with relief and crawled out of the tent.

The guys all laughed and slapped me on the back. "No hard feelings. Right, Brian?" Kevin asked.

I opened my mouth to say no. But all that came out was a low rumbling sound, from deep in my throat.

"Hey, Brian, the joke's over," Phil said.

Another deep rumble escaped my throat.

I felt strange. Prickly. Itchy all over.

I glanced down and saw the shaggy fur growing on the backs of my hands.

My fingernails grew, stretching into pointed claws.

I rubbed the thick, bristly fur that covered my cheeks and chin.

Snapping my jaws, I let out a sharp growl. Then I raised my face to the full moon — and howled.

Still holding their masks, the other guys stared at me in horror.

I didn't blame them. I used to be scared of werewolves, too!

I let out another long howl. So this is what Mom meant when she said everything would change soon!

My stomach rumbled. I realized I was really hungry!

I snapped my jaws. My terrified friends all started to run.

But I knew they wouldn't get far. Four legs are faster than two!

I guess Thunder Lake is going to be fun after all! I told myself.

Then I started to run.

P.S. DON'T WRITE BACK

Camp Timber Lake Hills. My new sleepaway camp. My new, really cool, sleepaway camp.

I've been here for eight days now. In Bunk 14. And I'm having a totally awesome time.

The guys in my bunk like to horse around and play tricks on each other. They're the best.

But Sam is crabby. He's the camp director. Sam is huge. Over six feet tall with a stomach that explodes over his belt. His gray, bushy mustache is the only hair that grows on his head. He's totally bald. And he never smiles. Never.

There's lots to do here. But softball is my favorite. The guys in my bunk are the best softball players in the whole camp.

Not to brag or anything, but I happen to be the bunk's star hitter. And I'm only twelve — a year younger than everyone else in the bunk.

Home Run Dave. That's what they call me.

As I said, camp is pretty excellent.

There is one problem, though.

146

I've been here for over a week, and I haven't received a single letter from home.

That might not sound so strange. But last summer Mom and Dad sent four letters and a carton of pretzels. And that was on the second day.

This year, so far, nothing. Not even a crummy postcard.

So when Sam grumbled, "Mail Call!" this afternoon, I raced out of the bunk. I knew he'd have a letter for me today.

Or a package.

Something.

Sam dug through his mail pouch and pulled out a bunch of letters. "Don Benson! Mark Silver! Patrick Brown!"

The guys jumped up to claim their mail.

By the time Sam finished, Don held up six letters. "Hey, guys. How many did you get?"

Jeremy waved three letters in the air.

Patrick paraded around with the new *Mutant Rat-Man* comic his dad had sent.

I had nothing.

"I can't believe this," I muttered. "Mom promised she would write!"

I know it's no big deal. Really. I mean, there must be lots of kids at camp who don't get mail.

But my parents had *promised*.

Three days later and still no mail.

I asked Sam to check with the post office. He

147

said he would. The post office is run by Miss Mildred. She's been in charge of the town mail forever. And in fifty years, she's never lost a letter. At least that's what she says.

I started imagining all these crazy things. Maybe Mom and Dad sent my letters to the camp I went to last summer. Or maybe there had been an earthquake, and they couldn't leave the house.

Dumb things like that.

Anyway, I finally decided to call home and find out what was going on.

"Sam," I said after mail call that day, "I need to phone home."

Sam shook his head no. "No calls home unless it's an emergency," he barked.

"But it *is* an emergency!" I insisted.

"No calls home."

The next day, after swimming, we all raced back to the bunk to change for our big softball game against Bunk 13.

"Mail Call!" Sam yelled as I tied my sneakers. I ran out to the porch in time to see Sam yank out the first letter from his pouch.

"David Stevenson! Today's your lucky day. Miss Mildred found this letter in the bottom of a drawer," Sam said, waving a crumpled envelope in the air. "She can't imagine how it got there. She mumbled something about elves. Anyway, she says she'll keep looking for more."

I practically ripped the letter from his hand. I checked the name on the front just to make sure it was really mine. Then I tore it open.

> *Dear David,*
> *We're not coming up for Visiting*
> *Day. Your sister misses you. See you*
> *in August.*
> > *Mom and Dad*
> > *P.S. Don't write back.*

Huh? That's it? I turned the paper over, then back again. I gazed around suspiciously. This had to be a joke from one of the guys. But they all had their heads buried in their letters. No one even glanced in my direction.

I sat down and read my letter again.

> *We're not coming up for Visiting Day.*

How could that be? They promised. They *always* came up for Visiting Day. Always.

> *Your sister misses you.*

No way. My older sister Carly danced around the house like a lunatic the day I left for camp. She said it was the happiest day of her life.

And *P.S. Don't write back.* That was the weirdest part of all. Why would Mom write something like that? She said she loved getting letters from me.

A huge lump stuck in my throat. I wanted to cry. But I didn't. Not until the next day.

The next afternoon, another letter came for me. Excellent! This will explain everything. I started to read.

> *Dear David,*
>   *We're sending you to live with your Great-uncle John. He's coming to pick you up on the 27th. We think it's for the best.*
>   *Mom and Dad*
>   *P.S. Don't write back.*

"What?" I choked.

The letter shook in my trembling hands. How can they send me to live with Great-uncle John? I mean, he's eighty-seven years old and lives in an old-age home!

I glanced up and stared into the trees across from my bunk. They started to spin around me. My hands grew numb. Then they turned to ice. My eyes filled with tears.

I leaped up and ran. All the way to the camp office. Up the steps. To the front door. It was locked.

I peered through the window screen. No one inside. But there — hanging on the wall. The phone! I had to get to that phone.

I twisted around to my left. Then to my right. No one in sight. Good. I gently raised the screen and crept over the windowsill into the office. Then I darted for the phone and dialed.

By the third ring, my palms dripped with sweat. Beads of perspiration clung to my forehead.

"C'mon! Pick up!" I shifted my weight from one foot to the other. "Come on already!"

Then, finally! On the fourth ring my mother answered!

"Mom!" I cried. "What's going on?"

" — not home right now. Please leave a message. And have a nice — "

Oh, no! I heard voices. Outside. Coming toward the office. No time to leave a message.

Think, Dave! Think! Get out of here quick!

Then I spied it. A window at the back of the office. I threw open the screen and dived out.

I charged back to the bunk. Panting wildly. I leaped up the porch steps. The door flew open.

And there stood Sam. A stone statue. Glaring at me.

"Stevenson! You're in big trouble."

"But, Sam — " I started to explain.

"No, Stevenson. You're late for the scavenger hunt. In the woods. Remember? Now you'll have to catch up with the other guys." He shuffled down the stairs and headed for the trees.

The scavenger hunt. Right. A hike through the woods. Then a campfire supper. Then the hunt. I had forgotten.

I tossed everything out of my drawers, searching for stuff for the scavenger hunt. My sweatshirt. Backpack. Flashlight.

How could my parents do this to me? I kept repeating over and over to myself as I searched the bunk frantically for my flashlight.

And then I saw it. Under my bed, *next* to the flashlight. The envelope. From the letter this afternoon.

I read the address again. David Stevenson, Camp Timber Lane Hills.

That's it! Why hadn't I noticed it before? My camp is Camp Timber *Lake* Hills!

Now it made sense. Camp Timber *Lane* Hills stood on the other side of the lake.

A mix-up. Simple as that. I breathed a small sigh of relief. Those letters weren't for me. They were for some other David Stevenson. At some other camp. And he probably had *my* letters!

I grabbed my flashlight and stuffed it into my backpack.

I knew what I had to do. While everyone searched for clues on the scavenger hunt, I would escape across the lake and find Camp Timber Lane — and the other David Stevenson.

As soon as the scavenger hunt began, I slipped away in the dark and headed for the dock.

The camp rowboats bobbed gently up and down on the moonlit water. I steadied one and climbed inside.

I leaned over and tugged on the rope that held the anchor. Heavy. Very heavy. I clutched the rope with two hands and heaved.

Uh-oh. Not as heavy as I thought.

The anchor flew out of the water — and crashed on to the boat floor.

The boat pitched from side to side. I crouched down and grasped the oarlocks tightly. And waited. Waited to be caught.

Silence.

I breathed a low, steadying sigh. Then I locked the oars in place and began to row.

As I cut through the water, the twinkling lights from camp grew smaller and smaller. I turned to glance at the opposite shore. Thick woods. Total blackness. Maybe this wasn't such a good idea.

But I had to get to the other camp. I wanted my mail.

I rowed faster. My arms ached. Tiny splashes around the oars thundered in my ears. My head throbbed.

Then, finally. A dock!

I dropped the anchor and stepped up. The

dock's rotted wood splintered and cracked under my sneakers.

Where is the path? I wondered, sweeping my flashlight over thick weeds.

I stumbled through the dark. Through the tall, scratchy grass that scraped against my legs.

Suddenly, the beam from my flashlight fell upon a big wooden sign. I stood directly in front of it to read the worn letters. CAMP TIMBER LANE HILLS.

I found it!

I gazed beyond the sign. I squinted in the darkness. Yes! Bunks.

But where were all the kids? And why didn't they have any lights in this camp?

Weird. Very weird.

I trampled through the grass to the first bunk. A skinny boy, about my age, hunched over the porch railing. He raised his head slowly. His hollowed eyes met mine.

"Uh, excuse me," I stammered. "Is there a David Stevenson in this camp?"

He lifted a bony arm and pointed to the blackened doorway behind him.

"Uh, thanks," I said. But I didn't budge. I wanted to go back. Back to my cheery, normal camp.

Just go in, I told myself. Just get your letters.

I inched past the boy and pushed open the

creaky door. My hand trembled as I searched the dark room with my flashlight. No one here.

I'm leaving, I decided. This place is too creepy. Way too creepy. But as I turned, I caught sight of something. No. Someone. Someone moving in the shadows.

"Who . . . who's there?" I choked out.

"What do you want?" a harsh voice replied.

"I'm, uh, looking for David Stevenson."

"Well, you found him," the voice snapped back.

I shone my light to the very back of the bunk. And there he stood. A scrawny kid with long brown hair and torn, dirty clothes.

"What do you want?" this David Stevenson demanded with an icy stare.

I couldn't answer. My heart thumped wildly.

"I said, what do you want?" he repeated.

I gulped loudly and began. "I have your mail."

His eyes narrowed angrily. "My what?"

I pulled the letters from my pocket and held them out. "Your mail. Letters from home," I explained. "And I'd like mine. If you have them."

"Who are you?" he demanded. He stepped closer to me.

"I'm David Stevenson, too," I replied. "You see, I go to Camp — "

"Leave!" he screamed, shaking his fists violently. "You can't let them see you here!"

Oh, wow! This kid is crazy!

"Listen," I pleaded. "Just give me my letters and I'll go."

"Go! Go! Go!" he shrieked.

I flew out the door and down the steps. The skinny kid had disappeared.

I staggered through the thick grass, darting around tree stumps and boulders.

Then I noticed a familiar smell. The smell of a campfire. I listened. Crackling. Loud snapping.

I crouched down behind a large rock. I spied the flickering light of the campfire. And kids, hundreds of kids, circling it. Arms wrapped around each other. Swaying back and forth. Moaning. Moaning.

What kind of camp is this? I wondered.

I swallowed hard. Something is really wrong here!

I jumped up, ready to bolt. But a long, skinny arm swooped down and grabbed my hand.

The kid from the porch! His eyes glowed an evil red as he tugged me toward the fire.

I struggled to break free. But I couldn't escape from the skinny kid's grip.

The swaying campers turned to face us. Moaning.

Their sunken eyes stared blankly into mine. Were they in some kind of weird trance?

They dropped their arms. And parted for us.

My face flushed in the heat of the leaping flames.

And then I knew what would come next. They were going to push me. Into the fire.

"Nooo!" I screamed.

With a hard tug, I broke free. And ran. Faster than I'd ever run before.

I leaped into the boat. I rowed swiftly across the lake. Then I charged up to my bunk.

Sam paced on the porch, back and forth. Back and forth.

"Sam! Sam!" I cried breathlessly.

"Stevenson! Where have you been? The whole camp is out searching for you! And your mother called. She said they had to go away — "

"Sam! Listen!" In one long breath, I told Sam about everything. The camp. The other David Stevenson. The sad, moaning campers. The skinny kid who tried to drag me into the fire.

Sam stared hard at me. "David, what are you talking about? We're the only camp on this lake."

"No! You're wrong, Sam. I saw it. The sign said Camp Timber Lane Hills!"

Sam rubbed his chin thoughtfully. "Well, there once was a camp across the lake," he said. "But it burned to the ground one summer thirty years ago."

"No!" I shrieked. "It's there. I'll show you!"

Sam ushered me up the bunk steps. "We're not going anywhere tonight. We'll straighten all this out in the morning."

157

"But — "

"In the morning!" Sam repeated sternly. "Now get inside and go to sleep!"

I staggered to my bed in a daze.

"I know what I saw," I mumbled as I climbed into bed.

I grabbed my flashlight and pulled the covers up over my head. I flicked on the light and flashed it on one of the envelopes that I had just received.

"See. I'm not crazy. It says right here. David Stevenson. Camp Timber Lane Hills."

Then I pointed the light along the top right corner of the envelope. And gasped.

The postmark.

It was dated July 10.

1964.

SOMETHING FISHY

"You mean I have to sit in this horrible, hot apartment ALL SUMMER! But, Mom — it's so boring here!"

We always go to the lake. Every single summer. And now she was telling me that we couldn't go.

"It's the money, Eric," Mom said. "It costs a lot to rent a house on the lake, and we don't have it this year."

This had been a terrible year for money. The year of the divorce. The year that everything had gone wrong.

Mom stood in the corner of my bedroom and stared at me. I guess she thought I was going to cry or something. But I didn't cry. I smiled and told her it was okay — even though it wasn't.

After she left, I sprawled on my bed. I closed my eyes and tried to picture the lake. The water was probably bluish-gray today. And clear.

I scrunched my eyes tightly and tried to imagine how it felt. Cold. Nice. I could almost feel the

159

sandy bottom of the lake squish between my toes.

"Eric?" It was my sister, Sarah. Her voice brought me back to my own room.

"Can't you ever knock!" I shouted.

Sarah never knocks. She's nine. Three years younger than me. But she should still knock.

Sarah and I are different in lots of ways. I have brown hair and brown eyes. She has red hair and green eyes. I'm nice, and she isn't. I knock, and she doesn't.

"Well?" I sighed as I rolled off the bed and stomped across the room to my fish tank.

"We're not going to the lake," Sarah announced.

"I know that, Sarah," I groaned.

"But it's boiling here in the city. And we don't have air-conditioning, or anything."

"Don't remind me," I said. "Leave me alone. It's too hot to talk."

She shuffled her feet for a while, but then she left my room. Of course she forgot to close the door behind her.

I gazed into my fish tank and thought about the sweltering city heat. My T-shirt was already sticking to my back. And it was only June. What would it be like by August?

I sprinkled some food into the water and sat down. The fish raced toward it. First the big fish. Then the medium-sized fish.

The little fish almost killed each other fighting over the leftovers.

Well, at least the fish will be able to go swimming this summer, I thought. Lucky fish.

I woke up early the next day. It was brutally hot. It must have been 100 degrees in my room.

I glanced at the clock and groaned. Eight in the morning, and the heat was unbearable. I didn't even bother getting dressed. I just put on my shorts and shuffled out to the kitchen.

Mom was frying bacon and wiping her forehead on her sleeve. "I'll buy some fans today," she promised. She slid a plate of pancakes and bacon under my nose.

I took a few bites. I wasn't very hungry. It was too hot to eat.

I walked back into my room and gazed into the fish tank. The fish seemed fresh and happy. They were flicking through the water like silver and gold flashes of cool lightning.

I wondered what it would be like to be a fish. It must feel fantastic, swimming around like that in the cool water.

I followed the fish for a long time. Back and forth. Back and forth. Until my mother came in.

"Allowance day, Eric," she announced. "Maybe you can buy something cold this afternoon. Like an ice cream. Or buy another fish. One of those exotic fish that you love so much."

I didn't want to buy a fish. I wanted to BE a fish. In the lake.

161

I called my friend Benny, but there was no answer. And then I remembered. Benny went to Colorado with his parents. My friend Leo was on his way to camp. And Dweezle the Weazel was at his grandmother's for the summer.

Wow. What a boring summer.

I spent my allowance at the pet store. I bought a castle for my fish tank. It was pink, with all kinds of doors and windows.

The fish seemed to like it. They swam in and out of it as if it were their new home.

They liked it so much that the next week I bought them a tiny purple rowboat. And the week after that, I bought them a new friend — a plastic diving figure with a long, sharp spear in his hand. They seemed to like that, too.

I gazed at my fish whenever I wasn't at the playground behind school or watching TV or at my computer. I couldn't stop staring at them.

And then, late one night, something seriously strange happened.

My room felt like a furnace. I lay on my bed without moving. My shorts were sticking to the backs of my legs. My socks were clammy and gross.

I turned and glanced at the tank. I stood up. The glow from the fish tank drew me across my shadowy room.

I pulled my desk chair over to the fish tank and gazed at the fish. My gourami streaked through

162

the castle and circled the boat. Again and again.

One of my platys disappeared under the boat. The bubbles from the filter kept swirling round and round and round. The bubbles faded in and out of focus. Gurgling, gurgling, gurgling.

I raised my left index finger and touched the cool water. I dipped my finger deeper into the tank and twirled it.

My finger seemed to have a mind of its own. It moved in a circle, then drew a perfect figure eight. It formed another, and then another. Five times clockwise. Two counterclockwise. Three to the side. Again, and again, and again.

In the hall, I heard the clock strike ten times. I drew one more figure eight through the water with my index finger.

And then, as I sat there with my eyes half closed, the weirdest thing happened.

As the clock struck ten, I suddenly felt wet. And cold.

I blinked several times, trying to understand. I spun around and kicked my feet.

And faced a fish. Eye to beady eye. It was right there, goggling me.

"Whoa!" I cried. "Did I fall in the fish tank?"

I plunged through the water and looked above me. The fish were staring down at me. And they were HUGE! Like whales. Even the smallest goldfish were gigantic.

"How did I get down here?" I gurgled. "What's

happened to me? I'm smaller than a goldfish! And I can breathe under water!"

I should have been scared. But this was too exciting!

I couldn't believe it! I dived to the bottom of the tank and did a somersault. Awesome!

I swam around for a long time. I did a dozen surface dives. I plunged down and touched the bottom. I stood on my head. Then I zoomed back up to the top and flicked some water at one of my goldfish.

The goldfish didn't seem happy. His jellylike eyes gazed at me menacingly. And then he began to move. Slowly. Straight toward me.

I raced to the purple rowboat and threw myself into it. The boat lurched and water poured in. But it didn't sink.

The goldfish took his time. Slowly, it began to circle the boat. Around, and around, and around, watching me menacingly.

Did it plan to attack?

I huddled in the bottom of the little boat all night. I wished the goldfish would stop circling me.

I lost all track of time. After a while, sunlight washed over the fish tank. Morning!

I heard a familiar voice from far away. "Eric? Eric?"

My sister! I was never so glad to hear her voice.

"Sarah!" I called. "I'm over here! I'm in the fish tank!"

Peering over the side of the boat, I could see her moving around my room. "Sarah! Over here!" I shouted, cupping my hands around my mouth. "Look in the fish tank! Over here!"

She didn't turn around. She couldn't hear me. I was about the size of an ant. How could I expect her to hear an ant's tiny cry?

Gazing through the glass side of the tank, I saw my sister step closer. "Yes!" I cried aloud. "Yes! She's coming over here!"

She bent down and stared at the fish.

"Here! Over here!" I cried. I jumped up and started waving both arms. I nearly tipped over the boat. "Sarah! Sarah!"

A big gourami floated in front of me, blocking me from view.

When the fish swam away, Sarah was gone.

Now what? I asked myself. I've had my swim. I've had my excitement for one summer. It's time to get out. It's time to get big again.

The enormous goldfish came rolling toward me again. "Look out!" I cried.

Too late. The big fish bumped up hard against the side of the boat. "Hey —!" I cried out as I felt the boat tip. I toppled into the water with a splash.

The fish slid past me. I could feel his scaly skin brush my side. Yuck!

I heard a disgusting sucking sound. I turned and saw the gaping round mouth pulling at the water. Pulling me toward the hungry fish.

I'm going to be fish food! I realized.

I tried to swim faster. But my side started to ache. The sucking sounds grew louder. The fish was pulling me into its mouth.

A desperate idea flashed into my mind. The deep-sea diver! I kicked my feet hard and dived down to the plastic figure.

I grabbed the spear away from the diver — and spun around to face my enemy.

The other fish all scattered to the sides of the tank.

The goldfish attacked, shooting through the water.

I dodged away. Kicked hard. Dived to the bottom of the tank.

I waited, watching it circle. I raised the spear.

I took aim — and sent the spear sailing toward it.

Missed.

That fish was too fast.

I saw its eyes flare with anger. It dived toward me. I pressed my back against the side of the tank. It whipped around and smacked me with its tail.

Stunned, my knees buckled, and I started to drop to the tank floor.

The spear floated down to the bottom. I grabbed it just as the fish attacked again.

The huge yellow body soared toward me. I drew back my arm — and drove the spear into the fish's underbelly.

What am I doing? I asked myself, watching it float onto its side. *I just killed one of my pets!*

But I couldn't worry about it. I mean, it had just tried to *eat* me!

The dead goldfish floated to the top. But I didn't have time to relax. The other fish were eyeing me now.

I grabbed the spear and held it ready. Was I going to have to fight them all, one by one?

Two neons darted close. They were my smallest fish. But now they were bigger than me! If they decided to attack together, I was doomed!

Then, from far away, I heard voices. The words were muffled by the water. But through the glass, I saw Mom and Sarah.

They were walking about my room. I guessed they wondered where I was.

I knew I couldn't call to them. Especially from the bottom of the tank! But how could I signal them? How could I get their attention?

My heart started to pound when I saw Sarah walk over to the fish tank. She stared down into the water. Then she poked a finger in and flicked the dead fish.

"Mom — there's a dead fish in here!" I heard her call.

I saw Mom step up beside Sarah and stare down

at the dead goldfish. Then I saw Mom pick up the white net I keep at the side of the tank.

The net! She's going to use it to lift out the dead fish, I realized.

I took a deep breath and leaped off the tank floor. I started swimming to the top as hard as I could.

I kicked and thrashed through the water. I had to get into that net. It was my only chance to escape.

Up, up, I swam. I reached the surface, gasping, every muscle aching. I grabbed the rim of the net with both hands — and pulled myself up and in.

Yes!

I tried to stand. Tried to wave to my mom. But the net wiggled in the water. It dipped low. I struggled to stay inside.

"Owww!" I cried out as something heavy landed on top of me.

Something heavy. And very smelly.

The dead goldfish.

I tried to shove it off me, but I wasn't strong enough. I couldn't breathe. It was *crushing* me!

And then I felt the water fall away. The net was lifted from the tank. The heavy fish bounced on top of me.

Mom was carrying the net out of the room. I tried to call out. But the dead fish smothered my face.

Where was she taking me?

Oh, no! I knew where! She was taking me to the burial place of all pet goldfish.

The bathroom!

"Please, Mom!" I cried, shoving the dead fish off me. "Please don't flush me! Please don't flush your only son, Mom!"

I climbed on top of the dead fish. But she still couldn't hear me.

"Please don't flush me! I'm in here, too, Mom! It's me! Please don't flush me!"

She tilted the net. I tried to grab the side. Missed.

And went sailing down.

Down, down.

I shut my eyes as I fell. I felt the air whip around me, drying my tiny body.

I waited for the splash.

But my feet hit the floor instead.

Startled, I opened my eyes. I stood face to face with Mom.

She was so stunned, she dropped the net. "Eric! Where did you come from?" she shrieked.

"Oh. Uh . . . I was in my room," I said, trying to sound casual.

But I didn't feel casual. I felt like leaping up and down and screaming, "I'm me again! I'm me!"

How did I get back to my old size? I thought about it a lot that day. I decided that getting dry was the answer. As soon as the air dried me off, I zoomed up to my old size.

169

And I'm going to stay this size, I promised myself.

I kept the promise for two days. Then the temperature outside soared to 102. I could barely breathe. I needed a swim — desperately.

I stared into the fish tank, remembering how cold and refreshing the water felt. Yes, I knew it was dangerous. I knew what a close call I'd had. I knew that going back in the tank was a crazy idea.

But it was also really exciting. *And* I was sweltering.

This time, I'll be more careful, I told myself. First I got a bag of little stones. I built a wall down the center of the tank. The fish could swim on one side of the wall. I'd swim on the other.

My own little swimming pool.

When I'm tired of swimming, I'll stand up on the rocks and let the air dry me. And I'll instantly return to my big size.

What could go wrong?

I slid my finger into the fish tank and traced a clockwise figure eight. I did it five times. Then I changed directions and traced five more figure eights.

The filter bubbles gurgled . . . gurgled . . . gurgled. . . .

And once again I was tiny, plunging into the water for a refreshing swim.

I had swum for only a minute or two when I heard voices at the top of the tank. Floating slowly, I glanced up. I was surprised to see Mom and Sarah.

"Where's Eric?" I heard Mom ask, her voice muffled by the water. "Where is he? I brought him such a nice surprise."

"Who knows?" I heard Sarah reply. "He keeps disappearing."

Mom leaned closer to the tank. She had a plastic bag in her hand. The bag held two fish. I stared up from the bottom of my private pool.

"Look, Sarah," I heard Mom exclaim. "Eric built a perfect little swimming pool for my present. He piled up rocks and moved the fish to one side. I'll bet he guessed what I was going to buy for him."

"What is it?" I heard Sarah ask. "What did you get him?"

Mom held the bag over the top of the tank. Then she dumped the two new fish into my private swimming pool.

"They are Siamese fighting fish," Mom told Sarah. "The meanest fish on earth! Look at them snap their teeth. Won't Eric be surprised?"

171

YOU GOTTA
BELIEVE ME!

I know you won't believe me. Nobody else does. I told my parents. I told my teachers. I told the police. I told the newspapers. I've even written to the President of the United States. Hah. I might as well have told my pet turtle, Mable. (Which I did.)

I just saved the world from weird aliens from outer space.

Uh-oh. I can almost hear you thinking, "Weird aliens from outer space? This kid must be nuts!"

But I'm not. Really.

The whole thing started because of the flying saucers. And the flying saucers started because of the no-TV rule. I must be the only kid in the entire *world* whose parents won't have a TV in the house.

"TV rots your brain," my dad says.

"There're plenty of things to do. You don't have to sit in front of a box that tells you how to think," my mom insists.

172

My parents are old hippies from the sixties. They believe that stuff. So the only TV I get to watch is at Robbie's house, and at Melanie's house. They're my best friends. I try to catch the most popular shows so I don't sound like too much of a geek when everyone talks about them. But I don't watch much.

To make up for no TV, my parents bought me a telescope a few years ago. It was nice of them, I guess. They knew I liked reading science fiction about outer space and stuff.

When you don't have a TV, there's not much to do after homework. So I started watching the sky every night.

And I started seeing flying saucers.

Some were round, with red and green lights. Some were shaped like paper-towel rolls. Some were big. Some were small. It was truly amazing how crowded it was up there.

Most of them turned out to be weather satellites and stuff from Earth. But others were real. I swear they were. Sure, nobody else saw the flying saucers. But nobody else watched for them.

My mom and dad just laughed. "It must be an airplane, Stanley," Dad would tell me. "Or a bird, dear," Mom would add.

"He just wants attention," my older sister, Laura, said. *She* was the one sneaking out early to put on makeup. To get the attention of Herbie, the high school heartthrob.

"Stanley is a geek," offered my little brother, Dan. *He* was the one who made giant balls out of aluminum foil. And *I* was a geek? Hah!

All my teachers thought I was telling stories. And when I called the police, they treated me like a nut.

Then there were my so-called best friends.

"Stan," said Robbie, best friend number one, "you are a total weirdo."

Now, I can tell you that I'm not a weirdo. I'm a perfectly normal twelve-year-old guy. I'm in seventh grade at Piscopo Junior High. I'm five feet four inches tall. I have brown hair and blue eyes, and I wear wire-rimmed glasses. I'm good at math and science. And I play a mean game of hoops.

"He just has a good imagination," said Melanie, best friend number two.

Well, that's probably true. But I don't make things up. Not things that count.

"Look," I told Robbie and Melanie, "I can understand if my family doesn't believe me. I can understand if my teachers don't believe me. I can understand if the cops don't believe me. But you are different. We've been best friends since we were wearing diapers."

Melanie sighed. "Stanley. We *are* your best friends. And we've been your best friends for a long time. That's why we think you should give this outer space thing a rest. There isn't enough room up there for all the flying saucers you've seen!"

And that was that . . . until two days later. Wednesday, July 12. The night that would change my life forever.

It was eleven o'clock, and I couldn't sleep. I felt crummy. It was really hot in my bedroom. Sweat dripped down my neck.

I stared at the green digital numbers on the clock next to my bed. 11:01. 11:02. 11:03.

I couldn't sleep. I got up and trotted downstairs. I poured myself a glass of carrot juice (my parents' favorite drink). Then I stood at the back door. I stared out through the window. It was hazy and dark.

A crack of lightning flashed across the sky. Then came the thunder. *Ka-boom!* It made me jump. Then it started to pour.

At first, I thought I saw another lightning bolt. I squinted and stared hard. Something flashed — but it wasn't lightning.

I ran upstairs to my bedroom. My telescope sat in the window. I pointed it at the flashing light to take a better look. And what I saw made me sweat harder than ever.

A flying saucer!

Round, big, and bright. With lots of white lights around it. The lights kept flashing, which is why it looked a little like lightning. It floated above the ground over one of Mr. Tribble's cornfields.

I rubbed my eyes. Was I dreaming? I didn't think so.

I pinched myself on the arm just to be sure. It hurt.

The saucer suddenly lifted off and shot away.

Mr. Tribble had a bad reputation. He used to chase kids off his land with a pitchfork. He acted mean and strange, and his wife seemed just as weird. Nobody showed up anywhere near his farm if they could help it.

But I couldn't help it. I had to go over there. I had to see what had happened in that field.

I pulled on my jeans and a T-shirt. I picked up my sneakers.

Carefully, I tiptoed downstairs. I didn't want to wake anybody. I wanted to see what was going on for myself. I opened the front door and sneaked out.

It was still raining, but I hardly noticed. I ran all the way. Finally I reached Mr. Tribble's big red barn. I tiptoed over to the end. Then I peered around the corner.

The cornfield was empty. But when I glanced down, I noticed something weird. It looked as if someone had burned a circle in the ground.

I walked slowly over to the burned part. I reached down to touch it. Something had been here.

When I turned around, Mr. Tribble stood behind me.

His eyes were glittery and angry. And he carried a pitchfork.

"What are you doing in my cornfield?!" Mr. Tribble demanded.

"Mr. Tribble!" I gasped. "Am I glad to see you! A flying saucer landed in your cornfield. Look at those marks — "

"There wasn't anything here," Mr. Tribble said sharply.

"But you *had* to see it!" I cried. "It was here a minute ago. Then it flew away. . . ."

"No. Nothing here!" Mr. Tribble repeated.

He started walking toward me. His eyes glittered. He bared his teeth. The pitchfork glimmered in the dark.

I ran.

The next morning at breakfast, I told everyone my big news.

"And I think Mr. Tribble knows something," I finished. "What do you guys think we should do?"

"Pass the whole-grain toast," Laura said.

"Mrph," Dan said with his mouth full.

"Dan, don't talk with your mouth full," my mom warned.

"Look at this. The factory is closing," my dad groaned. "Another defeat for the workers. It says right here. . . ."

And that was that.

My friends were no better.

177

"Look, Stan," Robbie said. "This has happened before. It's just your imagination."

"Imagination my foot!" I yelled. "Come on over to the field and see for yourself!"

"There is no way I'm going over to Tribble's farm," Melanie shivered. "He is totally creepy."

"All right," I said angrily. "Suit yourself! I'll figure out what to do alone."

And I did. I came up with a brilliant plan. I decided to get my dad's camera and take pictures of the burned circle. Then they'd have to believe me.

Wouldn't they?

The next night, I wore my clothes to bed. I pulled the covers up to my chin so my parents couldn't tell.

I had Dad's camera under my pillow. I was ready. I just had to wait until everyone fell asleep.

I stared at the clock. 11:46. 11:47. I planned to leave at midnight.

I looked out the window. And then I looked again.

The spaceship slid down into Mr. Tribble's cornfield.

I grabbed the camera and quietly ran out of the house.

I crept past Mr. Tribble's house. I could see the light from his TV through the window. I breathed a sigh of relief. If he kept watching TV, maybe he wouldn't come looking for me.

When I reached the barn, my heart practically stopped beating.

The flying saucer stood there.

It was much bigger than I thought. It was about as big as half a football field!

It was bright and shiny. There were stairs going up into the center of it. And walking up and down the stairs were THEM.

The aliens! The things from outer space!

They were big, too — the size of Mr. Tribble's cows. But they didn't look anything like cows.

They didn't look like anything else I'd ever seen, except in nightmares. Their skin was a mucus-green color.

They had giant, mushed-in heads with big, glittery eyes. They had tentacles all over their heads where their hair should be. They walked on six legs. Two arms grew out of their backs. And instead of hands, they had giant claws.

A slimy green goo dripped from their bodies.

My mouth dropped open, and I started to shake. I wanted to get out of there . . . fast.

But I couldn't leave. I had to see what they were doing there.

A few aliens held strange-looking silver instruments. Every few minutes, they pointed them at the sky.

And then two aliens slithered right toward me. Had they seen me?

No.

The aliens started to talk. Their voices sounded gloppy, as if they had bad colds. And to my surprise, they were definitely speaking English!

"We are almost at stage three," slobbered Alien Number One. "This signal will be the final one."

"It is the Earthlings' own fault," slobbered Alien Number Two. "Sending television waves out into space gave us the idea."

"Once we learned their language," Alien Number One said, "and we understood the importance of television to them, it was just a matter of time."

"It has been ten long years. The invisible messages we have been broadcasting through their TV programs have made them weak and stupid. Earthlings do not believe in flying saucers. They think we are science *fiction*." Alien Number Two snuffled. Maybe it was laughing.

"This last message will finish them," Alien Number One continued. "They will not be able to resist. They will be helpless before us. They will simply give up."

"When do we broadcast?" Alien Number Two asked.

"In exactly twenty Earth hours," Alien Number One answered. "We start at eight o'clock tomorrow. What the Earthlings call 'prime time.'"

I couldn't believe my ears.

All these years, TV really *had* been weakening the human race! Just as my parents said!

Maybe the no-TV rule had been a good idea after all.

The two aliens slithered away. Then I saw a big door open in the top of the spaceship.

All the aliens stopped what they were doing and turned around to watch. I heard a whirring sound. A big silver dish rose out of the ship.

It looked a lot like a TV satellite dish.

That's when I remembered the camera. I had to take some pictures. With my luck, they probably wouldn't come out. But I had to try.

My hands were shaking so hard, I almost couldn't work the buttons.

When I had taken about five pictures, it happened.

I felt a tickle in my nose. It grew and grew. I didn't want to make any noise. But I couldn't help myself.

I sneezed.

Five aliens turned around and stared at the spot where I hid. Before I could move, they darted toward me.

My heart pounded in my chest. I tried to yell. But all that came out was a croak.

I couldn't breathe. I tried to run. But my feet felt as if they were stuck to the ground.

One of the aliens carried a silver bag. The creature took out a kind of tube.

181

Another alien grabbed me. The first one jammed the tube into my side.

"Ow!" I cried. Then everything went black.

When I woke up, it was dark. I tried to get up, but I couldn't. Someone . . . some*thing* . . . had strapped me to a table.

I was on the spaceship.

I picked my head up and gazed around. The only light in the room came from a giant TV. It hung in the air about six feet in front of me.

"Just watch the television," a gloppy alien voice said in the darkness.

A rerun of *Space Trekkers* was on. I had heard of the show, but never seen it.

I closed my eyes. I didn't want to watch. But the alien voice said, "Open your eyes, human." Something in its tone told me I'd better listen. So I did.

And I watched.

For three hours.

I expected to feel strange. I expected to get hypnotized or something.

But nothing happened.

I guess you had to watch a lot of alien TV for their waves to work.

Suddenly, the TV went blank.

"How do you feel?" asked the alien voice.

"Fine," I replied in a flat voice. I tried to sound hypnotized.

"Good," said the voice. "Now, go home. You have not been here. When we come, you will be ready."

"I will be ready," I said again in my hypnotized voice.

The next thing I knew, I found myself outside the spaceship. I wanted to run, but I thought it wouldn't be a good idea. I had to pretend to be under the aliens' spell. So I just strolled away, slowly.

Inside the house, I raced upstairs to my parents' bedroom. My legs were weak. My chest burned. I could hardly breathe.

"Mom! Dad! There's a flying saucer!" I gasped. "They caught me. And they're sending a TV signal out that will make us all slaves! Tomorrow night at eight! We've got to do something!"

My dad sat up in bed. My mom opened her eyes.

"You had a bad dream, Stanley," Dad told me. "Go back to sleep."

"No, no! It was real!" I yelled. "You've gotta believe me. You've got to!"

"Stanley." Mom sat up, too. "It was just a dream. But I'm glad you're beginning to under-stand why we don't watch television."

"Go to bed, son," my dad said. "We'll talk about it in the morning."

"The entire world is in danger, and you don't believe me!" I wailed.

Then I remembered the pictures. "I have pictures!" I cried. "I took them tonight! They prove it!"

I reached around my neck for the camera.

It was gone.

The next day, Saturday, I called Melanie at eight o'clock in the morning. I think I woke her up. I didn't care. I told her everything.

"Uh, Stanley." Melanie sounded unhappy. "This is really getting too strange. Could you just stop it?"

"I can't stop it," I told her. "I'm telling the truth."

"Yeah, right," she muttered.

When I called Robbie, it was the same story.

"Sure it happened," Robbie said. "And I come from Jupiter!"

I decided to try the police.

"Hey!" Officer Banks cried when I walked up to the station. "It's the flying saucer kid. See another one, kid?"

A couple of the other officers laughed. I just stared at them. They wouldn't believe me, either.

I left the station. I looked around. It was a normal, sunny day. People walked around. No one knew that aliens were about to take over the world. No one seemed to care.

I cared.

And I had an idea.

The aliens had built something to send out their

weird waves. Maybe I could build something that would get in the way of them, so they wouldn't reach anyone's TV set.

Maybe I could build a mirror, to reflect the alien waves back at them. I raced over to Robbie's house.

"I need to borrow some money," I told him. "As much as you have."

"How come?" he asked.

"To save the world, of course!" I told him.

Robbie didn't believe me. But he did lend me the money.

So did Melanie. They're pretty good friends. I raced over to the supermarket. I grabbed a cart. And I filled it with every single roll of aluminum foil in the store.

When I got to the checkout, Mr. Barnes looked at me and blinked. "What do you want with all that foil, Stanley?" he asked.

"Science experiment for school," I lied.

The total came to $134.59. I didn't have enough money.

"My parents will come in tomorrow and pay you," I told him. *If the aliens don't win,* I added under my breath.

I dragged the foil home to my garage. I started building my giant mirror.

I ran out of foil when the mirror was about twice as big as my dining room table. Then I carried it to Mr. Tribble's farm. Luckily, silver foil doesn't weigh a whole lot.

I made sure no one saw me with my mirror. I hid it in the woods behind the barn. Then I crawled closer to see what was going on.

The alien ship sat there. The satellite dish appeared ready.

It looked awfully big. I didn't think my little foil screen would do the trick. But I was running out of time. It was already six-thirty. Then I had another brilliant idea.

I raced home. I crept into my brother Dan's room. And I stole his gigantic foil ball.

I never thought it would come in handy. I guess Dan isn't such a dweeb after all.

The foil from the ball made my screen a lot bigger. I still didn't know if it would work. But I had to try.

I managed to haul the screen up to a high branch of a big maple tree. From there, I could see the alien satellite dish.

I only hoped the aliens couldn't see me. But they didn't seem to be around. Maybe they were in their ship, getting ready.

I pointed my screen in the right direction.

Then I waited.

At exactly eight o'clock, a blue light came streaming from the alien dish.

I held my breath.

The light hit my reflector and bounced right back to the alien ship.

I waited. That's when the blue light went out. I held my breath.

The alien dish pulled back into the ship. And then the ship took off, straight up into the air. The last I saw of it, it was soaring toward the stars.

I left the silver foil up in the tree. I don't know what happened to it. Mr. Tribble probably thought some kids were playing a joke on him.

And then I went home.

What was I supposed to do? Tell somebody? No way.

Maybe the flying saucer will come back. But I doubt it. My guess is, the aliens got a dose of their own medicine. They're probably flying through outer space right now, watching reruns of *I Love Lucy* and slobbering all over each other.

I saved the world from weird aliens from outer space. But no one will believe me.

I finally did tell Robbie and Melanie, a few days later. But they just asked for their money back.

Then I tried telling my parents, one last time.

"I totally agree," my mom said. "TV could definitely take over the world."

"Pass the tofu," my dad said.

"How do I look, Mom?" my sister Laura asked. "I'm going out with Herbie later."

"You stole my aluminum foil ball!" My brother Dan glared at me. "I just know it."

So that's the end of my story. Unless the aliens come back. And I can get some pictures to prove that the whole thing happened.

I spend a lot of time behind my telescope these days.

Hey. Over there. Did you see those flashing lights?

It's back! Look — the alien ship is back!

You believe me — *don't* you?

SUCKERS!

"Gross!" I shrieked.

Alex Pratt shook the wiggling jellyfish in my face. "What's the matter, Ashley? Scared of a little jellyfish?"

"She's a wimp! All summer people are wimps!" Jimmy Stern exclaimed. He's Alex's best friend.

Alex and Jimmy are fourteen years old. A year older than me. They think they're really cool because they live on Black Island all year round. And anybody who doesn't live here is a wimp.

And that includes my little brother, Jack, and my cousin Greg.

"Drop it on her head! Go on! Do it!" Jimmy urged, pushing his dark, greasy hair out of his eyes.

Alex snickered. He dangled the jellyfish over my head. Then he lowered it. Slowly.

"Leave her alone!" my cousin Greg yelled. He was hiding behind me. You know, I think they might be right about Greg. He is kind of wimpy.

Alex pushed me aside. Not hard to do. Alex stands at least a foot taller than me and is twice as wide!

"I smell gummies," Alex crowed. He moved in closer to Greg. He shoved him back hard. "Hand them over, Greggie."

"No way," Greg replied. "And quit shoving me. Please."

"Yeah," Jack echoed. "Quit shoving him. Or you'll be in big trouble. I take karate, you know."

"The Karate Kid," Jimmy sneered.

"And Gummy Boy," added Alex. "Get them!"

Alex and Jimmy jumped. They knocked Greg and Jack down into the sand. Then Alex sat on top of Greg.

"Look what I found!" Alex said, pulling out a big bag of gummies from Greg's pocket. He lifted the bag and emptied it into his mouth.

Then the two tough guys jumped up and ran.

"Alex and Jimmy are ruining our whole summer!" I wailed.

We walked along the beach. Greg plucked a piece of driftwood from the shore and hurled it into the ocean.

"I hate those creeps more than anything," he muttered. "I'm going to make them pay."

"Yeah," Jack cried with enthusiasm. "When I earn my black belt, I'll karate them. My teacher says I'm lightning!"

Greg rolled his eyes. "You have about ten belts

to go," he reminded Jack. Then he slid his hands into the front pocket of his shorts. His face lit up.

"Hey! They didn't get all my gummies!"

He fished a crumpled bag out of his right pocket. Then he dropped a few of the slimy candies into his mouth. Greg chomps a few dozen of them a day.

He passed the bag to Jack. "Want one?"

Jack chewed away in silence. Quiet for once.

"How about you, Ash?" He offered the bag to me.

"No way!" I replied. "Worm candy. Ugh. Totally gross."

"You're nuts," Greg replied. "These are awesome. They're the best." He raised the bag to his mouth and gobbled the rest of the worms down.

"Hey, Ash. Look." Greg grinned at me. Little bits of green, purple, and red gummy worms stuck to his teeth.

"Yuck! You are gross. Totally gross. Right, Jack?" I asked. "Right?"

Jack didn't answer. "What's that?" he said, pointing to a big trunk up ahead on the beach. At Bowen's Cove.

The three of us raced through the sand to the trunk. Jack reached it first.

The rusty old chest was as long as a coffin. Draped with barnacles and seaweed. And padlocked.

Jack hopped up and down. "It's a pirate's chest! Full of treasure. Gold and jewels!"

"It's not a pirate's chest," Greg replied. "It probably just fell off a boat and washed ashore. I bet it's full of fishing gear."

I wrinkled my nose. The chest smelled moldy and sour. "I bet it's full of rotten fish."

Jack danced around the chest. "Let's open it. Hurry!" He slammed the lock with the side of his left hand. It didn't budge.

"I'll open it!" Greg bragged. "Stand back." He lifted his foot. Then smashed it down hard on the lock. Nothing.

I scanned the beach. A few yards away I spotted a sturdy piece of driftwood. I hurried over and carried it back.

Then I shoved the wood into the tiny space between the lock and the lid. With two hands, I slowly pushed down on the wood.

Pop! The lock shot open.

"Way to go!" Jack cried.

Then the three of us started to lift the damp, heavy lid. Inch by inch.

"Whoa!" I cried as it banged wide open.

A big, green, quivering blob sprang out. And flew right at me! It latched on to my leg.

"Help! It's got me!" I shrieked. "Pull it off! Pull it off!"

I shook my leg wildly. But the thing held on. Cold and slimy. Clammy. And as smelly as a hundred dead fish.

It wrapped itself tightly around me. It covered my leg from my ankle to my knee.

"Help!" I yelled to Jack and Greg. But they stood frozen with fear.

I pushed frantically at the slimy blob. My fingers sank into the cold, green gunk. "Ohhh!" I let out a moan as I felt underneath the skin.

The thing had suckers!

Suckers that twitched and tugged at my skin. And the more I struggled, the tighter they grasped my leg.

THWOCK!

It moved! It dragged itself up my leg by its suckers. Leaving a burning, itchy trail.

"Get it off!" I moaned.

Greg and Jack awoke from their trance. They grabbed for the blob. They yanked at it. But the suckers dug deeper into my leg.

THWOCK. THWOCK.

The blob inched up my thigh. Squeezing harder.

Greg pounded the blob with a stick. "Off, slime-ball!" he yelled. "Off!"

"Greg! Stop!" I cried. "You're smashing my leg."

THWOCK. The blob yanked a moist sucker off my thigh. And wiggled it in the air. Almost as if it were sniffing. Then it nosed the sucker into Greg's T-shirt pocket.

"Whoaaa," Greg cried and jumped back.

The sucker emerged with a gummy worm. Schlop! It sucked the candy into its slimy body!

"It — it ate a gummy worm!" Greg stammered. "Did you see that?"

"But it doesn't have a mouth," Jack shuddered. "It doesn't even have a head."

Now the blob quivered up my stomach. The suckers jerked at my skin. Would it slurp *me* down, too?

"Stop talking! Do something!" I screamed.

Greg grabbed a bunch of gummy worms from his pocket. He dangled them in front of the blob.

THWOCK. THWOCK. The creature flew off me and heaved itself at the gummy worms. Then it slurped them down.

"Yes! You did it!" I cried.

"But now it's on me!" Greg moaned. "And I'm out of gummies!"

I stared in horror. The blob clung to Greg's arm. Writhing. Pulsating.

Jack gaped at the creature. "I think it's growing!"

Jack was right. The creature strangled Greg's arm and oozed across his chest.

"More candy!" Greg choked. "In my bedroom. Hurry! It's squeezing me."

Jack and I raced to the front door of our beach cottage. We turned the doorknob.

Locked.

Nobody home.

194

Jack flung the doormat aside and found the key hidden there for us. He opened the door, and we sprinted up to Greg's bedroom.

"Check his dresser," I ordered. I yanked open Greg's closet door. I pawed through his sweatshirts and jeans.

Not a single gummy.

"I can't find any in the dresser," Jack cried.

"Check under the bed," I said. "Check *everywhere*."

I dug through the bottom of the closet. Sneakers. Dirty socks. Finally I spied the familiar bags. Dozens of them.

"I found gummies!" I cried in triumph.

I snatched up a bag. Empty! Then another. And another. All empty.

"What are we going to do?" Jack wailed.

"We'll go to the store. Come on — hurry! Let's find our bikes!"

We pedaled furiously to Simpson's General Store.

We dropped our bikes outside the store and dashed inside. Packages of gummy worms were piled up on the counter.

I snatched about twenty bags. All I could carry. Jack did the same.

"That will be — " Mr. Simpson started.

Oh, no! *Money!* I didn't have any money!

"Mr. Simpson. Please. I don't have any money.

And I need these gummy worms," I explained frantically. "It's a matter of life and death. They're for Greg."

"Greg? He's my best customer. Always buying gummy worms. Okay. Go ahead. I'll charge it to your parents' bill."

"Thanks, Mr. Simpson!" I called. We rushed out of the store.

Jack and I tossed the bags of candy into my bike basket.

"There's the shortcut to Bowen's Cove," Jack cried. He pointed to a dusty road off Main Street. "Let's take it!"

I hesitated. "Okay," I agreed. "But you'd better be right."

We raced to the road. Then skidded into the turn.

"Oh, no!" Jack cried. "My gear chain slipped. I have to fix it. Go ahead without me. Just stay on this road. Then turn at the cutoff. It's not far."

"Perfect," I mumbled, rolling my eyes. I zoomed down the deserted dirt road. I whizzed by the tall dune grass. So quiet. So still. No one in sight.

And no cutoff for the cove.

I braked to a complete stop. Turned my bike around. "I think I'm lost," I said out loud.

"You're found now."

The dune grass parted. Alex and Jimmy came lumbering out. They gripped my handlebars.

196

"Roadblock," Jimmy smirked. "No summer people allowed."

Alex peered inside my bike basket. "Yum. Gummy worms. Hey, Jimmy. Ashley wants to share her candy."

"No!" I shrieked. "I need those."

Alex and Jimmy began tearing into the gummy worm bags. I tried to yank my bike away, but Alex grabbed on to the handlebars again.

Then, Jack came pedaling up. Hair flying. Racing up the path. His tires throwing huge dirt clouds up in the air.

Alex and Jimmy turned to face him. I quickly moved my bike to the roadside.

"Clear the path, jerks!" Jack cried out.

"Uh-oh. Watch out, Jimmy. The Karate Kid is going to run us over." Jimmy laughed.

Jack kept coming. When he was nearly on top of them, he flung his legs out. And kicked them both into the dirt.

With a cheer, I jumped on my bike. We sped away.

"You'll be sorry!" I heard Alex call after us.

"Yeah. You guys are in big trouble!" Jimmy yelled.

We flew down the road. And there it was — the cutoff to Bowen's Cove! We reached the beach in minutes.

We scooped up the candy and sprinted down to Greg.

And gasped. The oily blob bulged and quaked. Much bigger. Bigger than Mom's beach umbrella.

And no sign of Greg.

Then I heard a faint cry. "Help me. Help me."

"Greg!" I screamed. "Where are you?"

THWOCK. THWOCK. The slimy blob quivered in the sand. And that's when I saw a sneaker. Greg's sneaker.

"He's *under* the blob!" I screamed to Jack.

"Can't breathe," Greg moaned.

"Hold on, Greg," I cried. I quickly ripped open a small bag of gummy worms. And placed six candies down in a thin line.

THWOCK. THWOCK. Schlop!

The slime monster slid forward and slurped the gummies up eagerly.

"More! Open more bags!" I told Jack.

He tore through the bags. And I flung huge handfuls onto the sand.

THWOCK. The blob plucked a slimy sucker off Greg. It quivered excitedly. *Let Greg go,* I thought. *Please let Greg go.*

I threw a mound of gummy worms on the sand.

RRRIP! The monster yanked its suckers off Greg. It rolled forward and slurped down the candy.

I spun around to Jack. "Lots more gummies. Fast! Try to lead the creature back into the chest."

Greg stumbled as he tried to stand on his wob-

198

bly legs. Then he and Jack tore open bags and bags of candy. I placed a thick trail of gummies in the sand. A river of gummy worms. Leading to the chest.

THWOCK. THWOCK. Schlop. Schlop. The creature followed our trail. Slurping down candy.

A foot from the chest.

"The chest! Throw some gummies into the chest!" I commanded.

Jack and Greg pitched the candy in.

THWOCK. The blob lurched forward. Inches from the chest.

"Throw the bags right in! There's no time to open them!" I shouted.

The blob wriggled its way up the chest wall. But it had grown too big. Too big to heave itself up.

"We have to push it in!" I cried.

Jack drew back. "*You* push it in!" he shouted. "I'm not touching that blob. What if it grabs me?"

"Not me!" Greg protested. "That thing nearly strangled me."

"But it's our only chance!" I wailed. "We have to boost it back in."

They didn't move.

I threw myself against the creature and shoved. But my hands kept slipping. "It's too slimy," I moaned. "I need your help. Please!"

Jack and Greg stepped forward. Then we all pushed. And pushed. And pushed.

Sweat ran down my forehead. The boys' faces turned a bright red.

Slowly we hoisted the monster into the chest. One oily bulge at a time.

Then we slammed the lid down and jumped on top.

"Hey! Look!" Jack pointed down to the front of the chest. A bag of gummy worms hung out.

"Gummies!" Greg cried gleefully. "Awesome! Exactly what I need right now." He leaned over to lift the lid.

"Are you crazy?" I shrieked. "That thing in the chest almost squeezed you to death. Don't lift that lid!"

"Uh-oh," Jack warned.

We glanced up to see Alex and Jimmy angrily charging toward us.

"Jack! Just the guy we're looking for," Alex called. "I think we owe you something."

We scrambled off the chest and headed full speed for the dunes.

I turned back and saw Alex and Jimmy stop in front of the trunk. "Look! Gummy worms!" Alex cried, pointing to the bag poking through the lid. "Excellent!"

"There's plenty more inside!" I called.

Then Jack, Greg, and I watched as Alex and Jimmy eagerly pulled up the lid.

DR. HORROR'S HOUSE OF VIDEO

"Help! Help!" Screams echoed through the crowded streets. Something huge and menacing and green rose above the steel-gray city.

A giant monster. A plant monster.

The plant had grasping leaves. Leaves that reached out like hands to grab frightened people below. The people twisted and screamed as the plant lifted them in its leafy grip. Up, up, up to certain death.

I yawned. *Bor*-ing!

I'd seen *The Plant That Squeezed St. Louis* three times already. I rewound the videotape. As far as horror movies go, this one just didn't hold up.

And I should know. I'm Ben Adams — I've seen them all. Movies with mummies, movies with werewolves, movies with creatures from other planets. I'm kind of an expert.

In fact, my best friend, Jeff, and I plan to make horror movies when we're older. Right now, we're twelve. Too young to be taken seriously. But we've already made some home horror movies with my dad's camcorder.

I usually play the victim. It helps that I have red hair that stands on end and very pale skin. I'm great at acting scared. But what good does that do me now? With Jeff at camp and me on vacation?

That's where I am. On vacation for the summer with my parents. My mom and dad rented a house near the mountains for the whole month of August. There's nothing to do here. Nowhere to go. And worst of all, no kids my age.

Mom and Dad say, "Go out! Have fun!" But where? I'd rather stay inside, watching horror movies.

And I have. For two whole weeks now, I've been watching videos I brought from home.

"Ben!" my mom called from the other room. "You've been stuck in front of that TV all afternoon." She walked in, then yanked open the blinds.

I blinked in the sudden light. "It's time you got some fresh air. It's not healthy for a growing boy to sit inside all day. I'm going into town for gardening supplies. Why don't you come with me?"

Dad works in the city during the week and is here on weekends. But Mom is a teacher, so she has the summer off. And what does she do? She works in the garden.

"Ben," Mom said in a voice that meant business. "Do you want to come to town?" It wasn't an invitation. It was an order.

"But, Mom," I argued, holding the monster video box so she could only see the plant. "I'm watching this educational movie about nature."

Mom rolled her eyes. "That's a horror movie, and I know it. You're wasting your summer, Ben, watching that stuff. Now let's get going."

In town, Mom headed straight for the garden supply store. I gazed up and down the street. I'd never been in this part of town.

Something caught my eye. A video store! "I'll meet you up the block," I called to Mom.

Hurrying away, I tried to control my excitement. I could get a fresh batch of videos! And best of all, the store was called Dr. Horror's House of Video. It must be all horror movies.

How lucky can a guy get?

I stopped outside the store. The frayed awning drooped in front. A layer of dust covered the window. I wiped the dirty pane and peered inside.

The inside looked as old and dusty as the outside. Videos were piled everywhere.

Fine with me, I thought. Who knows what I'll find under all that mess?

The door creaked open — and I hadn't even touched it. This just got better and better! Quickly, I slipped inside.

"Can I help you?" someone asked in a low, whispery voice. I whirled around. An elderly man with flowing white hair stood behind me. He had white bushy eyebrows and a face creased with a thousand tiny lines.

"My name is Dr. Horror," he said in that whispery voice. He leaned heavily on a cane, then waved it at all the shelves. "Welcome to my store."

Dr. Horror smiled, and I saw that he was missing most of his teeth. "Do you like horror movies?" he asked.

"Are you kidding?" I replied. "I think I've seen every horror movie ever made."

"I bet you haven't seen any of these," Dr. Horror said, chuckling. "I make my own in the old garage behind the store."

I grinned. "Really?" Just wait until I tell Jeff about this, I thought. He'll be totally jealous. Even if he is having a great time at camp, I'll bet he hasn't met anyone like Dr. Horror!

"Go on. Look around," Dr. Horror told me. "I'm sure you'll find something to frighten you."

This was so cool! I hurried to check out the videos. *Ten Tales from the Mummy Files. Monsters at Midnight. A Boy and His Werewolf.*

"These are terrific!" I said, lifting a vampire video. The vampire on the front had deathly white skin. A drop of ruby-red blood ran down his pale chin.

But it was his expression that really grabbed me. His eyes bored into mine — as if he were gazing into my soul.

Which video should I get? I couldn't decide. They all looked so good!

Then I saw a movie playing on one of the video monitors, off in a corner. On screen, a huge monster — half man, half lizard — stepped out from a slimy swamp. He was searching for something to eat.

Squish, squish, squish went his webbed feet as he spotted a boy in the distance. Lizardman advanced.

I watched, spellbound.

The monster crept closer and closer to the boy. I moved closer, too. The boy's face twisted in fear.

I could feel the boy's fright. I sensed his horror — right in my gut.

Creak! A noise from behind me. I started to turn. But then Lizardman clutched the boy's shoulder. And I felt something grab *my* shoulder.

Something cool and smooth. I looked down. A green hand gripped me. Hard!

"Lizardman!" I screamed.

"Excuse me?" said Mom. She let go of my shoulder and took off a green glove. "I just wanted to show you my new gardening gloves."

She shook her head and stepped in front of the set. "These horror movies make you so jumpy,

Ben. I don't think you should be watching them. Let's go home."

I peered around Mom, trying to see the screen.

"Now!" Mom insisted, and she dragged me out the door.

The next morning I woke up early. I wanted to get to the video store. I had to see how *Lizardman* ended. But I couldn't say that to Mom. She wouldn't understand.

"I'm going for a bike ride," I told her.

Mom's mouth dropped open in surprise. "You're going *outside*?"

Before she could ask any questions, I wheeled my bike down the driveway and hopped on. Fifteen minutes later, I stood in front of the video store.

A CLOSED sign hung on the door. The store was dark.

I hopped from one foot to the other. When would it open? When would I find out about Lizardman?

I peered through the dusty window, hoping to spot Dr. Horror inside.

No such luck. But I did see a flickering light in the corner. A movie played on one of the sets. I squinted at the screen. Lizardman!

"Dr. Horror!" I called, knocking. "Are you in there?" I jiggled the doorknob.

The door swung open with a creak. "Dr. Horror?" I called in.

206

No answer.

The only sounds I heard were the voices in the horror movie. And the only light came from the TV.

I'll sneak in, I decided. I'll watch the movie, then sneak back out. No one will even know.

I edged forward, staring at the TV. . . .

An hour later, the movie ended. Lizardman gobbled the boy in a few quick bites. Then he had the other townspeople for dessert.

Cool! Definitely one of the best horror movies I'd seen all summer!

The VCR switched off. The room suddenly fell dark. Time to leave.

I made my way to the door and pulled at the knob. Nothing happened. I tried pushing. The door wouldn't budge.

"Oh, no," I groaned. "I'm locked inside."

Now what? I thought, squinting in the darkness. To my right, I spotted a sliver of light. Another door? A back exit? I crept toward it.

Yes! A door! Behind it, I heard noises. Thumps, and muffled shouts. What was going on?

I leaned against the door, pushing with all my might. The door swung open easily. Startled, I stumbled and fell.

I landed hard on my side. My eyes opened wide. A big webbed foot stood an inch away. Make that two big webbed feet.

"Huh?" I let out a cry and jumped up.

Lizardman in all his green glory towered over me like . . . like . . . a monster!

A living, breathing monster, flicking his long sharp tongue. His hot breath hit me like a blast from a furnace.

Bright lights beat down on me. Blinding me. I turned to run. Lizardman stretched a long sinewy arm to stop me. He had me in his grip! A grip as strong as an iron band.

I let out a frightened squeal and squinted into the bright light. Was anyone else here?

I heard sounds. Feet pounding.

Hands grasped me. But they didn't pull me from Lizardman. The hands held me in place. Hairy hands. Pale white hands. Hands wrapped with cloth.

Werewolves! Vampires! Mummies!

"Wait a minute!" a familiar voice shouted. I squinted into the light. Dragging his cane, Dr. Horror shuffled over. "Hello again," he said.

"H-h-h-i," I stammered.

Dr. Horror's eyes gleamed. I twisted hard. But I couldn't break the monsters' hold.

"I see you found the door to the garage," said Dr. Horror. He waved his cane around. "What do you think?"

For the first time, I took it all in. The monsters. The lights. The cameras.

I gazed around the huge room. The monsters

all looked familiar. The deathly white vampire. The mummy. And, of course, Lizardman. The horror movie monsters!

This garage was their film studio! How could I have forgotten?

I grinned at Lizardman. "Love your work," I said.

Lizardman nodded and released his grip.

"And these costumes!" I went on. "They're the coolest!"

Dr. Horror smiled. "Yes, you're a horror fan. Right?"

"The biggest!"

"Good, good, good." Dr. Horror rubbed his hands together. "How would you like to be in *Return of Lizardman*?"

"Excuse m-me?" I stammered.

"We're filming the *Lizardman* sequel, and we need a new victim."

Me in a real horror movie? I couldn't believe it!

"Do you have acting experience?" Dr. Horror asked.

"Some," I said, thinking of our home movies.

Dr. Horror tilted my head and examined my profile. "Well, you seem like a natural. It's a small role. You don't even have lines." He thrust a bunch of papers at me. "Here's the script."

I leafed through the scenes. Lizardman emerging from the swamp . . . destroying a school . . .

one boy escaping. "Is that me?" I asked Dr. Horror.

"Yes. Any other questions? We're ready to start now."

Now? I wanted to call Jeff at camp. Tell Mom and Dad. Maybe phone a few more friends. I wanted to play this for all it was worth.

"Can I make some phone calls first?" I asked.

Dr. Horror checked his watch. "You have time for just one. I suggest you call your parents. We like to have their permission before filming. We can take care of your contract later."

The phone rang ten times before Mom answered. Of course she had been outside gardening.

"I'm not sure," she said when I explained about the movie.

"But, Mom!" I shouted. "This could be my big break. Please, please, please! It's so important to me!" I took a deep breath.

"Just be home in time for dinner," Mom said, finally giving in.

I hung up the phone, then turned back to Dr. Horror. "It's all set."

Small alien-creature actors wheeled a swampy backdrop behind me. Everyone bustled around, getting things ready. A four-armed actor plopped a tree right next to me. The vampire and mummy stood behind the cameras. The werewolf set the lights. "There!" he said. A murky glow bathed the room.

Dr. Horror motioned for me to stand against the tree. "We'll tie you up," he whispered, strapping me to the trunk. "For your big scene with Lizardman."

"Oh, right," I said, remembering the part in the script. All I had to do was act frightened. Simple enough.

Dr. Horror shuffled over to his director's chair. "Now," he said. "You lost your way in the swamp, and fell asleep. When you woke up, you were tied to this tree. You know Lizardman is coming back. But when?"

He turned to the vampire actor running the camera. "Roll 'em," he said. "Okay . . . action!"

Lizardman crept through the swamp. I tried to look scared. But I was too excited. Too happy.

"Cut!" shouted Dr. Horror, shaking his head. "More feeling!"

I tried again. I opened my eyes wide.

Lizardman glided closer. His tail swept from side to side. His eyes darted back and forth. He really seemed hungry. What an actor!

Lizardman flicked out his tongue to catch a fly. Great effect!

And the makeup! As Lizardman slid nearer, I saw just how monsterlike he looked — even up close. Green skin, red bloodshot eyes. Long, slimy tongue.

"Hey, wait," I called out.

"What?" snapped Dr. Horror impatiently.

"Don't I need makeup, too?"

Lizardman stood inches away. "I know I'm supposed to be an ordinary boy. But these other actors look terrific!"

I reached up to touch Lizardman's face. "Is this a mask?" Ugh. The skin felt bumpy and cold. It had to be a mask.

"Hey, can I see it?" I tugged at the mask. It didn't budge. "It's stuck," I announced. The other actors crowded around. How nice, I thought. They want to help.

The vampire actor stretched his mouth into a teeth-baring grin. His sharp teeth glinted in the light. Coming closer, he pulled my arms back around the tree. Then he tied them with another rope.

I didn't remember this from the script. "Hey!" I shouted. "What's going on?"

Nobody answered.

Instead, the mummy unwound the wrapping from his face.

I gasped when I saw its decayed flesh hanging from its bony frame. And its eyes — glowing red eyes.

The werewolf shimmered for a moment, growling deep in his throat. He raised his paws, and deadly nails popped out. Two sharp fangs burst from either side of his mouth. His nose quivered with excitement.

This couldn't be trick photography. What was it?

I started to tremble as I answered my own question. These weren't actors from a horror movie! They were *monsters* — real monsters.

"Let me go!" I cried, struggling to get free. The heavy ropes cut into my hands.

I had to escape! I had to! But the ropes held me tight.

I was trapped!

His eyes glowing excitedly, Lizardman breathed in my face. His hot breath hit me full force. A smell like the bottom of a swamp. My stomach turned.

Lizardman's teeth scraped my face. His scaly hand gripped my neck. His tail sliced through the air.

"Dr. Horror!" I shrieked. "Save me! Please — *do* something!"

"Whoa! Stop, monsters!" Dr. Horror called out. "Stop at once!"

The monsters stepped back. Lizardman froze in place.

Oh, thank goodness! I thought. I'm okay. It was all my imagination.

I let out a relieved sigh. How could I get so carried away?

Dr. Horror reached out — to untie me, I thought.

But I was wrong.

He reached up to my head. And he fixed my hair!

"Okay, monsters. Now we're ready for the big eating scene," he said. "Roll 'em!"

THE CAT'S TALE

"Come on down, Marla," my little brother, Scott, called. "We're telling ghost stories!"

"No thanks," I shouted back. Then I covered my ears so I wouldn't hear the next blast of thunder. Thunderstorms weren't so loud when my family lived in the city. Here in the country, the lightning flashed so close — and the thunder boomed so hard — it shook the house.

Last year when I turned twelve, my folks decided it would be safer for my brother and me to grow up in the country. So we moved from New York City up here to River Falls.

Scott loves living in an old house with a big yard. But not me. I hate it. I miss Central Park. I miss taxis. And most of all, I miss my friends.

I listened to the tree branches brush against my window. I suddenly pictured ghosts trying to claw their way through my window and into my room.

I'm not a *chicken* or anything. I'm not even

really afraid of the thunder and lightning. I just like it better when there isn't any.

I gasped as the room went black. Now the only light in my room came from the lightning. With every flash, the trees left frightening shadows on my wall.

Downstairs I could hear my parents and Scott still telling ghost stories — in the dark! I wanted no part of *that*.

I couldn't stand the sound of the branches scratching against the glass. I opened the window. Then I felt my way around the room in the darkness. I touched my desk. My chair. My headboard.

"Oh!" I cried out as something big, wet, and hairy flew through the open window. It slammed into my chest — and I fell to the floor.

Long, sharp nails scratched at my arms and neck.

High-pitched screeches rang in my ears.

I stared into two glowing green eyes. Then I started to scream.

Mom and Dad bolted into the room. "Marla, what's the matter?" Dad cried. He held a candle in one hand and Scott's Little League bat in the other.

"A hairy monster!" I shrieked. "It flew into the room! And-and — "

"Is this the monster?" Mom asked sweetly. She held up her candle so I could see. In her arms she carried a small, wet, shaking black cat.

216

"It's just a cat, honey," Mom said softly. "She must have climbed up the tree and jumped in here to get out of the storm." She examined the cat. "A stray. No tags around her neck."

"Meow!" A loud roar from behind me. I spun around. "Stop it, Scott!" I cried. He laughed. "Meow! Meow!" He thought it was a riot.

I ignored him and reached for the cat. My mother placed her in my arms. "You're nice and safe here," I said to the cat. I turned to my parents. "Can I keep her?"

Mom and Dad glanced at each other. "Marla, a cat is a big responsibility," my Dad began.

My face fell. "Please, Dad," I pleaded. "She needs me. She's all alone. And I need *her*. I have no friends around here."

"Well, we'll talk about it in the morning," my mother said. "She can stay tonight, anyway. Come on, Scott, it's bedtime."

I petted the black cat. The storm had stopped. The air was filled with a fresh mist. "I think I'll call you Misty," I said. "And don't worry. You'll be able to stay here — for life! I'll make sure of it."

Misty spent the night curled up at the foot of my bed. And the next morning, she did the weirdest thing. She followed me into the shower!

Misty purred happily as the hot water pounded on her fur.

I'd always heard that cats hate baths and

217

showers. They keep themselves clean by licking themselves.

Not Misty. Misty was special.

When we went down to breakfast, we both had wet hair. "I see you two have washed up," my father said.

I smiled. Misty also showed her pointy white teeth in a grin.

We all laughed when Misty tried to eat my eggs. "You must be hungry, you poor thing," my mother said.

She gave Misty a saucer of milk and some tuna. "I've spoiled you now," Mom told Misty. "You'll never go for cat food after that." I knew then that Mom would let me keep Misty.

"Kids, I have a great surprise!" Mom said excitedly. "I've joined the swim club. You two can bike over there today and take a swim. There will be lots of kids your age there."

Scott jumped out of his seat. "All right! A pool! Right here! And we don't have to take a taxi to a stinking old gym. I love it out here!"

I frowned at my brother. He was so easy to please. All it took was a few ghost stories and a swimming pool. I still missed New York.

But since I was stuck here, meeting some other kids didn't seem like such a bad idea. Besides, I love to swim. And the heat wave was starting to get to me. I ran upstairs to put on my swimsuit.

"Hurry up, Marla!" Scott called from the front door. If you're not here in one minute, I'm going without you."

"See you later, Misty," I said, waving. Misty leaped up on my desk and meowed. She sounded so sad, like a baby who had lost her mother. She cried and cried. I cuddled the cat in my arms and tried to calm her.

"I know how you feel. I don't like being alone in a new house, either," I said, petting her black fur. Then I called downstairs. "Hey, Scott, you go on. I think Misty and I are going to hang out here today."

At dinnertime, Scott told us about the great kids he met at the pool. I felt a little jealous. All I did was read a book while Misty napped.

But when I gazed down at Misty, snuggled in my lap, eating pieces of my frankfurter, I knew I had done the right thing. Misty needed me.

That night I dreamed about my old neighborhood. My friends and I were rowing a boat in the park. We were having a picnic lunch, and laughing. Then, suddenly, a stranger grabbed me from behind and covered my mouth. I tried to lift my head, but couldn't! I couldn't breathe!

I woke up. I *still* couldn't breathe!

Misty! The cat was sitting on me. Covering my nose and mouth.

I tugged at her with all my strength. But I couldn't budge her.

I started to feel dizzy and weak. The room spun around me.

I struggled to get air into my lungs.

I grabbed at Misty's fur. But the cat pressed even harder against my face.

Beads of sweat dripped from my forehead. My skin turned cold and clammy.

Finally, I curled my hands around Misty's neck. I ripped her off my face and held her far from my body.

Then I gasped in breath after breath. Holding the cat tightly, I carried her downstairs to the family room. My parents were watching a video.

"Mom! Dad!" I cried. "Misty tried to kill me!"

"What?"

"She tried to kill me. She plopped on to my face. She wouldn't get off! She — she tried to suffocate me!"

My mother took Misty from me and petted her back. "Marla, Misty was probably just cold. You know you like to turn the air-conditioning up too high. She was trying to get warm."

Maybe what Mom said made sense. I don't know. But that's when I started getting afraid of that cat.

The next day, when Misty started crying again, I ignored her. I locked the front door on my way out, hopped on my bike, and took off for the swim club.

The club seemed to be a really fun place. And there were lots of kids my age.

Scott ripped off his shirt and did a belly flop into the deep end. I took my time climbing the ladder to the high diving board.

I was about to dive in. I stared down at the water. And stared again.

For some reason, I suddenly didn't feel like diving. I began to edge back down the board. I didn't want to go in that water.

"Hey, Marla. What's your problem?" Scott called from the pool.

I cupped my hands and started to answer Scott. But I suddenly realized I wasn't the only one on the diving board.

Something brushed up against me and scratched my leg.

"Ow!" I screamed out in pain and surprise.

I lost my balance. I tumbled into the water below.

Cold, blue water poured into my mouth and nose. I thrashed my arms and legs in a panic.

I couldn't swim.

I struggled to reach the surface. But everything went black.

A crowd of people huddled around me. I could hear them congratulating the lifeguard who had jumped in and saved my life.

The lifeguard helped me to a lounge chair. He wrapped my cut leg in a towel. "Stay here," he said. "I'll call your parents and get you some bandages for that cut."

The blood seeped through the white towel. Ow! That was some cut! Who could have scratched me so badly?

Scott raced over to me. I thought he wanted to make sure I was okay.

Instead, he dumped Misty into my lap.

"Mom told you to leave this dumb cat at home," he said. "She followed you all the way up onto the high dive!"

Mom and Dad showed up a few minutes later and drove me home.

"Marla, to celebrate the fact that you're all right, I've made your favorite meal — spaghetti and meatballs!" Mom said.

I felt queasy. I really craved something else. "Uh, Mom?" I asked. "Do you have any of that tuna casserole left? And how about a big glass of milk?"

That shocked my parents. "Are you sure you're okay?" Mom asked. "It's not like you to give up your favorite dinner — especially for leftovers!"

I had a very restless night. I kept hearing whispers. Soft, breathless whispers.

Then the whispers became a creepy chant.

"Nine lives, nine lives. I will have thy body before I've lived my nine. Thy life is mine, and mine is thine."

My eyes darted around the room. No one there. No one — except Misty.

Was I going nuts?

After that, I couldn't sleep at all. I sat straight up in my bed and stared at Misty as she slept.

Had she really spoken?

The next day at the swim club, I stayed as far as I could from the water. Instead, I joined a volleyball game on the back lawn.

I'm not a great volleyball player. But I managed to spike the ball hard enough to earn my team the winning point.

After the game, Sarah and Melissa, two girls from my team, asked me to go to the snack bar for ice cream.

"You're a pretty good player," Sarah said. She twirled her ponytail around her finger. "We've got a volleyball team at school. You should join. What grade are you going into?"

"Sixth," I replied shyly.

"Oh, I thought you were older. We're in junior high," Melissa said.

"A mouse!" Sarah cried. She jumped up onto a wooden picnic table.

I saw the little gray creature scurry by. Melissa leaped up next to Sarah.

I didn't join them. I crouched down on the ground and pounced on it.

"Gotcha!" I cried.

I picked up the wriggling mouse by the tail and held it up.

Melissa and Sarah stared at me in horror.

"Yuck!" Sarah cried. "That's so gross! Get that thing away from me!"

"Eew!" Melissa turned her head away from me. "Marla — *why* did you do that?"

The mouse thrashed about in my hand. I tossed it into the nearby bushes.

Why did I do that? I asked myself.

I hate mice!

Any other day, I'd have been up there on the table with Melissa and Sarah. Instead, I acted really stupid in front of two junior high girls.

I acted like a real jerk. I acted absolutely . . . catlike!

Thy life is mine, and mine is thine.

It was all becoming clear to me. Now I knew why I was afraid of water. Why I had a sudden craving for tuna casserole. Why I found it so easy to pounce on a mouse.

Misty had just about taken over my mind. And, little by little, she was taking over my body.

I'll have thy body before I've lived my nine.

Misty didn't want to share a body with me. She wanted my body all to herself!

I needed a plan. I had to fight back. I had to get rid of Misty before she got rid of me!

I raced home and grabbed Misty by the collar. "We're going for a little ride," I said, trying not to frighten her. Then I placed Misty in the basket in the front of my bike and pedaled off to the local animal shelter in town.

"Don't worry, Miss," the man at the shelter said. "We're sure to find a nice home for a pretty cat like this."

I watched as he tied a name tag around Misty's neck and placed her in a large cage with other cats. Then I biked home.

For the first time in days, I felt relaxed. Happy.

What a relief! I had done it. I had gotten rid of Misty and saved my life!

I parked my bike on the side of our garage. I glanced toward the house and gasped. A black cat with deep green eyes stood on the porch.

No! I told myself. It can't be Misty. It just can't! I locked Misty up in a shelter a mile away. My legs trembled as I walked over to the porch. I lifted the tag on the cat's neck and read it.

Misty! It *was* Misty.

But how did she get home? How?

I feared going to sleep that night. What would Misty do to me? I lay there staring into the darkness.

Then I heard that same, horrifying, breathless voice, whispering ever-so-softly in my ear.

"Nine lives, nine lives. I will have thy body before I've lived my nine. Thy life is mine, and mine is thine."

That was enough to keep me awake for a long, long time!

Just before dawn, I shoved Misty into her cat carrier and sneaked out of the house. The carrier had a heavy lock. It could be opened only from the outside with a key.

No way Misty could escape this time! I told myself.

I strapped the carrier to my handlebars and rode through the gray morning to the bus station. The time had come for Misty to take a trip across the country!

We reached the station about half an hour before the bus was scheduled to leave. I watched the morning sun come up over the little town.

Suddenly I felt so thirsty. I set the cat carrier down on the sidewalk and hurried to the soda machine.

I had just dropped two quarters into the machine when I heard the deafening *screeeech*.

The screech of brakes.

A shrill cry.

I spun around in time to see the big red truck squeal to a stop. The driver leaped out of the cab. His face was bright red. "Was that your cat?" he called to me.

I ran over to him, my heart pounding.

"I didn't see her until it was too late," the truck driver told me. "I'm so sorry. Really. Why did you let her walk in the street?"

I opened my mouth to reply, but no words came out.

How had Misty escaped from the carrier? How

had she broken the lock and climbed out of the case?

I didn't really care. Misty was dead. Dead and gone.

I wasn't exactly sorry.

That night, I slept soundly, peacefully, for the first time in days. I pulled the covers up high and snuggled my head into my soft pillow. I'm sure I had a smile on my face as I drifted to sleep.

The smile faded when I heard the whispers.

I sat up with a shiver. And listened to the soft chant of the words:

"Eight lives, eight lives left. I will have thy body before I've lived my nine. Thy life is mine, and mine is thine."

SHELL SHOCKER

"Oh, no, you don't!" Tara Bennett yelled to her eight-year-old brother, Tommy. "That's my shell! Mine!"

Tara jumped up from the beach blanket and ran to the shore. She saw the waves wash over Tommy's toes as he rinsed the sand off the shell.

"Give it to me," Tara demanded, wrenching the gleaming white object from her brother's hands. "It's for my shell collection!" she sneered. "The biggest and best shell collection in the world!"

"No fair, Tara. I saw it first."

"No fair!" Tara mimicked. She narrowed her blue eyes. "You're a baby."

Tara held the seashell up to the light and admired its smooth curves and pointed spiral. It sparkled like a jewel in the afternoon sun.

"It's the most perfect shell in the world!" she announced. "Everybody is going to be jealous when they see it."

She closed her eyes. And pictured herself back at school. Winning the seventh-grade science fair with her new shell. All the kids in my class will be green with envy, Tara thought happily.

"Can I hold it?" Tommy asked softly.

"No way!" Tara snapped. "You can't even look at it without my permission!"

Clutching the shell tightly, she turned and marched across the beach. Far away from her annoying little brother. Then she flopped down on the sand to examine her newest treasure.

"It's beautiful," she gasped, turning the shell back and forth in her hands. "And it's mine. Not Tommy's. Mine!"

Whenever Tommy found a seashell, he pressed it to his ear. He said he could hear the roar of the ocean inside.

Tommy is such a jerk, Tara thought. She turned the shell over and over in her hand. Everyone knows you can't really hear the ocean inside a shell. Just the same, Tara held the white shell up to her ear.

"Oh, gross!" Tara cried.

A clump of wet seaweed slid down her cheek.

She wiped the green slime away. Then she placed the shell against her ear again.

And listened.

"Help me!" a tiny voice called from inside.

Tara screamed and dropped the shell.

"Who — who said that?" she stammered, gazing down at the shell. Then she jerked her head up. Expecting to see Tommy laughing at her.

But no one stood there.

Tara sat alone.

She jumped up and backed away from the shell. She stared suspiciously down at it. "Was it you?" she whispered. "Did you talk?"

Don't be silly, Tara, she told herself. Shells can't talk.

Creeping forward, she kicked the shell gently with her toe. It rolled across the sand, then stopped.

"Help me!"

The voice cried louder this time.

Tara screamed again. She began to shiver under the rays of the hot summer sun. She wrapped her arms tightly around herself. Then took a deep, steadying breath.

"Who's in there?" she demanded.

"I'm trapped," the tiny voice wailed. *"Help me!"*

Tara gasped. "I can't believe it!" she cried out. "The shell is talking. To me!"

Tara's head reeled. Beads of sweat dripped from her long blond hair.

"Of course I'm talking to you. I need your help!" the tiny voice pleaded. *"I'm a prisoner! Please. Pick me up."*

Tara didn't know what to do. She inched closer

230

to the shell. She leaned over and peeked inside. It appeared to be empty.

I have to find out where that voice is coming from, Tara thought. I just have to. Tara carefully lifted the shell from the sand.

"How can I help you?" Tara asked. Her voice trembled.

"Take me to the cave. To help me escape. Please. Trust me," the voice begged.

"Trust you?" Tara asked breathlessly. "I can't even *see* you!"

"Come to the cave. To help me escape. Then you'll understand. Then you'll see me!"

Tara hesitated. A talking shell, she thought. What an opportunity!

She grasped the shell in her hands and smirked. "Why should I help you escape?" she asked. "You're the world's first talking shell! I can make a fortune with you! I'll be rich and famous! People will pay a lot of money to hear a seashell talk!"

Tara's mind raced with all the possibilities. Maybe she would star in her own TV show! Tara and Her Amazing Talking Shell!

"But, Tara, I will talk to you only. When you're alone. So no one will believe you," the voice replied. *"But listen to me! There's something inside the cave that will* really *make you rich and famous."*

"What is it?" Tara demanded, shaking the shell. "Tell me!"

231

"It's the biggest seashell in the world," the voice told her.

The biggest shell in the world?

Tara pretended not to care. "Oh, really?" she muttered. "The biggest shell in the world? Where is this cave?"

"I'll show you," the voice answered. *"Just walk along the shoreline. To the north end of the beach. I'll show you where it is. I promise."*

Tara bubbled with excitement. I'll be the most famous shell collector in the world, she thought. I'll be Tara, the Shell Queen!

"Okay," she agreed. "I'll do it! I'll take you to the cave!"

"Yesss!" the voice hissed.

Tara took a small step across the sand. "What about my mom and dad?" she asked. "I should tell them where I'm going."

She gazed across the crowded beach. She spotted her mother and father sprawled out under their neon-pink beach umbrella. Mom turned the pages of a book. Dad slept.

"Don't worry. They won't even notice you're gone," the voice urged. *"Let's go."*

Tara turned toward the north end of the beach. The sun cast an eerie glow over the towering sand dunes. The ocean waves hammered the shore.

"Maybe I'll bring Mom with me. There's no lifeguard over there," she muttered.

A loud screech echoed inside the shell.

"Help me!" the voice screamed out. *"Help me — now!"*

"Okay, okay," Tara snapped. "I'll help you. But remember your promise! The biggest shell in the world belongs to me."

Clasping the seashell in her hands, Tara stomped across the beach. The hard, wet sand hurt the bottom of her feet, but she was determined to find the cave . . . and the biggest shell in the world!

Tara walked and walked. "Aren't we there yet?" she whined.

"Keep going," the voice replied.

"But it's getting late!" she moaned.

Tara gazed out over the water. The sun floated on the edge of the sea like a big red beach ball.

"I'm kind of scared," Tara mumbled. "I'm all alone out here."

She turned and searched for her mom and dad and Tommy. She thought she spotted them alongside their pink umbrella on the edge of the beach. Three tiny specks in the sand.

"I want to go back," Tara whimpered. "We've wandered too far."

"But we're so close," the voice said softly. *"We can't turn back now. Look to your right. By the rocks."*

Tara scanned the beach.

There! The opening of the cave! Practically in front of her!

"Finally," Tara gasped.

She dashed to the cave's dark entrance. And listened. From deep inside the cavern she heard a frightening earsplitting screech!

"What's that?" Tara whispered.

"It's only the wind," the tiny voice explained. *"Let's go in."*

"But . . . but I'm a little afraid," Tara admitted. "It's so dark in there!"

"Don't worry," the voice replied. *"I can guide you through the cave. Just do exactly as I say. Walk straight ahead . . . and don't touch the walls."*

Tara took a deep breath and stepped forward. The darkness swallowed her up. She stumbled blindly ahead.

The cave floor dipped and pitched. Tara reached a hand out in front of her. She groped at the curtain of dark. She staggered on.

A rock. A huge rock stood in her path. Her foot slammed into it.

"Oh, no!" she screamed as she stumbled. Her arms flew up from her sides. Up to the walls of the cave.

Tara shrieked.

The walls. They moved. They squirmed.

With thousands and thousands of black hairy spiders!

The spiders crawled over Tara's neck. Through her hair. Up her arms.

234

Tara leaped away from the wall. She swatted frantically at the spiders. Their hairy legs tangled her hair. Pinched her skin.

"I'm getting *out* of here!" she shrieked, frantically batting them off.

"But you can't go now!" the tiny voice in the shell pleaded. *"You've got to help me! We're so close now. Don't you want to own the biggest shell in the world? Don't you want to be rich and famous?"*

Tara hesitated. Her skin still prickled from the spiders.

"Wait until you see it," the voice crooned. *"It's the biggest, most beautiful shell you could ever imagine!"*

Tara closed her eyes.

Yes, she thought. The most beautiful shell. MY shell!

"This had better be worth it," she grumbled.

"Oh, it is," the tiny voice replied. *"Just wait. You'll see."*

Tara sighed. She crept deeper into the cave. Slowly. Very slowly.

"Keep walking," the voice in the shell whispered. *"We're almost there. Almost there."*

Tara staggered ahead. Barely breathing. No turning back now, she thought to herself. She had to find this huge shell! She had to have it!

CRUNCH! CRUNCH! CRUNCH!

Something cracked beneath Tara's feet.

"What's that?" she asked nervously. "What am I walking on?"

"*Nothing to worry about,*" the voice in the shell answered. "*Keep walking. But watch your step!*"

Tara took another step and felt something shatter under her toes. "What is it?" she demanded. "It hurts my feet! I want to know!"

Tara spun around and slipped.

"*Look out!*" cried the voice. "*Don't fall!*"

Too late! Tara tumbled down. Into a huge pile of large white stones. Sharp stones. She cried out as the rough edges cut into her skin.

What are these? She peered closer.

Tara shrieked. And shrieked again.

Her horrified cries echoed through the large cave.

These weren't stones. They were bones. A carpet of bones!

"Nooo!" Tara wailed. She scrambled to her feet. "You can keep your big shell! I'm going home!"

"*Wait! Wait! Don't go!*" the tiny voice begged. "*There's nothing to fear!*"

Tara stopped. "Nothing to fear?" she yelled. "Look at all the bones in here!"

"*They're only fish bones,*" the voice insisted. "*The tide carries dead fish into the cave.*"

Tara gazed at the huge pile of bones on the floor. "Fish bones? They look awfully big to be fish bones."

"They're very big fish," the voice explained. *"But not as big as the biggest shell."*

"Really?" Tara said. Her heart raced with excitement.

She lifted the little shell up to her eyes and shook it hard. "Tell me where it is!" she demanded. "Tell me now, or you'll be a prisoner for the rest of your life. Where is the biggest shell in the world?"

"It's close," the voice told her. *"It's right around the corner. You can almost reach out and touch it. Turn the corner, Tara."*

Tara gasped.

The biggest shell in the world, she thought. It's almost mine!

Tara rounded the corner. She stopped. Listened.

POUND. POUND. POUND.

From the darkest depths of the cave. The beating of a giant monster heart!

"Wh-what's that sound?" Tara gasped.

"It's the pounding of the waves," the voice replied. *"Hurry up now. If you want to see the shell before the tide comes in."*

Tara trembled. She carefully stepped toward the back of the cave. The pounding grew louder. Clutching the shell nervously, Tara inched forward.

A shaft of light filtered down through the cave-

237

top. Tara followed the ray. Down. Down. Down. And there it sat.

The biggest shell in the world.

Tara's eyes popped open wide with wonder.

The huge shell filled the whole cavern. Its pointed spiral nearly touched the top of the cave. It glistened white and pink. So big. So beautiful.

It stole Tara's breath away.

It was a perfectly formed shell — like the little one in her hand, but a thousand times larger!

"The biggest, most beautiful shell in the whole wide world," Tara whispered in awe.

"See? I told you," the little voice crooned.

Tara rushed forward, hugging the gigantic shell in her arms. It was so big. Her arms didn't even stretch halfway around it! She stroked its smooth pink curves and gazed up at its tall, twisting spiral.

I have found the biggest and best shell of all! Tara thought. "I'll be famous!" she crowed. "I'll be rich! I'll be the greatest shell collector in the whole universe! And everyone will be so jealous!"

"There's something I forgot to tell you," the little voice said. *"This is truly the biggest shell in the world. And inside it lives — the* biggest hermit crab *in the world!"*

With that, the huge shell rose up. Tilted back. And out crawled a monstrous hermit crab!

The biggest, ugliest sea creature Tara had ever seen.

238

Its bulging red eyes bounced on the ends of two long stems. Its huge green mouth slammed open and shut with a hideous slurp.

Its enormous, cruel claws were the scariest part of all.

They waved frantically in the air. And snapped hard over Tara's head!

Tara shrieked. And tried to run.

Too late.

The monster crab snatched Tara up in its giant claws!

"Help me!" Tara screamed. "Somebody! Help me!"

The tiny voice in the shell burst out laughing. *"Help me! Help me!"* it mocked.

The huge claws of the monster crab pinched Tara's waist. Its pounding heart thundered in her ears. Slimy drool dripped from its hungry jaws.

Tara dropped the small shell to the ground. It rolled across the cave. And stopped.

A tiny hermit crab popped out.

"Look, Mommy, look!" the tiny voice screeched. *"I caught another one!"*

Tara screamed, and the giant claws snapped shut around her.

POISON IVY

Camp Wilbur.

What kind of a name for a camp is *Wilbur?*

I still can't believe my parents sent me here.

"Matt," they said, "you'll love it."

Well, I've got news for them. I don't love it. I don't even *like* it.

I've never been to sleepaway camp before. I'm a city kid. Why would I want to sleep away?

I like hanging out with my friends all summer. Rollerblading up and down the sidewalks. Hanging out at the playground. Going to the movies.

I like the city. How am I supposed to get used to all this fresh air?

Oh, well. I have four weeks to get used to it. Here I am in a tiny cabin. Not even any screens on the window.

I've got three bunkmates. Vinny and Mike aren't bad. They're twelve, like me.

Brad is the problem. He arrived on the first day

240

with *three* trunks. All filled with perfectly ironed clothes. Name tags sewn on every item.

Brad has blond hair pulled back in a ponytail down to his collar. He has blue eyes and about a thousand teeth when he smiles. He's real preppy-looking.

As soon as he walked into the cabin, Vinny and I held our noses and cried out, "What's that smell?"

"Yuck!" Mike sniffed several times and made a sour face. He turned to Brad. "What did you step in?"

"It's probably my aftershave," Brad replied calmly. He began carefully unpacking his trunks.

"Huh? Do you shave?" I asked him.

He shook his head. "No. I just like aftershave."

"Smells like sour milk," Vinny whispered. I don't think Brad heard him.

"It keeps my face fresh," Brad said, rubbing his smooth cheeks. "It comes in a spray can. Great stuff. You can borrow some if you like."

I groaned and hurried out the door. How was I going to stand living with a skunk for a whole month?

The cabins are on a low hill that overlooks the baseball field. I jogged down the hill, taking deep breaths, trying to forget that incredible odor.

Some guys from other cabins were starting a softball game. I asked if I could play, too.

The rules at Camp Wilbur are really loose. The place isn't organized at all. The rule is pretty much "Do whatever you want. Just don't get into trouble."

"You can play left field, Matt," a kid named David told me. He waved me to the outfield.

"Anybody got a glove?" I called, trotting over the grass.

"You won't need it. No one here can hit that far!" David joked. At least I *think* he was joking.

"Matt — watch out for that poison ivy," a kid named Jonathan called.

"Huh?" I glanced around. "What poison ivy?"

It wasn't hard to find. I spotted a large patch of the stuff at the edge of the outfield. It was starting to grow over the path that led to the main lodge and the dining hall.

Three leaves. A plant with three leaves. That's how you identify poison ivy. Even a city kid like me knows that.

I gazed at the square patch for a second. Then I stepped away from it and turned to home plate.

Just in time to see the first batter send a high fly ball sailing out to left field. Leaping around the poison ivy patch, I raised my hands and got under it.

"I've got it!" I called.

I didn't have it. The ball sailed over my head.

By the time I chased it down, the batter had

run the bases and was sitting in the grass drinking a Coke.

I told you I hate camp.

That night I was awakened by a loud scratching sound. I sat up in my bed and listened.

Scratch. Scratch. Strettttch.

The mosquitos are doing push-ups, I decided.

I settled back on my pillow.

But the sound repeated. Scratching. Stretching. A dry rustling from outside.

It wouldn't let me get back to sleep. I climbed out of bed and crossed the cabin to the window. My three bunkmates didn't stir.

I peered out at the purple night. The trees were tall black shadows against the clouded sky. Nothing moved. The leaves didn't rustle.

Something else was making the sound.

Scraaatch. Scraaaatch. Strettttch.

I was wide awake now. I decided to check it out. Silently, I pulled on my high-tops and crept out into the night.

I glanced up and down the hill. Totally dark. Not even any lights on in the counselors' cabins at the top.

No moon. No stars. No breeze.

I turned and followed the sound down the hill. It grew louder as I approached the baseball field.

Scraaatch. Scraaaatch. Strettttch.

I pictured giant snakes — as long as trains — stretching across the grass.

What could be making that weird sound?

I stepped on to the outfield. The grass was wet from the heavy dew. My sneakers slipped and slid.

What am I doing out here? I asked myself. Has all this fresh air warped my brain?

And then the clouds slowly pulled away from the moon. And as pale white light washed over the ground, I saw the creature.

Its head bobbed on its slender shoulders. Its hands shook on either side of its skinny body.

It rose up. Up.

"Ohhh!" I let out a low moan as I realized I was staring at a plant.

Or rather, a whole bunch of plants — rising up together!

I swallowed hard and started backing up.

The poison ivy patch! It was alive! Alive!

The three leaves formed a head and two hands. They bobbed as the plant stretched on its vine. Stretched over the baseball outfield.

Scraaaatch. Scraaaaatch. Strettttttch.

I couldn't believe it. It was horrifying.

Long tendrils reached out toward me, curling through the darkness. I turned and ran.

I slipped and fell in the dewy grass. But I scrambled to my feet and ran even faster.

I burst into the bunk. The screen door slammed behind me.

"Hey — !" Vinny cried out sleepily.

"Poison ivy!" I screamed. "Run! Run!"

"Huh?" Vinny sat up, rubbing his eyes.

"What's up?" Mike jumped down from his bunk. "Matt — what is it?"

Brad groaned. "Give me a break. It's still night!"

"Run!" I cried. "Poison ivy! It's coming! It's coming up the hill!"

They laughed.

Do you believe it? They laughed at me.

I guess it sounded kind of stupid. And I guess I was exaggerating just a little. It was so dark out there. I probably imagined the whole thing.

Vinny and Mike accused me of having a nightmare. Brad just groaned, rolled over, and went back to sleep.

It took me a while to calm down. But then I fell back to sleep, too. And dreamed about long green snakes.

The next morning, the poison ivy patch had crept over the entire baseball diamond. It covered the outfield and the bases. And it had spread over the path that led to the main lodge.

"Hey — watch out!"

Some guys playfully shoved each other into the poison ivy patch as we made our way to breakfast. Some kids showed off by rolling around in it. They picked up clumps and tossed them at each other.

They claimed it couldn't be poison ivy since it grew so fast.

They were wrong.

By that afternoon, about half the kids in camp had horrible red rashes all over. They scratched and moaned and groaned. The camp nurse ran out of lotion by dinnertime!

That afternoon, the poison ivy had spread over the soccer field and the archery ground. And it had climbed halfway up the hill to the cabins.

Luckily, no one in my cabin had touched the stuff. We sat at dinner at our table in the corner and watched the other kids scratch and complain and carry on.

The sun was sinking down behind the trees when we came out of the dining hall. We saw Larry and Craig, two of the counselors, carrying weed whackers and weed poison.

"See you later, guys!" Craig called. "We're going to knock out that poison ivy patch if it takes us all night!"

Craig and Larry slapped each other a high five. I watched them make their way into the evening mist, heading toward the poison ivy.

We never saw them again.

Late that night, all four of us in the cabin were awakened by the frightening scratching, stretching sounds. We hurried to the window and peered out.

A thick fog had lowered over the hill. We couldn't see a thing.

I shivered. The scratching sounds were really close. I wondered if I looked as scared as Vinny, Mike, and Brad.

We went back to bed. But I don't think any of us could fall asleep.

The next morning, I wearily pulled myself out of bed. I slipped into the T-shirt and shorts I had worn the day before. Still yawning, I crossed the cabin to the door.

Started to push it open.

Pushed harder. Harder.

The door was stuck.

"Hey — what's up?" Vinny called, yawning.

I told him the problem. "I can't get out the door."

"Then climb out the window," he suggested.

Good idea. I turned to the window.

"Oh, no!" I shrieked. I *wondered* why it was such a dark morning!

The window was completely covered over. Covered by a thick curtain of POISON IVY!

"It — it climbed up here!" I stammered, pointing.

My three friends were on their feet now. We were all wide awake. Staring at the heavy curtain of leaves that blocked out all light.

"The poison ivy must have grown over the door, too!" Vinny cried.

As we stared in horror, the ivy started poking into the cracks of the cabin. Long tendrils uncoiled and reached in for us.

"Help! Somebody — help!" Brad shrieked.

"Come on!" I cried. "Let's all try the door!"

Vinny, Mike, and I ran to the door and started to shove. We lowered our shoulders to the door and pushed with all our might.

Brad hung back, clinging to a wall, trembling in fright. I turned and saw the ivy tendrils reaching, reaching into the cabin.

We pushed again. A desperate shove.

Yes! The door budged. Just an inch. We could see the thick poison ivy that had grown over the entire cabin.

"Don't touch it!" Mike cried.

"Brad — come help us!" I called to him. "Hurry. We moved it a little. But we need your help."

"Hurry! We've got to get *out* of here!" Vinny urged.

His eyes on the uncoiling tendrils, Brad obediently joined us at the door.

"Everyone push on the count of three!" I cried. "One . . . two . . ."

Brad stepped to the front and lowered his shoulder to the door.

And to our surprise, the poison ivy appeared to creep back.

We pushed the door open another inch. Then another inch.

"Shove hard!" I cried. "It's retreating or something!"

"We need only a few more inches. Then we can slip through!" Mike shouted.

Brad leaned forward.

The plant backed up.

Brad leaned further.

The plant moved back.

"Why is it doing that?" Brad asked, turning to us.

"I think I know!" I cried excitedly. "It's your aftershave! The plant can't stand your aftershave!"

"That's impossible!" Brad cried. "*Everyone* likes my aftershave!"

"Get the can," I cried. "Let's try to spray the poison ivy!"

Vinny quickly ran to the shelf over Brad's bed. He grabbed the can of aftershave and brought it to the door. Then he raised the can, aimed it at the thick poison ivy — and sprayed.

The can went, *Phhhht.* Nothing came out.

"It's empty!" I shrieked. "We're doomed!"

"No! I have twelve more cans!" Brad cried. "But I don't want to waste them!"

Ignoring Brad's protests, we pulled the twelve cans from his trunk. I ran to the door. I raised the can. I sprayed.

The ivy slid back.

I sprayed again. The ivy slid back some more.

"It works!" I cried. "The horrible smell of the aftershave makes it retreat! Come on, guys — let's get it!"

The three of us edged out the door, spraying the thick plant as we moved.

"Don't use it all up!" Brad called. But his cry was nearly drowned out by the loud *whisssssh* of the spray cans.

Back, back, we pushed the poison ivy. It had covered the whole camp. All the cabins. All of the fields. It had even covered the dining hall.

We had our work cut out for us. But we knew we could do it.

We held our noses and sprayed. Pushing the poison ivy back. Watching it retreat with every smelly whiff.

Finally, after hours of spraying, we backed the plant into the lake. Its tendrils rose up as if surrendering. And then the whole plant sank beneath the water with a loud *whoooosh*.

"YAAAAAY!" A cheer rang out through the camp as everyone shouted out thanks and congratulations. The counselors carried my three friends and me around on their shoulders. And we danced and laughed and celebrated.

But not for long.

I was the first to spot the black funnel cloud in the sky.

"A t-tornado!" I stammered.

The black cloud whirled and spun toward us.

But it *can't* be a tornado, I realized. The black cloud was making a buzzing sound. A droning buzz.

Closer. Closer. The buzz grew louder as the dark cloud lowered over the camp.

"Uh-oh!" I heard Brad exclaim over the droning roar.

"Uh-oh?" I demanded. "What do you mean *uh-oh?*"

"I forgot one bad thing about my aftershave," Brad replied.

"One bad thing? What is it?" I asked.

"It attracts mosquitoes," he said.

THE SPIRIT OF
THE HARVEST MOON

Before last weekend, I'd never heard of the Pine Mountain Lodge. Neither had my parents. But then a brochure came in the mail. It advertised the lodge as "Wood Lake's 100-Year-Old Best-Kept Secret."

That's all my parents needed to hear. They have a thing about visiting out-of-the-way places. And the older the better.

"Oh, Jenny," Mom said to me, "doesn't it sound perfect? We'll go in September, over the long holiday weekend."

So here we were. At Pine Mountain Lodge. The only guests here.

"The whole place to ourselves!" Dad exclaimed as he carried in our luggage from the car.

"We'll be like part of the family," Mom said, signing the register. She gave Mr. Bass, the owner of the lodge, her cheeriest smile.

Mr. Bass grunted. He looked like Frankenstein without the green skin.

His son, Tyler, who is twelve like me, helped Dad carry our fishing poles. I nearly choked when I saw Tyler. He reminded me of a goldfish. He has light orange hair, bulging blue-gray eyes, and skin pulled so thin that you could see his veins right through it.

So far, I had only glimpsed the back of Mrs. Bass. She sat like a sack of laundry, in front of the TV.

The only normal-looking one here was Bravo, the Basses' golden retriever. He nuzzled his warm nose in my hand. "You're a good boy. Aren't you?" I said, reaching down to pet him.

"Don't get too many guests here after August," Mr. Bass said gruffly. He handed Dad the room key. "Too cold."

Dad grinned. "That's how we like it."

"Absolutely," Mom said. "We love the mountain air."

Mr. Bass led us down a long, narrow hallway to our rooms. One dirty lightbulb hanging from the ceiling cast a creepy yellow glow on the walls.

"Well, here it is," Mr. Bass said as we approached the end of the hall. He opened the door to two connecting rooms. The first room had knotty pine paneling, a rickety bed piled high with scratchy woolen blankets, and a worn braided rug on the floor.

Across the room, next to a beat-up old dresser, I saw a small, smudged window. On the other side of the dresser stood a green door that led outside.

Everything in the room smelled like my dirty gym socks.

I walked through the first room to the second room and peeked inside. It looked exactly the same as the first.

I wandered over to the green door, jerked it open, and poked my head out. It was growing dark out. So I couldn't really see much — just a porch, and, beyond it, trees. Lots and lots of trees.

"Time to close up now," Mr. Bass barked. I jumped. I hadn't seen him there.

I ducked out of his way, and he tugged the porch door shut. Then he locked it. Next, he pulled a set of heavy wooden shutters across the front of my window and latched them securely on the top and bottom.

"What are you doing?" I asked.

"Locking up," he said.

"Excuse me, Mr. Bass," I replied in my most polite voice. "I like to sleep with the window open."

Mr. Bass stared hard at me. "Too cold at night to do that," he said flatly. "Don't want to catch a chill, do you?"

"I guess not," I answered. I glanced into Mom and Dad's room. Their window was shuttered, too.

After Mr. Bass left, I unpacked my clothes. He was right. It was freezing up here. I climbed into bed wearing two pairs of socks, sweatpants, and a T-shirt with a sweatshirt over it.

I pulled the blanket up to my chin and studied the room once again. No TV. Just like Mom and Dad to find the one place on the planet without TV!

I spent the next hour or so reading. Then called good night through the connecting door.

"Sleep tight, Jenny," Mom called back. "See you in the morning!"

I guess I was pretty tired because I fell asleep right away. But I kept waking up. I couldn't find a really comfortable position. As I fluffed up my pillow for the tenth time that night, I heard a voice call out my name.

No. Can't be. It's the middle of the night. I plopped my head down on the pillow and closed my eyes.

"Jen-ny."

There! Again! I did hear it! Was it Mom or Dad? It didn't sound like either one of them. Too low and gruff.

I sat up and shivered in the dark. A strong wind rattled the shutters.

"Jen-ny."

"Is that you, Dad?" I quivered. No answer. I knew it wasn't my dad. The voice wasn't coming from his room. It came from outside. From the porch.

"Jen-ny," it cried again. "It's cold out here."

My heart hammered away. What should I do? I crept out of bed to the green door. I leaned my ear against it. "Who's there?" I croaked.

No answer.

I flew back to bed and yanked the covers up to my ears. And waited.

"Jenny! Jenny!" My eyes jerked open. Sunlight peeked through the shutters. I must have fallen asleep.

"Time to get up!" Mom chirped in the doorway. "Did you sleep well?"

"Uh, I was cold," I mumbled. "How did you sleep?"

"Like a rock," Mom sang out happily. "I love this crisp mountain air."

Did I really hear a voice last night? It must have been a dream. Just a weird dream.

After breakfast, Mom and Dad decided to hike up to Devil's Peak.

"Aren't you coming along?" Dad asked as he and Mom buttoned up their identical red-and-black-checkered jackets. Then they tugged on matching red-and-black caps with furry red ear-flaps. Boy, did they look dumb.

"Mr. Bass says the view up there is spectacular," Mom explained. "Come on, honey. Put your jacket on."

I hate hiking. "Um. Can I hang out with Tyler? And, uh, explore the woods around here?"

"Well, okay," Mom replied. "But don't go too far. We won't be gone long."

Tyler and I played a few games of horseshoes. Then he gave me a tour of the lodge while Bravo tagged along. The tour took two minutes. There was the lodge and then there was the woods. Period.

By now, things were getting pretty boring. Tyler didn't talk much. We sat cross-legged on the porch, staring at each other.

"So, Tyler," I began. "Do you have any friends around here?"

He stared at me with those bulging eyes. "Not really," he answered. "But I don't mind. I like playing alone."

"Oh," I said. I kind of expected him to answer that way. Then I thought about the strange voice from last night.

"Does anybody live near here?" I asked.

"No," he replied. "The next house is a mile away."

"Are you sure there's no one else around here?" I asked. "Because last night I thought I heard someone out here on the porch."

Tyler's body stiffened. "What do you mean?"

I told him about the creepy voice calling my name. "But I'm sure I dreamed the whole thing," I ended.

"Well, you didn't," Tyler said.

257

"What do you mean?" I gasped.

Tyler moved in close. "There's something I should tell you," he whispered. "I'm only telling you this for your own good. Okay?"

I nodded.

"This lodge is haunted. That voice you heard was the spirit, calling to you."

"The sp-spirit?" I stammered. "What kind of spirit?" I reached out for Bravo and hugged him close to me.

Tyler's eyes narrowed. "A long, long time ago, a tourist hiked up Devil's Peak and never came down."

I gulped loudly.

"They say," Tyler continued, "that his spirit turned into a wandering mist. And the mist takes over a different body every year."

"Really?" I croaked.

"Uh-huh," Tyler said. "A different body every year. At the end of each summer, during the harvest moon, it finds a new body. A warm body. That's why we lock the doors and shutters at night. To keep the spirit from coming inside."

I swallowed hard. I knew we shouldn't have come here. I *knew* it.

"What exactly happens if the spirit comes inside?"

Tyler lowered his voice. "If you let it inside, it will jump out of the body it's in and enter yours.

Then *you* will be forced to live on Earth for a year as a wandering mist."

"That's ridiculous," I blurted. "You're making this up. You're just trying to scare me."

"*Jen-ny!*" I nearly jumped out of my skin. I turned to see Mom and Dad waving from the end of the trail. I was never so happy to see my parents. Even in those dumb jackets.

I ran to them, practically knocking them down. "Mom! Dad!"

"Hi, Jen." Dad smiled. His cheeks glowed rosy red from the crisp mountain air. "Did you have fun?"

"Uh, sure," I answered. "I'm glad you're back, though." And I meant it, too.

That night, I didn't look forward to bedtime. But I kept telling myself that Tyler was just trying to scare me. Nothing would happen. Tyler was just a creep. Who had no friends. And I could see why.

After Mr. Bass came by to close the shutters, I crawled into bed. I tried really hard to fall asleep. I couldn't.

I was so wide awake, I heard Dad snoring through the door. I hummed along with his snores. And began to drift off. . . .

"*Jen-ny! It's cold outside.*"

My eyes popped wide open. I instantly began

to shake all over. The voice. It was real. Not a dream.

"Jenny!" it called louder. *"It's cold outside."*

I flew out of bed. "Mom! Dad!" I screamed. I shoved open the door to their room and jumped into bed with them.

Mom bolted straight up. "Jenny! What's wrong?" she cried.

My heart pounded in my chest. "A ghost is after me," I sobbed. Then I told them Tyler's story.

"Oh, honey," Mom said. "Tyler's just playing a mean joke on you. Dad will talk to him in the morning."

"But I heard the voice, Mom. I know I did." I sobbed even harder.

"Calm down, Jen," Dad said softly. "It's only your imagination."

"It is not," I wailed. "I'm not kidding about this. I'm really not."

"We know, dear," Mom replied.

But they didn't know. They had no idea.

The next morning, I shuffled into the dining room. Tired and confused. I sat with my parents, even though I could tell Tyler wanted me to sit with him. But I wasn't going to let that creep near me.

Bravo curled up underneath my chair. As I ate my scrambled eggs, I fed him little scraps of bacon. He took my mind off Tyler.

260

But I couldn't help stealing a glance at the window. I saw that Tyler hardly ate a thing. In fact, he never seemed to eat much at all. No wonder he was so thin and pale.

Tyler shoved his chair away from his table and headed for ours. Bravo whimpered and nudged my knee. My stomach churned.

Tyler grinned at me. "Want to play some more horseshoes, Jenny?"

My heart began to thud. "No," I said, my eyes glued to my plate. Suddenly I knew. Tyler was pale. Tyler never ate. Tyler's own dog feared him. *Tyler was the spirit!*

"Please, Jenny?" Tyler begged.

"I'm busy," I told him. Then I gave Mom and Dad a look that said don't butt in.

I hung around with Mom and Dad all day. I even hiked up a nature trail with them. I'd do anything to avoid Tyler.

At dinner that night, I hardly touched my food. On the way back to our rooms, Dad gazed outside. "Look, Jenny! The harvest moon!"

A chill shot through my entire body. Hadn't Tyler said that the spirit finds a new body during the harvest moon?

"What's wrong, honey?" Mom asked. "You look upset."

"I want to go home right now!" I wailed. "If we stay here, the wandering spirit is going to take over my body."

"Jenny," Mom cooed, "you know better than to believe a silly ghost story."

"But there is a ghost!" I cried. "Why won't you believe me?"

Mom just shook her head from side to side. But she walked into my room with me and sat on the bed for a long time.

Then, just before Mr. Bass came to lock the shutters, Mom peered out the window to check the porch. "Jenny! Look!" she said. "Bravo's out there. He'll protect you."

Knowing Bravo sat out there did make me feel a little better. And even though I'm too old to be tucked in, I let Mom tuck me in that night.

"Sleep tight," she said, kissing me good night. "If you need us, Dad and I will be in the lounge playing bridge with the Basses."

"Bridge!" I shouted. "You aren't going to be next door?"

"Jenny," Mom said firmly. "Stop this. You're acting like a baby." Then she left.

I lay very still for a long time. The wind howled through the woods. It blew hard against the porch door. A tree branch scraped against my window. I covered myself with three blankets, but I still shivered underneath them.

I was all alone.

I waited.

Waited for the spirit to call my name.

No voice. Nothing but the sound of the howling wind and the rattling shutters.

BANG! Someone knocked hard on the door. "Jenny. It's cold and windy out here. Let me in. It's me, Tyler!"

I clutched the blankets close to me. He was here. Here to steal my body. "Go away!" I shouted. "You're evil!"

"Please! Let me inside! I lost my key! Jenny, please! Don't leave me out here. It's so cold. Please!"

"No!" I screamed. "Never. Never!" The wind shook the shutters hard now. Tyler kept banging. Tears ran down my face. My whole body trembled. "Go away!" I yelled.

Then I heard Bravo barking. Good boy, Bravo! He must have heard my cries. His paws clattered up the porch steps. He snarled angrily at Tyler.

"Stop it!" Tyler shouted at the dog. "Leave me alone!" I heard Tyler stumble down the stairs.

And then — silence. Bravo had chased Tyler away. The horror had passed.

I was safe.

I let out a long, relieved sigh.

Soft whimpering cut through the quiet. Bravo!

I rushed to the green door, opened it, and Bravo trudged in.

Bravo gazed up at me gratefully. His sad brown eyes stared up to meet mine. "Thanks, Jenny," he said. "It's cold outside."

Even More TALES TO GIVE YOU

Goosebumps®

THE CHALK CLOSET

I wiped the sweat from my forehead. It was only seven-thirty in the morning. But the thermometer had already hit 95 degrees. And the air conditioner on the bus was broken.

This was not going to be a good day.

"Hey, kid," the bus driver yelled. "End of the line!"

End of the line was right, I thought. I jumped off the bus and checked out the school.

Millwood Junior High. It was a wreck.

The school stood four stories high. Its red brick — blackened with years and years of city soot — was chipped and crumbling. All the windows on the second floor were boarded over with plywood. And the roof sagged.

"Better get used to it, Travis," I told myself. I dragged myself up the steps. "You're going to be here all summer."

No matter what my mom says, I didn't exactly *try* to mess up sixth grade. Like lots of major disasters, it just happened. I tried to study. But stuff kept getting in the way.

Like when my cat, Lillie, had her kittens.

Or when my brother got a new computer game.

Or when something was on TV.

So . . . I messed up. And now, here I was in summer school. And looking at the school, I could see it was the pits.

I opened the rusty door and stepped inside. The main hallway was dark. I could barely see. The air was dry and smelled really stale. I started to cough.

I took a drink from the water fountain beside me. The water was warm and cloudy. And it tasted old.

I glanced up and down the hall. The place seemed deserted — no kids, no teachers.

No one.

I made my way down the hall and found a door marked PRINCIPAL. I jiggled the knob. Locked.

I checked out the classrooms. Empty. Except for the squeak of my sneakers, the place was totally dead.

What was going on? Was I here on the wrong day? Or was it the wrong school?

Then a voice broke the silence: "Travis Johnson?"

I nearly jumped out of my skin. I spun around and faced the tallest, palest man I'd ever seen.

"Y-yes?" I stammered.

"You're late, Travis," he said. His lips were unbelievably thin, and they hardly moved when he spoke.

Just great, I thought. My first day in summer school and I'm already in trouble. Way to go, Travis.

I followed the tall man to the classroom at the end of the hall. Of course, it was the only room I hadn't checked out. It was filled with kids. Many of them I'd never seen before.

Dooley Atwater and Janice Humphries were there. They came from my regular school. Janice was shy but okay. Dooley was the biggest goof in my whole school. He knew a million ways to get out of homework.

"The last row, Travis," the teacher said. "Be quick about it." Then he picked up a piece of chalk from the chalk tray and wrote MR. GRIMSLEY on the board.

Mr. Grimsley folded his arms across his chest and scanned the room. From the sour look on his face, I could tell he wasn't too thrilled about what he saw.

"Let me warn you, boys and girls," Mr. Grimsley announced. "I have very little patience with students who don't care to study. Got that, Dooley?"

"Me?" Dooley asked. "Why me?"

"I know about you, Dooley," Mr. Grimsley said, thumbing through a stack of cards. "I know about

269

every single one of you. You're bright kids. But you're all lazy. Hear this warning. You won't get away with anything in my class."

Dooley smirked.

Mr. Grimsley glared at him. Then he continued, "You must do your homework every night — or be prepared to go to the chalk closet."

"The chalk closet?" one of the girls asked nervously. "What's that?"

"If you don't turn in your homework tomorrow morning, you'll find out, Amanda," Mr. Grimsley said.

"No teacher gives homework the first night!" Dooley protested. "You've got to be kidding!"

"I do not kid," Mr. Grimsley declared. "Now let's get down to work."

The first night for homework, we had to write five reasons we'd want to be a Pilgrim. As soon as I reached home, I sat down at the kitchen table and wrote down three:

1. Get to travel a lot.
2. Eat dinner with some really cool Indians.
3. Don't have to recycle.

Then my brother, Chris, came in. "Want to go to the Ice Cream Igloo?" he asked. "They have a new flavor — peanut butter marshmallow mint."

I didn't have a choice. I had to go — right?

After dinner there was a *Lethal Weapon* movie on TV. No way I could miss that.

So, when I arrived at school the next morning,

I still had only three reasons why someone would want to be a Pilgrim.

But it was three more reasons than Dooley had.

"Your homework, Dooley," Mr. Grimsley demanded.

"You have to give me a break," Dooley replied, "just this once, Mr. Grimsley."

"I have to?" Mr. Grimsley asked, arching his eyebrows.

"It kind of looks that way," Dooley began. "You see, a car alarm went off right outside my window. And it was so loud, I couldn't think. And by the time someone turned it off — "

"It was way past your bedtime?" Mr. Grimsley asked.

"Well, not exactly," Dooley admitted.

"But you did your homework anyway — and then when you woke up, the cat had eaten it. Is that what happened, Dooley?"

"Well, something like that," Dooley said, smiling a little.

"Sorry, Dooley. I don't give breaks," Mr. Grimsley declared. "It's time to go to the chalk closet." Then he stepped into the hall.

Dooley started to follow. But when he reached the doorway, he stopped. "I forgot my textbook," he said, turning back.

Mr. Grimsley grinned. A creepy grin. "The chalk closet isn't study hall, Dooley."

"So what is it?"

Mr. Grimsley didn't answer.

Dooley shrugged. Then he followed the teacher down the corridor. I heard their footsteps fade as they walked up the stairs to the second floor.

Mr. Grimsley returned in a couple of minutes — without Dooley. At recess, Dooley didn't show up. Or at lunch. Or the next day. Or any day after that.

I didn't miss him, and I didn't feel sorry for him either. I figured he was kicked out of school. And he had it coming to him.

But at the end of the week, the same thing happened to Marty Blank. Marty sat next to me. I didn't know him too well, but he seemed okay.

Grimsley handed back the homework he had graded the night before. I heard Marty groan when he received his. There was a big red *F* at the top.

"You didn't study, did you, Marty?" Mr. Grimsley asked.

Marty shook his head. "I couldn't," he said. "I had Little League."

"Little League was more important than your schoolwork?" Mr. Grimsley demanded coldly.

"It was the big game," Marty explained. "The team was counting on me."

"The chalk closet, Marty," Mr. Grimsley replied.

"But I did my homework, Mr. Grimsley," Marty

protested. "I'm not like Dooley. It's not like I didn't try!"

Mr. Grimsley picked up Marty's homework. "*F*," he stated. "I guess you didn't try hard enough — did you, Marty? Let me show you to the chalk closet."

Marty's mouth dropped open. It looked as if he were about to say something. But he didn't. He just followed Mr. Grimsley down the hall.

Four days later, Marty still hadn't shown up at school.

"Maybe Grimsley kicked him out of school," I told Janice. "Or maybe Marty convinced his parents to let him quit," I suggested. "For all we know, Marty could be having a great time at the lake."

"For all we know," Janice said, "Marty could still be in the chalk closet."

Janice and I gazed up at the second floor.

"That's probably where Mr. Grimsley took them," she said. "Those boarded-up windows give me the creeps."

We stared up at the windows in silence. "Travis, what do you think is in the chalk closet?"

"Chalk."

"Very funny, Travis. You might not be scared, but I am. I'm really scared. I got *D*'s on my last three assignments. What if I'm next?"

What if *I'm* next? I thought with a shiver.

273

The next morning, Janice's hands shook when Grimsley handed back our assignments.

"B-but I worked really hard on it," she stammered. "I really did."

I didn't need to see her grade. I knew from Janice's voice that she had failed.

Grimsley didn't say a word. He just walked to the door. And waited.

Janice stood up.

Grimsley waited.

She slowly made her way to the door. Then they both disappeared down the hall.

Mr. Grimsley returned in a minute or so, and the class went on as usual. Right before the bell rang, Mr. Grimsley made an announcement. "We're going to have a math test tomorrow. And I expect everyone to get an *A*."

An *A*? I'd never gotten an *A* on a math test — ever.

The bell rang and I dashed outside to wait for Janice. I thought about the test while I waited.

And waited. And waited.

Janice never showed up.

I ran all the way home and grabbed the phone. I dialed Janice's number. The phone rang and rang. No answer.

I looked up Marty's telephone number in the phone book and called him. A recorded message

274

announced that the Blanks' number had been disconnected.

That night I tried to study. I never tried harder at anything in my whole life. But I was just too frightened to concentrate. What if Grimsley sends me to the chalk closet? I asked myself over and over again.

When I finished the test the next day, I knew I had blown it. I'd be lucky if I passed. But I'd have to wait till Monday — two whole days — to find out.

The weekend dragged. I couldn't think about anything except that stupid math test. And the chalk closet.

Monday morning finally arrived. My feet felt like lead as I walked up the steps to school. This was not going to be a good day.

I took my seat and stared straight ahead at Mr. Grimsley. He sat at his desk. The pile of test papers was neatly stacked in front of him.

He cleared his throat. "I'm going to return your test papers now," he said. "Most of you did very well."

He didn't look at me when he said that, I thought. But what did that mean? Was it good? Or bad? I didn't know.

"Bennett, Amanda," he began. "*A.*"

Oh, no! He's calling out the grades, too!

"Drake, Josh — A. Evers, Brian — A. Franklin, Marnie — A."

Wow! I couldn't believe it. Everyone was getting A's.

I broke out into a cold sweat. I wiped my sweaty palms on my pants. Hey, don't worry, I told myself. Everyone's getting A's. I probably got one, too.

Grimsley continued calling out names and grades. I was next.

My temples pounded as I watched him stare down at my paper.

"Johnson, Travis — D."

The whole class gasped.

"You know, I — I can do better than that, Mr. Grimsley," I stuttered. "Let me take a makeup test. Okay? You'll see."

"No makeup tests in my class," the teacher replied sternly.

"Please, Mr. Grimsley!" I cried. "Don't take me to the chalk closet! Please!"

"Come, Travis," Mr. Grimsley said. "You don't want to upset the other students, do you?"

I glanced around the room at the other kids. A few of them stared at me. Their eyes filled with horror. But the others had their heads buried in their textbooks. They pretended that they didn't even know what was going on!

"Don't you care?" I screamed at them.

No one answered.

Mr. Grimsley stood at the door.

"Come, Travis."

My knees shook so hard I could barely walk.

I followed Mr. Grimsley into the hall.

The front door was at the end of the hall. Mr. Grimsley's legs were longer, but I was younger. Could I outrun him?

"Don't even think about it," he said, without turning back. "It's locked."

I followed Mr. Grimsley up the stairs. It was almost pitch-black on the second floor. The only light came from a naked bulb dangling from the ceiling.

I trailed behind Mr. Grimsley. Past Room 269. Then 270. Then 271.

When we came to 272, he stopped and turned toward me. "Good-bye, Travis," he said.

I took a step back. I couldn't speak. I was terrified.

Mr. Grimsley twisted the doorknob. Then he gave the door a little push. It creaked open.

I peeked in over his shoulder. My heart pounded. What would I see in there?

I couldn't see anything. It was totally dark.

Mr. Grimsley gripped my shoulder and shoved me forward.

I stumbled inside.

The door slammed shut behind me!

I was locked inside — inside the chalk closet!

I squinted. Waited for my eyes to adjust to the darkness.

And then I saw them.

Dooley. Marty. Janice.

And behind them, shadows of other kids I'd never seen before. Transparent figures. Ghosts.

I squinted harder. They were all doing something. They were all holding their hands up in the air.

Why? I wondered. Why are they doing that?

That's when I heard it.

That's when I knew the chalk closet was the worst place on earth to be.

My hands flew up in the air, too.

Up to my ears. To cover them.

To drown out the screeching.

The horrible screeching sound of chalk on a chalkboard — the sound that I'd have to listen to forever.

HOME SWEET HOME

"Sharon!" my little sister screamed. "Sha-RON!"

It always makes Alice nuts when I fool around with her dollhouse. That's why I keep doing it. I just can't resist.

It's bad enough to be twelve and still sharing a room with my little sister. But that dollhouse takes up way too much space.

Alice is always playing with it. She has a family of dolls that are the exact right size for the tiny furniture. They even have names — Shawna and Bill, the mom and dad dolls, and Timmy and Toni, the kids. They all have plastic hair.

"SHARON!"

I strolled down the hall to our room. Alice knelt in front of the dollhouse, putting everything back the way it had been.

"You called?" I asked.

She glared at me over her shoulder. "You changed the furniture all around again."

"So?"

279

"And you stuck Shawna upside down in the sink."

"Give me a break, Alice. Shawna is a doll. And in case you hadn't noticed, that's a fake sink. It's not like it's going to mess up her hair or anything."

"You are so mean!"

I made a face. "Get a life. Normal nine-year-olds don't spend all their time playing with stupid dollhouses."

"It isn't stupid!" she shouted.

"Is so!"

She stuck out her bottom lip and pouted. I felt bad. Well, a little, anyway. "Look, I'm sorry, okay?" I muttered.

I flopped down on my bed. Alice didn't say anything for a while. Then she set the roof back on the dollhouse and stood up.

"Sharon?"

"Yeah?"

"Want to ride over to a garage sale with me?"

"Don't you have any friends?" I asked.

"None of them can go. Besides, it's on East Bay Street, and none of us are allowed to go that far by ourselves. Please?" she begged.

I don't know why I agreed to go. I really don't. Maybe because I felt guilty for messing up her dollhouse. Whatever. A few minutes later, we hopped on our bikes and headed out.

*　　*　　*

We turned onto East Bay Street. Alice stopped in front of a big, old house set way back from the road. I spotted the name on the mailbox. "Hey, this is Mrs. Forster's place!" I cried.

"Uh-huh."

I glanced up at the house. A curtain twitched, and I had the feeling that somebody had peeked out at us. "Mrs. Forster is really strange," I told Alice. "At least, that's what I've heard. Some kids told me she has weird powers. They said she can change herself into animals."

"No way!" exclaimed Alice.

"I saw her one time," I insisted. "She's totally scary. She's got big, black eyes that glare right through you. Her hair is as black as her eyes, with a streak of white right down the middle that looks like a lightning bolt."

Alice stuck her tongue out at me. "What's the matter, Sharon? Scared?"

That got me. "Of course I'm not scared."

"So come on." She started pedaling up the long gravel driveway. I followed slowly. I didn't want to be there. Mrs. Forster *did* scare me. But no way was I going to look lame in front of my little sister.

Alice stopped in front of the garage. Two long tables had been set up to hold the stuff Mrs. Forster wanted to sell. But nobody else was there, not even to take the money.

"How come no one is around?" I asked.

Alice shrugged. "Maybe she's gone to lunch or something."

I turned to stare at the house. The windows seemed to stare back like black, rectangular eyes. "I guess we'd better go."

"Not yet." Alice pointed toward the nearest table. "There's a sign. It says 'Leave payment on the table.' "

"Too weird," I muttered.

"Well, I'm going to look," Alice replied. She dove in. I mean, this stuff was heaven for Alice. And I knew exactly what she was looking for.

"You don't really think Mrs. Forster is going to have dollhouse furniture, do you?" I teased.

"Even if she doesn't, maybe she's selling some lace or something I can use to make curtains. She's got some really old stuff here, and . . . hey!" Alice cried. "Look!"

She picked up a tiny object from the table and held it up. "It's a little doll lamp."

"Let's see." I ran my finger along the shade. It felt cool and grainy, like a frog's skin. A shiver went up my spine. "Yuck!" I exclaimed.

"It's perfect for my living room," Alice protested. "And she only wants two bucks for it — exactly what I brought."

She set the money on the table and tucked the lamp into her pocket. "Aren't you going to buy anything?"

No way. I didn't want anything that creepy woman owned. But I didn't want Alice to know how frightened I was. So I started poking through the pile of stuff on the far table. A big china bowl caught my eye. I thought it was kind of pretty, so I picked it up.

"Be careful with that," Alice warned.

A huge, hairy spider crawled over the rim of the bowl. It scuttled over my hand. I screamed and flung the bowl away from me. It shattered into a thousand pieces across the concrete.

"Sharon! Look what you did!" Alice gasped.

"I hate spiders!" I cried. "Hate them, hate them, hate them!"

I gazed up at the house. A woman stood at one of the upstairs windows, staring down at me. I could see the stripe of pale hair glinting in the sunlight. Mrs. Forster!

I panicked. I totally panicked. "Let's get out of here!" I cried.

We grabbed our bikes and rode like crazy down the drive. I glanced over my shoulder. Mrs. Forster remained at the window, glaring at me with her round, black eyes.

We didn't stop until we reached home. Alice ran upstairs with the lamp. I guess she forgot all about Mrs. Forster once she returned to her weird little dollhouse world.

But *I* didn't. That night, I dreamed about the old woman. In the dream, she knew me. She talked to me. "You broke my bowl," she whispered in a harsh, raspy voice. "And you didn't pay for it. But you will pay, Sharon. I promise. Now you are my problem. And I always take care of my problems."

She leaned over me. Her hair fell down and tickled my face. I opened my eyes.

And found myself staring at the biggest, ugliest spider I'd ever seen. It dangled from the ceiling on a long white strand. As it swiveled to stare down at me, I saw a white stripe down its back.

It tickled my face with its hairy front legs.

"Mom!" I screamed. "Dad! Help!"

A few seconds later, Mom and Dad came running in. I scrambled out of the bed and flung myself at them.

"It's a spider!" I shrieked. "A big, hairy spider right on my pillow!"

Mom clicked the light on. No spider. No spider anywhere in the room.

Only Alice, sitting up in her bed, her mouth open wide in surprise.

Dad checked under the covers and all around the bed. I kept watching for it to scuttle across the carpet.

But no. No sign of it. "It was right there," I insisted. "It talked to me."

Alice giggled. "Wow, are you messed up, Sharon. A talking spider?"

284

I forced a laugh, too. It *was* really silly —
wasn't it?

The next day, I rode my bike over to a friend's
house. I stayed longer than I had meant to. When
I realized how late it was, I jumped on my bike
and raced home.

By the time I reached our neighborhood, trees
cast long shadows across the ground. One more
block, and I'd be home. I checked for traffic, then
started across the road.

"Huh?" I cried out as a car roared out of nowhere. I froze. Stared into bright headlights.

Then I swerved so hard my bike nearly flipped
over. Tires squealed. I could feel a breeze as the
car sped past me.

My legs started to shake, so I got off my bike
and sat down on the curb. Wow! A close one! I
couldn't understand where that car had come
from. I'd looked both ways, after all.

A faint scrabbling sound floated up from the
storm sewer beside me. I peered into the dark
opening. I couldn't see anything at first.

Then something moved in the darkness. Something small and quick. My heart began to pound.

A big hairy spider clambered out of the sewer
onto the curb. It had a pale stripe down its back.

I leaped up and ran down the block and into my
house. It took me a while to get my breath back.

This didn't make any sense. Where were all the spiders coming from?

I didn't know the answer. But I did know one thing: I hadn't been dreaming last night. I kept picturing that pale stripe down the spider's back.

I shuddered. I suddenly felt so afraid. I didn't even go back out to get my bike.

After dinner, I headed upstairs to do my homework. Alice had dragged the dollhouse out into the middle of the room. Tiny chairs and tables, beds and bathtubs littered the floor.

"Hey," I protested. "You're trashing my side of the room. I can't even get to my desk to do my homework."

"So do it on your bed," Alice shot back.

I started to my bed — and heard a *crunch*.

"Oh!" I gazed down and saw that I had stepped on one of the dolls. Shawna. Her hand had broken off.

Alice instantly burst into tears. "Look what you did!" she wailed.

"It was an accident!" I cried. "I didn't mean to!"

"You did. You hate my dollhouse. And you hate Shawna. That's why you always stick her head in the sink. And that's why you stepped on her!" Sobbing, she grabbed the broken doll and ran out of the room.

With a sigh, I flopped down onto my bed. "Stupid dollhouse!"

I glanced up. My breath stopped. "No!"

The spider.

The spider with the white stripe.

It clung to the ceiling with its thick, hairy legs.

If it let go, it would land on my face.

I shrieked and rolled off the bed.

When I glanced up, the spider was gone.

For the next couple of days, Alice wouldn't even talk to me. She walked past me as if I were invisible.

Just before dinner on Friday, I caught up with her in the hall. "Alice, listen," I pleaded. "I'm sorry about Shawna. I didn't mean to step on her. I really didn't."

She stared at me for a moment. "It's okay. Dad fixed her hand."

I felt better. But I just couldn't keep from teasing her. "I promise I won't put Shawna's head in the sink again," I offered.

"You won't?"

"Nope. I'll work on Bill for a change."

She stuck her tongue out at me. Then she spun around and headed for the dining room. Probably to tell.

I started after her. But then I heard the sound of glass tinkling above me, and gazed up at the chandelier. Its glass prisms quivered, sending rainbows shooting around the room. It happened every time a breeze blew in from the front window.

Except the window was closed.

The tinkling of glass grew louder. The prisms shook wildly. Before I could move out from under it, the chandelier broke away from the ceiling.

I dove to the wall.

The chandelier crashed to the floor beside me.

I shrieked and stared down at it.

Stared. Stared down at the spider.

"You — you tried to kill me!" I shouted at it. "I know who you are. I know what you're trying to do!"

I spun away. I had to get out of there. Away from the vicious old woman in her spider body.

I took three steps — and felt something drop heavily into my hair.

My eyes moved to the hall mirror. I saw it. I saw the spider in my hair.

I felt its hot breath on the back of my neck.

Felt its hairy legs slide through my hair, over my scalp.

"Noooooo!" With a cry of horror, I pulled at it with both hands. But it clung tightly to my hair. Clung so tight. So tight.

I screamed again. Couldn't anyone hear me?

I ran into my room. "Alice — help me! Help!"

She wasn't there.

And then I felt the spider legs — the points, the sharp points — digging into my scalp. Digging into my head.

Into my brain!

"Noooooooooo!"

Over my scream, I heard dry laughter. "You are a *tiny* problem," the spider rasped. So close to my ear.

The pain shot through my head. Through my whole body.

"You are a tiny, tiny problem."

Was the spider growing bigger? I felt its hot, spongy body press against my back.

Was it bigger now? No. It wasn't bigger.

I was smaller.

I was shrinking. Shrinking fast. Standing in the shadow of the hideous spider that still clung to me. Still drilled its forearms into my scalp.

"I have my revenge," the old woman's spider voice rasped in my ear. "You are a tiny problem now."

"Noooo!" With another cry of horror, I broke free. Broke free and ran into the dollhouse. Hid inside the dollhouse.

I was as tiny as a doll. I could hide there. I could be safe.

My life now? It isn't as bad as it sounds.

Alice has fixed up the dollhouse really nice. I'm comfortable inside it. My room is really great. She even put in a little color TV!

I feel very safe and protected.

I just have one big problem.

Alice.

Here she comes now.

"Hey — put me down! I mean it, Alice! Put me down!"

Why does she think it's so funny to stick my head in the sink?

DON'T WAKE MUMMY

The day the deliverymen brought a mummy case to our house, I tried not to act scared. I knew my older sister, Kim, would tease me forever if she knew how I felt.

"Oooh! A coffin," Kim said. "Are you scared, Jeff?"

Kim thinks that just because she is thirteen and I'm only eleven that I'm some kind of scaredy-cat. She's always jumping out at me and trying to spook me. That's Kim's only hobby. Teasing me and telling me I'm a wimp.

Dad is the curator of the town museum. So I've seen a lot of mummy cases — at the museum. This was the first one delivered to our house.

It was all a big mistake. But Mom had the men carry it into the basement. She warned us not to go near it.

After the men left, Kim and I stood at the top of the stairs, looking down into the basement.

"I've heard about these mummies," Kim said,

narrowing her eyes. "They wake at night and search for prey."

"I don't believe you," I said.

"No, really," she insisted. "Mummies are jealous of living people. So they creep around after dark and steal the life from people."

"Well, that mummy isn't stealing anyone's life. That box is chained up tight."

"You know, Jeff, the worst thing about you is that you're such a wimp," Kim declared.

"I am not," I protested.

"If you're not a coward, then why don't you go down there and check out the mummy?" she demanded.

"No way!" I told her. "Are you crazy? You heard what Mom said."

"Why don't you go down there and touch the box? Touch it one time. I bet you're too scared to even do that," she said.

"Fine," I said. "I'll do it." I regretted it even before the words finished coming out of my mouth.

The light switch was broken in the basement. It was so dark down there, it even smelled dark, like clay. I walked down the stairs slowly.

The box sat in the middle of the room. Everything else was covered in a layer of dust. But that box was spotless. The lid was so glossy it seemed to glow.

Step by step, I drew closer to the coffin. The only sound I could hear was the beating of my heart.

The air felt cold and moist. I rubbed my chilly, sticky palms together, working up my courage.

You can do it, I told myself. There's nothing to be afraid of.

I reached out my hand to touch the shiny black box — and the lid moved!

The chains clanked.

My heartbeat stopped for a moment.

I couldn't help it — I screamed.

Then I turned and hurtled up the stairs without looking back.

The basement door was shut! Kim had closed it behind me!

I threw my body against it and burst into the kitchen.

Kim sat at the dinner table, laughing at me.

"The mummy is alive!" I shouted. "The chains rattled! The lid moved!"

She roared with laugher. "You're such a jerk."

She strode over to the basement door, threw it open, and peered down at the box. "There's nothing to see," she announced.

She was right. The lid was closed. The chains were in place.

My imagination had tricked me again.

Or had it?

                    *   *   *

I had a hard time getting to sleep that night. No matter how I twisted my body, I couldn't get comfortable.

Why couldn't I get to sleep? I looked around my room. Everything was in its place. My books stood up straight on the bookshelf. My computer sat on my desk, casting a shadow over a pile of notebooks. I had thrown my clothes on the floor and they were clumped together near the closet door.

Go to sleep, I told myself. Everything is fine.

But then I heard a *THUMP*.

I sat up in bed. It sounded like someone dropped the phone book on the floor.

I waited. I listened.

THUMP.

Again.

What could it be?

THUMP.

There was a rhythm to the sounds. One after another. . . . Sort of like . . .

FOOTSTEPS!

Each heavy sound was a footstep!

THUMP.

And the steps were coming closer.

Then I heard an eerie clanking. I strained to hear it better.

THUMP. CLANK.

My heart raced.

It was a chain.

THUMP. CLANK.

I gasped. The mummy! Searching for a victim. Searching for me.

I screamed, for the second time that day. I heard someone running.

My door swung open.

The mummy! It had long tangled robes and wild frizzy hair. I screamed again and dove under the covers.

"Shhhh," a soft voice said. "Honey, everything's fine. I'm here now."

"Huh?" Mom. Wearing her terry-cloth robe.

She sat down on the edge of the bed and rubbed my neck. "Did you have a nightmare?" she asked me.

"No!" I exclaimed. "The mummy is out. I heard it coming for me, coming up the stairs."

"You had a bad dream, that's all." Mom bent over and kissed me on the top of the head. She smelled like cinnamon and soap.

I listened to her footsteps padding off down the hall.

The soft sound her slippers made on the floor was nothing like the heavy steps I had heard before.

I wanted to believe her, but I knew what I had heard. The mummy was out. It would be coming for me again.

*   *   *

The next day, I biked to the library to try to find out how to protect myself from mummies. Would you believe that the only books they had on mummies were scary novels and art history books? Not one practical how-to book?

As I pushed my bike home through town I noticed a new shop on Main Street. The sign read SAM BONE'S MYSTICAL MERCHANDISE. In the window a tapestry was laid out, with all sorts of crystals spread on it.

Through the glass I could see a guy, sitting up on a counter, leafing through a big book. He had long, bushy hair and a beard. Maybe he could help me. No one else was taking me seriously. What did I have to lose?

I locked my bike up on a No Parking sign. Then I pushed open the door to Sam Bone's Mystical Merchandise. A tiny set of chimes hanging on the door rang out.

"Good afternoon, sir," the man said, hopping off the counter and closing his book. "How may I be of service?"

"Are you Sam Bone?" I asked him.

"The one and only," he said, doing a corny little bow.

"I'm looking for some information on mummies," I said hesitantly.

"Is this for some kind of school project?" he asked me. "Or are you planning a trip to Egypt perhaps?"

"No, you see, my dad is the curator at the Museum of Natural History here in town. We had a mummy delivered to our house by mistake. . . ." The whole story poured out of me.

When I finished, Sam Bone began pacing up and down the crowded aisles of the store. Every so often he would grab a book off the shelf and rip through it, searching for something. Or he would rummage through a box full of oils or candles or crystals.

"Of course!" he shouted suddenly. "I've got it!"

He disappeared into a back room for a moment. When he returned he was grinning from ear to ear.

He held a closed fist in front of my face and then opened his fingers one by one. In his palm lay a small purple sack, with pictures of gold eyes sewn all over it.

Sam opened the neck of the pouch and poured a tiny bit of blue powder into his hand.

"Mummy dust!" he exclaimed. "This is an ancient mix of minerals. It is said that the Egyptians would scatter this dust around the entrances to tombs to keep the spirits from crossing into the world of the living. One puff of this dust and a mummy loses its power."

Then he blew the dust right in my face. I coughed. The dust smelled bitter and old.

"I'll take it!" I shouted. "How much does it cost?"

Would you believe mummy dust costs twenty bucks?

"Aren't you scared to be in the kitchen, Jeff?" Kim teased me during dinner. "After all, the basement door is right there."

She gestured over her shoulder. "Doesn't it bother you that down in that box there's a dead body all wrapped up." She rose from her chair and started staggering around the kitchen like a mummy. "He's waiting for the night to fall so that he can sneak up to your room and — "

"Shut up!" I cried. What is her *problem*, anyway?

"That's enough!" Dad groaned. "Kim, you're not funny. Stop scaring Jeff."

While our parents were doing the dishes, I scooped out the ice cream. Kim leaned over the table and whispered, "If you think you're so cool, wait until tonight."

"What are you talking about?" I demanded.

"You know," she teased. "The mummy. I heard it last night, too, you know. And I also heard you screaming like a baby."

So I didn't imagine the sounds! Kim had heard them, too.

"I'm not worried," I replied. "I'm protected. I'm not scared at all."

"Yeah right," Kim said. "We'll see about that."

* * *

After everyone had gone to bed, I lay awake. It was chilly in my room. A storm picked up outside. The glass in the windows began to shudder as a sharp wind started up.

I clutched my pillow. Waiting. Waiting.

I gripped the pouch of mummy dust in my right hand. The feel of the small sack in my palm reassured me.

Rain drummed at the window. The room filled with white light. Thunder crashed outside.

Then I heard it.

THUMP.

From the room below me. From the kitchen.

The sound terrified me.

THUMP. CLANK.

I heard a low wailing moan. Was it the wind — or the mummy?

THUMP.

The mummy was coming for me.

But I wasn't going to wait for it.

I jumped from my bed and threw open my bedroom door. I couldn't stop shaking, but I made myself step out into the upstairs hall.

CRASH! Lightning lit up the hallway for a second. No mummy in sight.

THUMP. CLANK.

I grabbed the banister and jumped down the stairs, two at a time. My feet felt all prickly as they hit the polished wooden floor of the front hall.

299

I turned the corner toward the kitchen.

THUMP.

Something blocked my way.

The mummy!

Too scared to scream. My throat jammed up.

There it stood, in the shadows of the hall. The mummy hunched over, its face wrapped in strips of cloth. Its skinny arms hung limply at its sides. The arms were weighed down by hands that were huge — gnarled claws, wrapped in layers and layers of cloth.

The chains from the case were draped over its shoulders. They clanked as the mummy lurched up to me. Through the gauze over its head, I saw the mummy's evil grin.

Quick! I tore my eyes away from the ancient monster. I fumbled with the powder. Struggled to get the pouch open.

It was tied in a knot! My fingers shook too hard to open it.

The mummy moaned a low, ugly moan and reached its arms out to me. Huge, hideous claws. Reaching. Reaching.

Finally the knot gave way. I turned over the pouch to empty the dust into my palm.

Grunting, the mummy swung both arms at me.

I lifted my hands to guard my face.

The rotting cloth brushed against my skin. I stumbled back.

I hit the floor hard. My teeth clashed together.

The dust! I dropped it! The pouch fell to the floor, spilling the dust all over.

I scrambled to scratch up a handful.

The mummy growled. Lightning flashed. The ancient mummy flickered in the jagged, white light. Again I saw its evil, leering grin.

"WHO'S THERE?" boomed my mother's voice from the top of the stairs.

The mummy stepped away from me. The hall light flashed on.

To my shock, the mummy turned around and ran!

I couldn't believe it! Mom had saved me!

The mummy staggered to the basement door. It disappeared into the basement.

I slammed the door behind it. Then I grabbed a chair and tried to wedge it under the handle the way they do in the movies.

Mom rushed into the kitchen, tying the sash to her robe. Dad stumbled in behind her, fumbling with his glasses.

"What on earth is going on down here, Jeff?" she demanded.

"Mom, the mummy . . . it's alive. . . ." I gasped. "It was coming to get me, I swear! It's trapped in the basement right now."

"This has gone far enough," said my mother. "Larry, for once and for all, tell your son that mummies are dead and don't stumble around at night."

301

"Well, actually, there's something I didn't tell you," my Dad replied, rubbing his chin. "You see, there's a rumor that this mummy really is alive. I thought it was a joke."

"Huh?" Mom and I both cried.

Dad explained. "This mummy was given to us by another museum. They didn't want it anymore because the night guards said the mummy rose after dark to wander the halls. But the curator promised there would be no problem — as long as nobody took the chains off the box. The mummy can't come alive, unless someone takes the chains off."

"Jeff, did you take the chains off the box?" Mom demanded anxiously.

"No, no. I didn't!" I exclaimed. "Of course not!"

Dad jumped up as if stung by a hornet. "We've got to lock that thing in!" he cried. He searched the drawers till he found a heavy padlock. Then he locked the basement door with a loud snap.

"I'm so sorry," Dad said, hugging Mom. "I can't believe I put my family in danger. I never thought that the rumor might be true."

"I'm sorry I didn't believe you, Jeff," Mom said, turning to me. They tucked me in upstairs. With the mummy safely locked up, I quickly fell asleep.

Wow! It's really dark down here. Dad should fix the light.

I can hardly see my way down these stairs.

This basement is creepy.

I can't wait until Jeff and my folks go to bed so I can get out of here and go upstairs to sleep.

Oh, man! I almost got caught. But it was worth it — just to see the look on my brother's face when I reached out to grab him. He almost fainted, the little wimp.

Kim, you are so mean! But he asks for it! He really does.

Okay. Sounds as if they're gone. I'll sneak back upstairs. . . .

The door is stuck. Really hard. It won't open.

They must have locked it.

"Mom! Dad! Hello, can you hear me? It's me — Kim. I'm locked in the basement!"

No. The wind is too loud. The storm is making too much noise.

I can't believe this.

"DAD! MOM! JEFF! SOMEBODY!"

They can't hear me. This is awful.

I'm stuck down here for the night.

Well, I guess these old sheets will keep me warm. I can even wrap the gauze back around my face the way I had it before.

Of course this chain is completely useless.

Maybe it wasn't such a good idea to take the chain off the mummy case. But mummies have to have chains. Everybody knows that!

Good. Some lightning from outside. I can see where to sleep. Is that our old couch over there?

Whoa. Wait a minute! The lid to the coffin —
it's off!

I didn't move the lid when I took the chains.

How did that happen?

Who opened the mummy case?

THUMP.

THUMP.

THUMP.

I'M TELLING!

It stood alone in the middle of the woods.

The most horrifying creature Adam had ever seen.

He crept toward it. Slowly. Silently. Through the bushes. Closer and closer to the hideous thing nestled in the clearing.

"I'm not afraid of you," Adam said under his breath. "I'm going to destroy you."

He ducked down in the tall grass and studied his enemy. He was only a few feet away from it now.

It was a gargoyle. And its huge, scaly wings rose over him. If the creature flew at him, he knew he could never outrun it.

I don't know if I'm brave or crazy, Adam thought. He crawled forward for a closer look. That's when he noticed the creature's claws. Long, sharp claws that could probably rip him in half.

"I'm not afraid of you," he whispered again. But

I am afraid of those fangs, he thought, peering nervously at the gargoyle's long, pointy teeth.

All the better to eat you with! Adam remembered the line from an old fairy tale.

Adam gazed up at the monster and took a deep breath. The creature sat silent and still. Good — it hasn't noticed me, he thought. Instead, it stared coldly at some twittering sparrows that had gathered at its feet.

It's now or never, Adam thought. He leaped to his feet and charged the monster.

"Eat this!" he screamed, lifting his weapon and squeezing the trigger.

Nothing happened.

The monster remained still.

Only the sparrows were surprised by his attack. They flew into the air with a soft flutter of wings.

"I don't believe it!" Adam cried. "I'm out of water!" He stared down at his empty water gun. Then he glanced back at the monster — a statue made of stone.

"You're lucky," Adam muttered. "If my gun was filled, you'd be dead now."

The monster didn't flinch. It was only a statue after all, stuck in the middle of a dried-up, old fountain.

Adam liked to come out to the woods and pretend to hunt. His best friend, Nick, said that pretending was for babies. "When you're in sixth grade, you've got to be cool," Nick told him. So

Adam came out to the woods by himself to play — when Nick wasn't around.

"If only I had more water . . ." Adam grumbled, shaking the water pistol.

To his surprise, the statue moved. Its mouth opened wide — and something green gushed out.

Adam jumped back.

Green liquid spurted from the statue's mouth.

Adam gaped at the gargoyle. "I don't believe this!" he cried. "It's amazing!"

Adam stared at the statue as the stream grew more powerful. The thick, green liquid splashed against the dry stones of the fountain.

"This is really weird," Adam said out loud. "Where is the stuff coming from?"

I guess I can refill my gun now, he thought. He pulled the plastic cap off one of the gun barrels and leaned into the fountain.

Then he stopped.

He felt as if the gargoyle were watching him.

He peered up at the monster. Its stone eyes remained frozen in a cold stare.

Get a grip, Adam, he told himself. It's only a statue. Nick would laugh his head off if he saw you now.

Adam reached up toward the gargoyle's mouth and held the plastic gun under the stream of liquid. His hand trembled as the gun's tank slowly filled.

"This stuff smells really gross! And it's kind

307

of gooey," he said, replacing the cap on the tank.

He turned to face the gargoyle. "Okay!" he yelled. "I've got you now."

Adam squeezed the trigger. Nothing happened.

He held the gun up to the light. He shook it some more. Maybe it's clogged, he thought. He turned and aimed at a large tree next to the fountain. He pumped the trigger, again and again. The gun suddenly jerked in his hands, and a green stream of liquid splashed the huge tree.

"Yessss!" Adam cheered.

The tree began to crackle.

Adam stared in shock as the brown branches faded to gray. The leaves crumbled. And fell heavily off the crackling tree.

A leaf dropped onto Adam's head.

"Ow!" he cried, rubbing his scalp.

The leaf was as hard as a rock.

Adam gaped at the tree. Was it true? Was it *possible*?

Yes. It had turned to stone!

Adam gazed down in amazement at the water gun in his hand. "Wh-what's going on?" he stuttered.

"I'm telling! I'm telling!"

Adam jumped at the sound of the high-pitched voice. A short, brown-haired girl with pigtails and freckles stepped out of the bushes. She pulled a red wagon behind her.

Adam groaned. It was Missy, his seven-year-old sister. The *second* most horrible creature in the world!

"What are you doing here, Missy?"

"Looking for *you*," she snapped. "Mom says you have to finish your art project. I told her she should take away your water gun. Or else you'll never finish it."

"You little brat," Adam muttered. "Why don't you mind your own business?"

"Why don't *you* do your schoolwork?" Missy shot back. "Do you want to stay in the sixth grade forever?"

"Go home, Missy," Adam said, fighting back the urge to tackle her.

"*I* always do *my* homework," Missy bragged. "*I* get straight *A*'s."

"Good for you," Adam growled. "Now leave me alone."

"What about your art project?" Missy demanded. "The contest is tonight."

Adam sighed. He gazed at the gargoyle in the fountain. Then at the stone tree. The crumbled leaves. He glared at his little sister.

"I'm busy," he said, clutching his water gun. "Art classes are for losers like you. I have more important things to do."

"I'm telling Mommy," Missy squealed. "You're in big trouble, Adam!" She stuck out her tongue. Then she started to sing. "I'm telling. I'm telling. I'm telling!"

Adam clamped his hands over his ears. "Shut up!" he yelled.

"I'm telling! I'm telling! I'm telling!" Missy sang louder.

Adam felt his face grow hot. Before he knew what he was doing, he raised the squirt gun and pointed it at Missy.

He didn't mean to squeeze the trigger. But he did.

Green slimy liquid squirted from the gun, splashing Missy's face.

Missy shrieked.

Then her small, round face turned chalky gray. Her lips froze in an open-mouthed scream. Adam stared in horror as the grayish-white color spread down her small arms and legs.

Then Missy's entire body stiffened. And a powdery dust swirled around her.

Adam's eyes bulged as he watched Missy turn to stone.

"Missy! No!" he shrieked. "What have I done?" he howled. "Don't worry, Missy. I'm going to hide you in the basement — until I can figure out what to do."

With a grunt, Adam hoisted his stone sister off the ground. She weighed a ton! He nearly broke his back lifting her into her wagon.

As he struggled to pull the wagon away, he heard gurgling. And hissing.

310

From the fountain? Yes.

Adam snapped his head around. Green slime dribbled down one of the gargoyle's fangs.

Adam shivered. His heart began to pound. He grabbed the wagon handle. Pulled as hard as he could. He didn't look back. He tugged the wagon until he reached the end of the woods.

All he had to do was pass by the school and turn the corner. His house stood on the corner of the next block.

He turned to Missy. "We're almost home," he said. "As if she can hear me!" he mumbled, rolling his eyes. He shook his head. My sister — a stone statue. How can this be happening?

Missy bounced heavily in the wagon. Adam glanced back nervously. He didn't know what would happen if she broke — and he didn't *want* to find out! He had to move fast. He didn't want anyone to see Missy like this.

"Adam! Adam!"

Adam recognized the voice. It belonged to the last person in the world he wanted to see. Mrs. Parker. His art teacher.

Mrs. Parker waved her arms in the air as she ran up the sidewalk after him. "Adam!" she cried out. "You finished your art project. I'm so proud of you!"

The tall, red-haired art teacher peered down at Missy's statue and clapped her hands together.

311

Adam gulped. "Well, Mrs. Parker . . . it's . . . not . . . um, really . . ."

"It's wonderful, Adam!" Mrs. Parker declared. "I had no idea you were such a talented sculptor. You've captured Missy in stone. It looks so much like her! It's a masterpiece!"

"But . . . but . . ." Adam fumbled for words.

"Hurry, Adam! Take your sculpture into the school. The art contest has already begun. Maybe you'll win first prize!"

Adam sighed. He stared at his stone sister. He wondered if she could hear. He wondered if she could *think*.

"Sorry about this, Missy," he whispered. "Nothing I can do now." He pulled the wagon into the school.

Adam won first prize. The judges placed a blue ribbon on Missy's stone shoulder. Mrs. Parker congratulated him.

His friend Nick came up and slapped him on the back. "Cool project," he said. "Really cool. It looks just like your bratty little sister! Want to come over and play video games?"

"Um. I can't," Adam stammered. "I — uh — have to get home and baby-sit Missy."

"Okay, see you," Nick said. He took one more look at Adam's statue. "Really amazing. How did you do that?"

Adam brought the wagon into the auditorium.

312

He crouched down to lift Missy up. And almost dropped her when he heard the voice. Missy's voice.

"Help . . . me . . . Adam."

Adam gasped.

"Did you say something, Adam?" Mrs. Parker asked.

"No," Adam replied. He grabbed the wagon handle, tugged hard, and raced out of the school.

Adam started toward his house when he spotted his parents in the front yard. Admiring their vegetable garden.

"Oh, no!" he moaned. "We can't go back to the house," he told Missy. "Not yet."

He didn't know where to go. So he hauled Missy back into the woods. "We'll hide near the fountain until I can sneak you into the house," he told her.

The sky was darkening as evening approached. The wind howled through the trees. A shiver ran down Adam's spine.

He pulled the wagon into the clearing.

And screamed. "Nooooooo!"

The gargoyle was gone.

"Where is it?" Adam cried. "Where — ?"

Adam didn't finish. A shadow slid over him. He glanced up in time to see the huge wings.

The gargoyle was flying!

No time to duck. No time to run.

In a gust of sour air, the ugly creature swooped

313

down. Its heavy wings pounded Adam's head.

"Get away from me!" he shrieked, throwing his arms up. "Get away!"

The giant creature swooped down again. Its eyes glowed a deadly red. Adam couldn't get away. The gargoyle dug its sharp claws into his shirt, shredding the sleeve.

"Noooo!" Adam uttered a terrified wail.

The gargoyle soared up again and began to circle. Prepared to dive again, its eyes flaming angrily.

Green ooze seeped from its gaping mouth. The liquid hit Adam's cheek with a sickening splat. His face sizzled.

Adam wiped the ooze away. He felt dizzy. Faint.

The gargoyle soared down at him. Adam dodged the monster.

As the gargoyle plunged toward him again, Adam spotted the water gun on the ground.

"Yes!" He grabbed it. Waited for the creature to swoop in closer . . . closer . . . closer.

When he could feel its sour, cold breath on his face, Adam pulled the trigger.

A blast of the slimy liquid splashed over the monster's glowing eyes.

The creature opened its mouth in a hideous howl. Then it dropped to the ground with a heavy thud.

And became a stone statue again.

Green liquid trickled from its leering mouth and dripped down its fangs.

"Yes!" Adam cried happily. "I did it! I did it!"

"Help . . . me . . . Adam."

"Missy!" Adam had forgotten all about her.

What am I going to do? he asked himself in a panic.

An idea flashed into his terrified thoughts. He reached for his water gun. It had some green liquid in the tank.

Adam shrugged. It was worth a try.

He aimed at the Missy statue. He held his breath and squeezed the trigger.

Nothing happened at first. Then, slowly, the gray stone cracked and crumbled. Layers of dust flaked from Missy's face. Her arms. Her legs.

"Adam, you jerk!" her voice rang out angrily from the rubble. "How could you do that to me?"

Adam grinned and hugged Missy. "You're alive!" he cried. He happily brushed the dust off her clothes.

"No thanks to you, stupid!" she snapped.

Adam ignored her angry words. He was so happy to see her. So happy! He threw his arm around her shoulders and led her through the woods.

"I can't believe you put me in the art contest," she complained, shoving his arm away. "They put that stupid blue ribbon on me. I felt like a total jerk!"

315

Adam sighed.

"Wait until I tell Mom. You'll be in big trouble! I'm telling her everything. I'm telling! I'm telling!"

Adam stopped walking. "Please, Missy — " he started.

"I'm telling! I'm telling! I'm telling!" she chanted nastily.

Adam sighed again. "I don't think so," he said softly.

Then he aimed the water pistol at her and pulled the trigger.

THE HAUNTED HOUSE GAME

I opened the closet door and reached up to the top shelf. It was dark up there. I couldn't really see anything, so I groped around until my fingers found what I was searching for.

"Aha. Here it is!" I said, carrying the box over to the table. "We're going to play Haunted House."

"Oh, Jonathan," Nadine moaned. "Not that dumb game again!"

"Come on," I replied, opening up the box. "It's fun. It's really scary."

"Yeah, that game is dumb," Noah echoed.

"Can't we play Parcheesi?" Annie complained.

"This is better," I said. "There aren't any ghosts in Parcheesi."

"But we've played it a hundred times before," Nadine mumbled.

"It's always different," I insisted. "Come on. Let's play Haunted House."

I unfolded the game board and lined up the

playing pieces. *BOOM!* A booming thunderclap shook the house.

We all turned to stare out the big picture window. The rain beat against it — hard. A bolt of lightning sliced through the sky. Then — *BOOM!* More thunder.

There are three things I really hate. The first one is thunder. The second — lightning. And the third — baby-sitting my seven-year-old brother and sister, Noah and Annie. Tonight I was a three-time loser.

At least Nadine is here, I thought. I stared at her across our long, oak dining-room table. Nadine is my best friend. We're in the same sixth-grade class. Whenever our parents go out together, Nadine gets to sleep over.

I dropped the dice in the little cup that came with the game. As I swirled them around, another burst of thunder startled us.

The house rumbled. Every window shook. And we have a lot of windows. Thirty-nine to be exact. I know. Because I counted them the last time I baby-sat the twins — when we played the Let's Count the Windows game.

"I wish Mom and Dad would get home," I said as I swirled the dice some more.

"Jonathan is afraid of thunder," Annie chirped.

"And lightning." Noah grinned.

"I am not," I protested, feeling my face turn hot. "Let's start," I said.

"What are the rules again?" Noah asked.

"The object of the game," I explained, "is to go around the board, through the haunted house — and try to find the hidden ghost."

"Oh, yeah. Now I remember," Noah said.

"And don't forget," I said in my best scary voice. "Be very careful. Don't land on SCARED TO DEATH!"

I shook the dice up and down in the little cup. Then from side to side. Then up and down again.

"Come on, Jonathan," Nadine said. "Roll the dice."

I tilted the cup and the dice spilled out. "Seven," I announced. "Lucky seven!"

"One-two-three-four-five-six-seven," I counted. I moved my green marker seven spaces.

And landed on YOU HEAR CREAKING FOOTSTEPS ON THE STAIRS.

I placed my marker down on the square.

Creeeak.

"Did you hear that?" I whispered.

Nadine and the twins nodded.

Creaking footsteps on the stairs. The stairs that led to our bedrooms.

"Maybe it's the cat," Annie whispered.

"Yeah, maybe it's the cat," Noah echoed.

"We don't have a cat," I replied.

We sat hunched around the table. Listening. Everything remained quiet. Everything except my heart pounding in my chest.

319

"Hey! I know what it was," Nadine said, straightening in her chair. "I bet the hall window is open upstairs. It was just the wind blowing through the window."

"That's it," I said, not totally convinced. It definitely sounded like a creak to me.

I studied everyone's faces around the table. No one appeared worried. "Okay, Annie. It's your turn. Spin," I said.

"You don't spin, Jonathan. You roll," Annie declared.

"Go ahead, Annie," Noah whined. "Take your turn."

"All right," Annie replied. She slowly tilted the cup and the dice dribbled out. "Three!"

Annie moved her red marker three spaces. "Onnnne. Twoooo. Threeee."

And landed on WIND RATTLES THE WINDOWS.

She placed her marker on the square and — the wind outside started howling. Really loud.

Then all the windows in the house began to rattle. All thirty-nine of them. First with a tinkling sound. Then more forceful. Vibrating in their frames.

The gusts outside grew stronger. Meaner. They whipped the windowpanes. I thought the glass would shatter.

My hands began to tremble. I hid them under the table.

I glanced over at Nadine. She stared out the big picture window.

I shifted my gaze to the twins.

The twins!

They were gone!

"Annie! Noah!" I cried.

"Here." Two small voices called from under the table.

"Come on out," I urged. "Everything's okay." But I wasn't as sure about that as I sounded.

"I'm staying here," Annie answered. "This game is too creepy. Every time we land on something, it really happens."

"It's not the game," I said. "It's the wind. And it's not blowing anymore."

It was true. The howling had quieted to a soft whistle. The windows stopped rattling.

"Jonathan is right," Nadine backed me up. Then she peeked under the table. "It's your turn, Noah. Don't you want your turn?"

"Of course I want my turn," he replied. He popped up and landed in his chair. He tossed the dice into the cup.

Annie slowly surfaced and plopped into her seat. "Let's play fast," she begged.

Noah swirled the dice and rolled a 2. He pounded the board with his blue marker.

My eyes darted to the board to see where he would land.

321

I found the square.

Noah plopped his marker down on it.

It said YOU HEAR AN EERIE MOAN.

A quick bolt of lightning pierced the sky. And then we heard it.

A moan.

A low, sad moan. From somewhere — inside the house.

"There's a ghost in here!" Annie shrieked. "Hide!"

"Where?" I yelled.

"In the closet!" Annie cried, jumping up from her chair.

"How do you know it's in the closet?" I shouted.

"She means we should *hide* in the closet," Nadine said. "Will everyone please stop screaming."

We stopped. The room fell silent. No creaking. No rattling. No moaning.

"There's no one here but us," Nadine continued. "This house always makes weird noises when it rains."

I guessed Nadine was right. She seemed so sure of herself. But I didn't think the problem was house noises.

"Now," Nadine said, scooping up the dice. "It's my turn."

She rolled a 4. I watched her closely. I was afraid — afraid to see where she would land.

Nadine moved her marker four spaces. And plunked it down on THE LIGHTS GO OUT.

And we all screamed as the lights went out.

"Everybody, sit still!" I shrieked. "I'll find some candles."

I groped my way into the kitchen. Mom and Dad kept candles in here somewhere. But where?

I couldn't see my own hands in front of my face. How was I supposed to find those candles? I opened every drawer in the kitchen, fumbling for them.

"Can you hurry up?" Nadine called from the dining room.

"Sure, Nadine," I muttered. "No problem."

Aha! Found them! Right on the counter. In their holders. Where they always are. I lighted them and returned to the other room.

We gathered at the end of the table — around the candles. Annie and Noah's eyes flickered with fear.

I was afraid, too.

"I don't want to play this game anymore," Annie whimpered. "It's too scary!"

"Our house is haunted." Noah's voice quivered.

"It's not the house," Annie whispered. "It's the game. This game is haunted."

I grabbed the dice and jiggled them in the cup. I glanced around the table. Everyone's eyes were opened wide. Glued to the board.

Lightning flashed outside the window. The candles sputtered in the dark.

323

Should I roll the dice? I wondered, gazing at our shadows dancing on the walls.

Should we stop playing?

Get serious, Jonathan, I told myself. It's only a game.

I spilled out the dice. 5.

I moved my marker. Slowly.

I held my breath as it landed on YOU HEAR A SCREAM IN THE ATTIC.

We sat quietly. Listening.

And then we heard it.

From upstairs.

A terrifying scream!

"Wh-what was that?" I stammered.

"Uh. The storm," Nadine replied. "Just the storm. Your turn, Annie."

I knew Annie didn't want to play anymore. But she rolled the dice. And moved her marker six spaces.

"YOU HEAR A BONY HAND TAPPING ON THE WINDOW." I read the words in the space.

No one spoke.

The room remained silent.

No tapping.

"See?" I said, walking over to the window. "Everything's — "

BANG!

A hand! A pale, bony hand — flew up out of nowhere! It banged the window hard.

The twins shrieked. I leaped back.

The wind picked up, and an icy draft blew through the dining room. The candles flared.

Nadine wrapped her arms around herself. Annie shrank back in her chair.

I studied the game board. Then I wiped my clammy hands on my jeans as Noah picked up the dice. *Not a three! Not a three!* I chanted to myself as Noah prepared to throw.

The dice tumbled out of the cup. They rolled. And rolled.

And stopped on — 3!

SCARED TO DEATH!

A candle blew out. Blinding white lightning flashed through the room. We screamed. And screamed. It seemed as if we screamed for hours.

The windows shuddered and quaked. Footsteps creaked on the stairs. An eerie moan floated up from the basement and flooded the room.

And then we heard the terrifying tapping.

Tapping. Tapping. Tapping.

We couldn't see it in the dark. But we knew what it was. The bony hand. Tapping against the window.

And then we were screaming again. Screaming so loud, it drowned everything out. Screaming so hard the whole house seemed to disappear.

I screamed until I couldn't hear myself.

Screamed until I couldn't breathe.

And then I stopped screaming, and the silence felt good.

I ran to the front door. I had to get out of that house. I had to!

But I stopped to pick up the newspaper on the mat. A yellowed newspaper.

The candle glow washed over the bold headline:

4 KIDS DIE IN MYSTERY DEATH!

My eyes rolled over the first paragraph:

Police were completely baffled when they found four kids dead in an old mansion last night. "It looked to me as if they were scared to death!" declared one police officer.

Scared to death. Scared to death.

I glanced at the date on the newspaper. March 14, 1942.

So *that's* when we died, I realized. We died over fifty years ago. And we've been haunting this old house ever since.

I couldn't stay at the door. Nadine and the twins were waiting at the table for me.

Rain beat hard against the windows. The lights flashed back on. I opened the closet door and reached up to the top shelf. It was dark up there. I couldn't really see anything, so I groped around until my fingers found what I was searching for.

"Aha. Here it is!" I said, carrying the box over to the table. "We're going to play Haunted House."

"Oh, Jonathan," Nadine moaned. "Not that dumb game again!"

"Come on," I replied, opening up the box. "It's fun. It's really scary."

"Yeah, that game is dumb," Noah echoed.

"Can't we play Parcheesi?" Annie complained.

"This is better," I said. "There aren't any ghosts in Parcheesi."

"But we've played it a hundred times before," Nadine mumbled.

"It's always different," I insisted. "Come on. Let's play Haunted House."

CHANGE FOR THE STRANGE

Jane Meyers, twelve-year-old track star. That's me. As I stepped up to the starting line, I could hear the crowd scream. The fans roared. They were waiting. Waiting to see my spectacular long jump.

"Jane? Jane? Earth to Jane."

"Huh?"

"Jane — stop daydreaming. It's time to go!" Lizzy called from across the practice field.

Lizzy Gardner is my best friend. I watched as she walked toward me, careful to keep away from the dirt patches. Lizzy hates to get her shoes dirty. Today she wore sparkly pink sneakers and a short pink skirt. A pink headband held her blond hair in place.

"Are you ready to go?" she yelled, cupping her hands around her mouth.

Lizzy doesn't understand anything about track or why I practice so much. She thinks I'd have more fun at her house, hanging out.

But I want to be a track star more than anything else. Unfortunately, I didn't make the school team. I heard one of the girls on the team say I wasn't good enough to carry their towels.

That was so cold. But I'm not giving up. Every afternoon after school, I practice out in the field. Some day I'm going to be an incredible jumper. No matter what it takes.

After I practice, I always hang out at Lizzy's house. First we watch *Animaniacs*. Then we put on the CD player and dance around to our favorite band, Fruit Bag.

Sure, it's fun. But lately I've been more into track than hanging out.

Lizzy has changed, too. She still wants me to come over and do the same things — only now she's added a new one. She likes to go through her closet, thinking up new outfits.

"Do these shoes go with my new skirt? Does this top match my eyes?"

We do that until Ivan the Terrible barges into her room. That's what we call Lizzy's little brother. Ivan has a dog. A really mean pit bull. He named it Lizzy — just to make his sister angry.

Lizzy the dog ate Lizzy the person's new yellow scrunchy last week. He swallowed it in one gulp.

Ivan also has a whole collection of mice, snakes, and other weird animals. He likes to chase us all over the house, dangling his disgusting creatures in our faces.

"Hello! Anybody home?" Lizzy tapped me on the shoulder. "I've been talking for five minutes. And you haven't heard a word I've said."

By now, I'd gathered my things together. "Sorry," I said as we headed off the practice field. "What's up?"

"Before we go to my house," Lizzy told me, "I want to go shopping. I found a great clothing store. It's called A Change for the Strange. Have you seen it? It's right around the corner."

I shook my head no.

A minute later, we stood in front of the store. A neon pink-and-orange awning stretched over its front door. A CHANGE FOR THE STRANGE ran across the top in glowing letters.

I walked through the door and gasped.

The place was so . . . strange. It didn't seem like a clothing store at all. All sorts of weird items crammed the aisles.

Rain slickers hung from moose antlers. Yellow umbrellas with duck-head handles bobbed in puddles of water.

Green capes with velvet flowers dangled from leafy trees. Fluffy bunny slippers peeked out of rabbit hutches. Shark's-tooth necklaces floated in a tiny wave pool.

Lizzy disappeared between the racks. I usually

follow her around stores like a little kid. But this time, I stood in one place, gawking.

A store clerk stepped up to me. "May I help you?" she asked.

Something *had* caught my eye — a bright red jacket. It had tiny cracks in the material and a yellow trim that ran around the middle.

"Can I see that jacket?" I asked.

The clerk reached up and unhooked the jacket from a tree branch. The jacket looked wet. Slick. But when I ran my hand down the front, it felt totally dry.

"It's a cool-looking pattern," I told her.

She smiled and pointed to the cracks. "Those are scales," she explained. "That jacket is snake-skin."

"Ugh!" I snatched my hand away.

The salesclerk slipped the jacket off the hanger. "Try it on," she urged. "I bet it will look great on you."

I slipped into it, then I turned toward the mirror. It looked great. I twirled around. A perfect fit!

"I'll take it!" I declared.

"You will?" Lizzy came over, surprised.

"Sure. It looks great with my eyes!" I joked.

Lizzy grinned. "I told you this store was great." She held out a pair of white bunny slippers. "I'm going to buy these."

I choked back a giggle. A snakeskin jacket was one thing. But bunny slippers? "Those will be great for when you get hopping mad!" I teased Lizzy.

"Ha-ha. Remind me to laugh later," Lizzy snapped.

We quickly paid for the clothes and rushed out of the store.

Out on the street, I zipped up the snakeskin jacket all the way to my neck. I hadn't taken it off since I tried it on — not for a second. I loved it!

I gazed at the bright snakeskin as we walked. It sparkled in the sunlight. It looked awesome — like something a model would wear.

When we reached Lizzy's house, we spotted Ivan crawling around the front yard. "Shh!" he whispered. "I'm on the lookout for caterpillars. I'm starting a new collection. So don't scare them away."

"No problem!" Lizzy shouted as loud as she could. Then she stamped her feet and waved her arms. "We'll be so quiet, you won't even know we're here!" she screamed.

I started to follow Lizzy into the house, then stopped. I felt kind of weird. Kind of weak. And dizzy.

"Are you okay?" Lizzy asked. "You look a little pale."

"I'm not sure," I answered. I took a few more

steps. Everything around me started to spin. I grabbed onto Lizzy so that I wouldn't fall.

"Maybe you're getting sick," Lizzy said. "Want me to walk you home?"

"No, that's okay," I replied weakly. "I can go by myself."

"Are you sure? You don't look good."

"I'll be fine," I told Lizzy. "I'll call you when I get home."

I started home, but I didn't get very far.

Suddenly I felt really hot. My skin felt as if it were burning up.

All I wanted to do was lie down, right there on Lizzy's lawn. Stretch out in the cool green grass.

But I forced myself to stand.

Then I flicked out my tongue.

It darted in and out. In and out.

I tried to stop. To hold it in. But I couldn't!

And each time it lashed out, it grew longer. Pointier.

I clamped my mouth shut. But my tongue shot back out. And I smelled something strange.

An animal.

A cat. Then I smelled a dog and a squirrel.

My mind raced with panic. I could never smell animals before. What was happening to me?

Then I sniffed something really tasty. A nice mousy smell coming from Lizzy's house. Ivan's pet mice! Mmm-mmm!

I clutched my head.

And then I screamed. "My head!"

I had no hair! No ears! My whole head was covered with dry, cracked skin.

I rubbed it frantically. I wanted to bring back my old head.

Then the world seemed to tilt. Everything swam out of focus, as if I were on a speeding merry-go-round. I couldn't hold myself up. I sank to the ground.

I closed my eyes. "I'll count to three," I said. "Then everything will be okay. I'll wake up and be back to normal."

Slowly I counted — one, two, three. I opened my eyes.

And I shrieked out in terror.

I wasn't Jane Meyers, track star. I wasn't even Jane Meyers, human being.

"I'm a snake!" I tried to shout. But a long *hisssss* was all that came out.

I felt sick to my stomach. I was a snake! A slithering, fork-tongued snake!

I need help, I thought desperately. I need Lizzy! She'll know what to do. I nosed aside a giant blade of grass and stared up at Lizzy's house.

How could I get inside?

I started to slither toward her front door — when her mother opened it! She stood in the open doorway, fumbling for something inside her bag.

This was it — my chance to get inside!

I slithered as fast as I could. Then a shadow fell over me.

Lizzy — the pit bull.

"Oh, no!" I tried to moan. But of course I hissed instead.

The dog lowered her head and growled. A low, menacing growl. Then she bared her teeth.

I tried to slither away.

Lizzy trailed me. Snarling. Drooling saliva on me.

I slipped under a bush. But she found me. She lowered her head to the ground. I could feel her hot breath on my skin.

With one bite, Lizzy was going to rip the skin off my back. She opened her mouth and —

"Lizzy! Go!" It was Mrs. Gardner. The dog jerked her head up and whimpered.

"Ivan! Come and get the dog. I don't want her in the garden! Ivan!"

No answer.

Mrs. Gardner grabbed Lizzy's collar and tugged the dog inside. I slid out of the bushes and followed right behind.

Mrs. Gardner put the dog in the basement while I slithered up the steps to the bedrooms.

"Lizzy!" I hissed to my friend. I glanced around the room. I spotted the TV. The CD player. The Fruit Bag poster on the wall. But no Lizzy.

And then the light snapped on.

335

There stood Lizzy in the doorway.

She was here! She would save me!

"Hey, Lizzy!" I cried, twisting my snake body into the air. "Help me! Help me!"

"Yaaaai!" Lizzy screamed. "A snake! Ivan, get in here!"

"No — it's me!" I wanted to shout. But of course I couldn't. What could I do?

Lizzy pressed against the wall as I wriggled over to the remote control on her night table.

I had an idea.

I pushed my head against the power button. The picture flickered on the screen.

So far so good.

I pressed another button until *The Animaniacs* came on. Now she'd understand!

"Ivan — !" Lizzy began. Then she stopped. A light came into her eyes. She did understand! She did! I writhed in happiness.

Lizzy stepped closer. She reached out. She was going to pick me up. To save me!

No! She grabbed hold of her tennis racquet and with a loud cry, swung it hard and whomped me across the room.

Splat! I hit her CD player. My tail struck a button. Fruit Bag began to play.

For a moment, I lay stunned on top of the player, while Lizzy shrieked for Ivan.

Then I got another idea. I began to dance.

336

"Lizzy!" I hissed. "It's me. It's Jane. I'm dancing the way we always do!"

Lizzy's eyes widened with fear. She cowered in the corner. "Ivan!" she yelled. "Get in here. Now!"

Ivan poked his head in the room. He grinned. "Got a problem?"

"One of your snakes is loose!" Lizzy shrieked. "Get . . . it . . . out . . . of . . . here. NOW!"

"Lizzy," I whimpered. I slinked off the CD player and slithered over to her feet. "You have to save me!"

Lizzy backed into the corner. I coiled around her leg. "Help me!" I hissed.

"Yaaiiii!" she screeched. She hopped on a chair, trying to shake me loose. "Please, Ivan. Take your snake. Take it!"

Ivan strolled over, taking his time. I threw a pleading look up at Lizzy. "Please!" I hissed.

Ivan crouched over me. He stared at me. "It's not my snake," he said. "I don't have any red ones."

Lizzy's voice screeched. "I don't care!" she shouted. "Just get it off of me!"

"All right. All right." Ivan said. He unwrapped me from Lizzy's leg and carried me to his bedroom.

Then he dumped me into his snake cage.

With two other snakes. Their fangs gleamed in

337

the light. Their hot snake breath washed over me.

I pressed myself against the cage. But they slinked closer and closer.

They know, I thought. They know I'm not a real snake like they are. And they're going to kill me!

They writhed forward — one on each side of me. Hissing. Hissing. They were going to surround me. And attack.

Their long tongues slid out. They darted forward with a sharp jerk and —

Ivan reached into the cage and pulled me out.

"You know, Lizzy," Ivan said, carrying me back into Lizzy's room. "There's something weird about this snake. It's got something on its stomach."

He flipped me over. Then he gasped. "Wow!" he said. "It looks like a zipper! A tiny zipper."

He shoved me into Lizzy's face.

"GET THAT THING OUT OF HERE!" she screeched.

"I mean it, Lizzy. Look! Let's try to unzip it." Ivan set me gently on the floor. He hesitated. Pulled back. Changed his mind again.

Then he took a deep breath, reached down, and tugged on the zipper.

RRRRRIPPPP!

I exploded into my full human body.

Ivan gasped. Lizzy screamed.

"Cool!" Ivan said, reaching over to touch me.

Lizzy kept screaming.

338

"Hey! How did you do that?" he asked.

My whole body shook as I told them the terrible story.

When I left to go home, Lizzy was still screaming.

A few days later, Lizzy and I sat out on the field. I had just finished practicing.

"That was awesome, Jane," Lizzy said. "That's the highest I've ever seen you jump."

I felt really proud. My jumping was totally excellent today. Yesterday too.

I hopped over to her.

She reached down and petted my soft white fur. "You're going to be the state high-jump champ," she said.

My pink nose twitched. "You're right," I said. "Did you bring any carrots?"

I had to admit it. Lizzy had been right back at that weird store. Those bunny slippers were *definitely* cool!

THE PERFECT SCHOOL

Going to boarding school was not my idea of a great time. It was not my idea at all.

Whose idea was it? My parents', of course.

I knew I was doomed the day the brochure for the Perfect Boarding School arrived in the mail. The slogan on the cover read: Why Settle for Anything Less Than Perfect?

"Perfect" is my parents' favorite word.

Unfortunately, they have me — Brian O'Connor — for a kid. And I'm far from perfect. I make my bed — sometimes. I take a shower — sometimes. I get my homework done — sometimes.

And I please my parents — never.

Before I knew what was happening, my mom and dad had signed me up for the two-week course. On the way to the train station, I begged. I promised to cut back on TV and video games. I promised I wouldn't tease the dog. I even swore I wouldn't eat three Snickers bars for lunch anymore.

But it was no use. They hustled me onto the train and told me to watch for the Perfect van when I got off at the Rockridge Station.

I found a seat across the aisle from a kid who appeared as unhappy as I felt. He was reading something I'd seen before. The brochure from Perfect.

"So what do you think of the place?" I asked.

"I think it stinks!" he snarled. He threw the brochure down on the train floor. "Perfect. Ha! How about a school to teach parents how to be perfect instead?"

"I'd send mine," I agreed. "I'm Brian. My parents are sending me to Perfect, too."

"I'm C.J. So why did your parents send you for training? What did you do?"

"It's more what I didn't do," I explained. "They're always telling me I didn't do this or I forgot to do that. Man, I wake up five minutes late, and the first thing I hear is that I didn't go to bed early enough, and that's why I can't wake up!"

We complained about our parents until the train man called out "Rockridge Station! Rockridge!"

I grabbed my duffel bag and followed C.J. to the door. "Here goes nothing," I muttered.

About half an hour later, the van pulled through the tall iron gates leading to the school. The driver parked near a row of kids standing behind a sign that said PERFECT GRADUATES.

These kids were *weird*. Their line was ruler straight. Each kid wore a gray uniform. Each kid stood straight up and faced forward. Each kid held a gray suitcase in his left hand.

They stood in silence waiting for their parents to pick them up.

Is that what my parents want me to turn out like? I asked myself. If it is, they can forget it right now.

The driver slid open the side door of the van. Another man stood next to him. "I am the director of the Perfect Boarding School," the new guy told us. "Line up in order of height. Tallest at the back. Shortest at the front. Leave your bags in the van. You won't be needing them here."

The director pointed to the first kid in line. "You are number one-twelve," he stated. He gave a number to each of us. I got 116.

"Your instructors will call you by number," the director explained. "You will call each other by number. You will call me and your teachers 'Guardian.' "

How am I going to make it through two weeks at this place? I thought. This guy is nuts!

A car pulled up in front of the other line. The director hurried over to present the parents with their perfect child — and get his envelope of money in return.

Were any of those kids like me when they got here? I wondered. What did the *Guardians* do to change them? What will they do to me? A shiver raced down my back.

Those kids were like robots. Robots!

Four more Guardians waited for us inside the door. One of them tapped me on the shoulder. "Follow me," he said in a low voice. He led me down a hallway and up a flight of stairs.

I caught sight of C.J. going into a room on the first floor. "See you later — " I started to call.

"No talking," the Guardian barked. At the top of the stairs, he turned left. A half-open door clicked shut as we passed it.

What are they trying to hide? I wondered. Why is every single door shut? Why don't they want us talking to each other?

The Guardian ushered me into the last room in the hall. "You will wear the clothing in the drawer. You will eat the meal on the tray. You will wait here until you are summoned," he ordered me. Then he shut the door.

I checked it — locked, of course.

I studied my new room. It didn't take long. There was a single bed with a small dresser on one side. A table with one chair on the other.

I wandered over to the dresser and opened the drawers. Only boring stuff. Gray uniforms, toothpaste, towels.

May as well check out the food, I decided. A

bowl of bumpy gray stuff sat on the table. I scooped up a little with my finger and licked it off. Tasted sort of like oatmeal.

Then I heard something. A rustling noise. From the heating vent near the floor.

The hairs on the back of my neck prickled. Is something down there?

I stretched out on the floor and pressed my ear against the vent. The rustling grew louder.

Not rustling, I realized. Whispering.

"Is someone down there?" I called softly.

The whispering grew louder. What were they saying?

"Can you hear me?" I asked.

"No talking," a Guardian called from down the hall.

The whispering stopped.

What was that? Did I hear voices from another room? Or was someone hiding down there between the walls?

No. That was impossible.

Right?

I was happy to find C.J. in my first training session. I wanted to ask him if he'd heard anyone whispering in the walls. "Hey, C.J.," I said softly.

"No talking," the Guardian in charge of our class ordered. "You will answer each question in the workbook on your desk."

How can he expect us to answer every question?

344

This thing is more than a hundred pages long. I flipped open the workbook.

Huh? I thought. These questions are strange: "What do you call your parents?" "What is your favorite food?" "What costumes have you worn for Halloween the last five years?"

Why did the Guardians want to know all this stuff? They already knew way too much about me.

So maybe I could confuse them a little. "I call my father Featherhead and my mother Jellyface," I wrote. "My favorite food is lumpy gray oatmeal. Every single Halloween, I've dressed up as a three-humped camel."

I tapped C.J. on the shoulder and held up my workbook so he could read my answers. C.J. snickered.

A strong hand grabbed my shoulder. Hard. "Number one-sixteen, you are a distraction to the others. You will be placed in the Special Training Course."

The Guardian marched me to the front of the room and hit a small buzzer underneath his desk. Another Guardian appeared at the classroom door.

"Take one-sixteen to the Pattern Room," the first Guardian ordered. "His training is being speeded up."

As the second Guardian herded me out the door, I glanced back at C.J. "Sorry," he whispered.

My mouth felt dry as I followed the Guardian

345

through the hallways. I tried to swallow, but I couldn't. I didn't know what the Special Training Course was — but I definitely didn't want to be in it.

The Guardian stopped in front of a wooden bench where a little girl sat swinging her feet. "Wait here," he ordered, then left.

As soon as the Guardian turned the corner, the girl leaned over to me. "Do you know what they're going to do?" she whispered. "I heard — "

A Guardian opened the door across the hall and called the girl inside. I slumped back against the wall. I was never going to find out what was going on in this creepy place.

I sighed and closed my eyes. Then I heard the whispering again. It was coming from the wall behind my head.

The whispers grew stronger. I pressed my ear against the wall. "Careful. Don't go in the Pattern Room," a voice cried.

My heartbeat thudded in my ears. "Why? What's in the room? Who are you?" I demanded.

"Don't go — "

The door to the Pattern Room opened. A Guardian ordered me inside.

I felt my legs trembling. I hoped the Guardian couldn't tell how scared I was. Slowly I stepped inside the room.

It looked like my doctor's office: a scale, an examining table, a counter with some cotton, bandages, and stuff.

"Step on the scale," the Guardian instructed. Maybe this won't be so bad, I thought.

The Guardian entered my height and weight into his handheld computer. Then he looped a tape measure around my head and recorded the information. He measured every part of my body, down to my toes. He even measured my tongue.

Why does he need all these measurements? I couldn't think of anything he could use them for. Did my special training take some special equipment that fit me exactly?

I remembered a movie my teacher showed in science class. Some scientists hooked wires up to a mouse and then dropped it into a maze. Every time it made a wrong turn, they gave the mouse a shock.

Maybe that's what the Guardians were going to do to me. Maybe they would give me a shock every time I did something my parents wouldn't like.

The Guardian picked up a color wheel from the counter. He held it up to my eyes, trying to find a color that exactly matched.

I felt more confused then ever. When the Guardian had recorded every detail about me, he sent me back to my room. Without a Guardian escort!

I had to find a way to escape. I paused at each

door and listened for voices. I didn't hear anything behind the fourth door. I opened it.

An empty office. With a phone. Yes!

I grabbed it and dialed my home number. The phone rang once. Please answer, Mom, I silently begged. Two rings. Three rings. Four rings.

I heard footsteps approaching the door. Answer. Answer.

Five rings.

"Hello?" my mom said breathlessly.

"Mom!" I whispered. "You have to get me out of this place! Something weird is going on here. I'm scared."

"Brian, you just got there yesterday. Give it a chance," Mom replied impatiently.

"But they — "

A cold hand pulled the phone away from me. I spun around. The director stood behind me.

"Hello, Mrs. O'Connor," he said. "This is the school Director. Your son Brian will be ready early. Truly special children often finish our program before the others. Yes. First thing tomorrow will be fine."

The director hung up the phone and marched me up to my room. "You have made your last error," he told me as he shut the door behind him.

What is that supposed to mean? I wondered. Are they still planning to give me the special training? Or are they sending me home — *un*perfect?

I flopped down on the bed. Every time I heard

footsteps in the hall, I thought a Guardian had arrived to take me for training.

I guess I finally dropped off to sleep. I had a dream about looking for my dog at the pound. All the dogs were whimpering.

When I woke up, the whimpering continued.

I jumped up and scrambled over to the vent. I peered down. Far below me, I saw dozens of glittering eyes.

"Save us!" a voice cried. "Save us — and yourself."

"Robots," another voice whispered. "The school makes a robot of you. They send home the robot in your place. A perfect robot. And then they make you live down here where no one can ever find you."

So *that's* why the Guardians asked those questions and took so many measurements! They were making a robot of me to send home to Mom and Dad!

My whole body trembled. I could barely breathe. "What do I do?" I demanded. "How can I — ?"

"Shhh. Someone's coming," another voice warned.

The eyes disappeared back into the darkness.

I had to get out of my room — now. I tore a piece of paper off the sheet lining one of the dresser drawers. Then I knocked lightly on the door. No answer. I knocked a little louder.

"Yes?" a Guardian called.

"I need to go to the bathroom," I said.

He opened the door. As I passed through, I shoved the paper into the lock.

The Guardian escorted me to the bathroom and then returned me to my room. He shut the door firmly behind him.

I waited a few minutes. Then I tried the door. It opened. The paper kept the door from locking!

I grabbed my spoon from the table and opened the door a crack. When the Guardian was looking in the opposite direction, I hurled the spoon down the hall as far as I could.

The Guardian heard the clattering sound and turned toward it. I slipped out of my room and ran down the hall the other way.

So far so good. I crept down the stairs.

"What are you doing down here?" someone demanded.

"N-nothing," I stuttered. Then my eyes adjusted to the dark hallway. "C.J., it's you!" I was so glad to see him! "We've got to get out of this school — now!" I told him.

His eyes bulged in surprise. "Huh?"

"There are kids trapped behind the walls. We have to save them — and us!" I exclaimed, tugging his hand.

"Follow me," C.J. answered. "I know where to go."

C.J. grabbed my arm and led me around the

corner and down a short hallway. He pressed on a wall panel — and it slid open.

"Quick. In here," he whispered. "It leads outside."

"Great!" I cried. I ducked my head and started into the narrow opening.

To my surprise, I saw only darkness. And heard whispering voices. Shuffling feet.

"Hey — !" I spun around to C.J. "This doesn't lead outside!" I protested. "This is where all the kids are hidden!"

"Sorry," C.J. replied in a cold, low voice. "This is where you will be hidden too, Brian. I work for the Guardians. My job was to guard you."

"No!" I shrieked. "No! Let me out! Let me out!"

But to my horror, the wall panel began to slide shut behind me.

"Thank you very much, Director," my mother said. "Brian looks perfect."

She admired my gray uniform, my perfectly brushed hair, my perfect smile. I stood straight as an arrow. I faced forward as a good robot should. I held the gray suitcase in my left hand, as all of the robots are programmed.

My mother shook hands with the Director. She handed him an envelope filled with money.

"He will be perfect now," the Director said. "We guarantee it."

351

That was two days ago. And I'm trying to be as perfect as I can be.

Because I don't want anyone to catch on.

It wasn't easy to pull C.J. into the dark chamber and escape before the wall closed up. And it wasn't easy to sneak into the robot room. To grab my robot and drag it up to my room. And then to sneak back into the robot room and pretend to be a robot.

Yes, I don't want anyone to catch on that the *real* Brian O'Connor came home. I don't want anyone to know that I escaped.

Some day soon I'm going back to that place and rescue those poor kids. But right now I'm being as perfect as I can be.

Okay, okay.

So I teased the dog this morning. And ate three Snickers bars for lunch. And spilled some grape juice on the white couch in the den.

But other than that, I've been perfect.

Really.

FOR THE BIRDS

"We're here!" Dad announced happily. "Happy vacation, everyone!"

Some vacation! I grumbled to myself.

My family piled out of the car. All five of us. I stretched my legs after the long ride. Then I gazed up at the lodge.

What a dump.

It looked like the log cabin on the maple syrup bottle. Except it was falling apart.

A log hung over the door with words carved into it: WELCOME TO BIRD HAVEN LODGE.

It should be called Bird *Brain* Lodge! I told myself, rolling my eyes. Only a birdbrain would come to a place like this!

Mom gave Dad's arm a squeeze. "Oh, Henry! It's so romantic!"

Romantic? Okay, maybe I'm only twelve. Maybe I don't think much about romantic stuff. But that wasn't exactly the word that came to my mind.

353

The word that came to my mind was *stupid!*

"Can't we go to a *real* hotel?" I pleaded for the thousandth time.

But Mom and Dad were too busy smooching to answer. They always acted this way on their wedding anniversary — which was today.

"Move it, Kim," ordered my fifteen-year-old brother, Ben. He had on his favorite T-shirt. It said: *So many birds, so little time!*

Do you believe it? A fifteen-year-old boy who's into bird-watching?

"Yeah, move it, Kim," echoed my other brother, Andy. He's thirteen. His hair hangs down over his eyes. I can never tell if he's looking at me. "We want to do some bird-watching before dark."

To me, if you've seen one bird, you've seen them all. But everybody else in my family is bird crazy! They spend all their time in the woods, staring through binoculars.

And if they spot a new bird to check off on their list, they go totally nuts.

It's sick. That's the only way to describe it.

And now here we are at Bird Haven Lodge. A whole week of bird-watching, bird talk — nothing but birds all the time.

Thrills and chills, huh?

Carrying my suitcase, I started up the gravel path to the lodge. Tall hedges lined the path on both sides. The hedges were trimmed into bird shapes. I passed what looked like a leafy pigeon. Then an eagle. I brushed by a bushy duck about ten feet tall.

"I'm going to hurl. Really," I complained.

My family pretended they didn't hear me. I guess they were sick of my complaints. But what was I supposed to do while they crawled through the trees gawking at birds?

"Check it out!" exclaimed Andy as we reached the lodge. "A pair of great horned owls!"

"No way," Ben scoffed. "Those are screech owls."

"Owls in the daytime?" I asked. "Where?"

"Right there, stupid," Ben said, pointing.

Then I saw them. They were standing guard on either side of the steps. Owls carved out of hedges.

Big deal — right?

"We're the Petersons," Dad told the big, jolly-looking man at the check-in desk.

"I've been expecting you," the man replied with a big smile. "I'm Mr. Dove."

"Mr. *Dove*?" I mumbled. "Give me a break!"

Mr. Dove's round, little bird eyes darted from Mom to Dad. "Mr. and Mrs. Peterson," he said, "you'll be in the Lovebird Suite."

Mr. Dove ran his fingers down the register. "Now . . . let . . . me . . . see. I have a double for the boys on the third floor in the Blue Jay Wing." Mr. Dove eyed me. "And for you — the Cuckoo's Nest."

"Cuckoo!" Ben and Andy hooted. "Cuckoo Kim!"

I shot Mr. Dove a dirty look. But he didn't seem to notice.

"Follow me," he said. "I'll show you to your rooms."

We followed him down the hall to the Lovebird Suite.

"These doors lead out to a terrace with an old-fashioned swing," Mr. Dove practically cooed. "Would you like to see it now?"

But Mom and Dad were too busy smooching to answer.

Uh-hmmm. Mr. Dove cleared his throat.

Mom giggled. "We can see the terrace later," she said. "Come on, Henry. Let's go see the kids' rooms."

We took the elevator up to the third floor. Ben and Andy dashed into their room, snatched binoculars from their backpacks, and ran outside to spot some birds.

"Now to Cuckoo's Nest," Mr. Dove announced.

"I'm the only one here who *isn't* cuckoo!" I muttered. I don't think anyone heard me.

Mom and Dad and I followed Mr. Dove again. We turned down a narrow hallway. We kept walking. And walking. We didn't see any other guests.

"Um, where *is* my room, anyway?" I asked.

"We're almost there," Mr. Dove sang out.

When we reached the far end of the hall, he stopped and opened a door.

"How unusual!" Mom exclaimed, stepping into the room.

Mom had *that* right. Cuckoo's Nest was small. Tiny, actually. And it was round. A round room.

"I don't know . . ." I began. "It's, um, so *far* from everybody."

"Don't be silly, Kim," Mom said. "It's a lovely little nest!"

I groaned. "Mom — can't you stop with the bird talk for one second? I'm sick of birds! Sick of them!"

I saw Mr. Dove staring at me, surprised by my sudden outburst.

Dad walked over to a window. "What a view!" he exclaimed. "Kim, you can see right into the famous Mockingbird Maze."

I joined Dad at the window. The maze looked like one out of my old *Pencil Fun and Games* book. Except that this maze was made out of twelve-foot-tall hedges. It went round and round and round. It seemed to have a hundred different dead ends.

I'd hate to get lost in there, I thought. "Hey!" I exclaimed. "There are Ben and Andy — inside the maze!"

Mr. Dove frowned. "You should save the maze

357

for tomorrow," he told Mom and Dad. "You'll need a full day to do it right."

"Why don't you go outside too, Kim?" Dad suggested. "Your mother and I have some unpacking to do."

Well, I went downstairs. But I didn't go outside. I don't really like to be outdoors at all. Too many birds.

I wandered around the lodge. I thought maybe I'd find someone else my age. Or a game room. Or a TV to watch.

But the place was empty.

Finally I sat down on a low couch in a room near the front desk. I guess it was some kind of rec room. I stared at the stone fireplace for a while. There were stuffed birds all around it on the wall. Pheasants and ducks and owls. Yuck!

I picked up an old magazine and settled back against the couch.

"Oww!" I cried out as a sharp pain shot up my back.

I jumped to my feet. A picture flashed into my mind. A huge, angry bird — a hawk or a falcon. It had dug its sharp beak into my back!

I spun around — and gazed down at a pair of hedge clippers.

"Huh?" I picked them up. Heavy, metal hedge clippers. I hadn't even seen them when I sat down on them.

I turned to see Mr. Dove enter the room. "You found them!" he cried. A smile crossed his round face. He hurried over to me. "Thank you! I've been searching all over for these!"

"I — I sat on them," I stammered. I handed them to him.

"I'm so grateful you found them." He beamed at me. "I owe you a big favor, Kim."

"No. Really — " I started.

"I owe you a favor," he insisted. His smile faded. "I guess you'd like revenge."

"Excuse me?" I thought I hadn't heard correctly.

"Revenge against your family. For bringing you here," he said, smiling again.

"Uh . . . no. That's okay," I replied uncertainly. "I'm . . . uh . . . enjoying it." I hurried out of the room. "Bye."

What did he mean by that? I wondered. He's just like my family, I finally decided. Totally nuts.

That night, we ate in the hotel dining room. I hoped to see some other kids at dinner. Some *normal* kids. Kids who couldn't tell a red hawk from a turkey buzzard. But we were the only ones in the dining room.

Mr. Dove was our waiter. Maybe he was the cook, too. Did anyone else work here? I wondered.

Ben and Andy couldn't stop talking about how

many birds they'd seen. They were so excited. "There are *thousands* of birds here!" Andy declared.

"No. Millions!" Ben corrected him.

Mom and Dad held hands all through dinner. They couldn't wait for us all to explore Mockingbird Maze in the morning.

I tuned out. I'd never been so bored in all my life.

Later, I was in my room, trying to get to sleep. I closed my eyes. I listened to the wind blow through the trees. I tossed and turned for hours. I twisted my covers into knots. No way could I fall asleep in Cuckoo's Nest.

The wind began to pick up. I heard flapping. Must be the awnings over the windows, I thought.

Then I heard a cry. My eyes popped open. I glanced around the room. It was flooded with moonlight. Shadows flitted on the bed, the floor, everywhere.

I threw back the covers and tiptoed over to a window.

I gasped!

The sky was thick with birds!

They circled in front of my room. Cawing and cackling.

An enormous crow landed on my ledge.

It stared at me with its bottomless, black-hole eyes. Then it pecked at the glass.

It's trying to tell me something, I thought.

A weird thought. But the whole thing was so weird. Why were the birds flying at night? Why were they circling in front of me? Cawing and chirping so demandingly?

They really did seem as if they were trying to communicate.

With a shudder, I pulled the curtain, hurried back to bed and slept with two pillows over my head.

The next morning, Andy and Ben woke me up at dawn. They insisted that I come with the family into Mockingbird Maze.

"I might as well," I said, yawning. "There's nothing else to do here." That was as enthusiastic as I could get.

The five of us ate a hurried breakfast. Then, armed with notebooks, bird books, and binoculars, we stepped out into a gray morning. The sun hadn't climbed over the trees. The morning dew still glistened on the grass.

What am I *doing* here? I asked myself, shaking my head unhappily. I hate birds. I *hate* them!

To our surprise, we found Mr. Dove at the entrance to the maze. He wore blue denim overalls, and he carried the hedge clippers. His round face was red and sweaty. I guess he had gotten an early start pruning in the maze.

361

"Good morning, everyone." He grinned at me. "I hope you enjoy the maze. Lots to see. Lots of surprises."

He chatted with Mom and Dad for a few minutes. Andy and Ben started chirping at me. "Cuckoo! Cuckoo! Cuckoo Kim!" They think they're a riot, but they're just dumb.

A short while later, we stepped into the maze. The tall hedges cast dark shadows over the path. I already felt lost!

We took about five steps — and stopped.

"Oh, wow!" I cried out. Standing in front of us was a huge hedge sculpture. Five people carved out of hedge. And the five people were *us*!

"Mr. Dove — !" Dad called. "What *is* this?"

We turned to see him grinning at us from the maze entrance. He waved the big hedge clippers. "All part of the program," he called. "Part of the program." He disappeared.

Dad shook his head. "What an odd bird," he muttered.

"Dad — *please!*" I begged. "Stop with the bird talk!"

We admired the hedge portrait for a while. I'm not sure why, but it gave me the creeps. Why did Mr. Dove do it? What did he mean, it was part of the program?

The questions repeated in my mind as we made our way through the twisting maze. Everyone else oohed and aahed over all the birds. There were hundreds of them. All different kinds. All chirping and cawing and crowing at once.

I had to hold my hands over my ears. It was deafening!

These birds are all chirping at once because they're trying to tell us something. That thought flashed through my mind again. That's totally crazy, I told myself. And I pushed the thought out of my head.

I shouldn't have.

I should have paid attention to my growing fear.

But now it was too late.

We stepped into a narrow tunnel — and came out the other end into a round structure. Dome-shaped. Made of metal wires.

It took us a few seconds to realize we had stepped into a cage. A giant bird cage.

"Wow — this is awesome!" Andy declared.

"What a great maze!" Ben agreed.

Then the wire door snapped shut behind us.

Andy's smile vanished. "Hey — how do we get out?" he cried.

"You can fly out," a voice replied. Mr. Dove appeared from a trapdoor in the cage floor.

"Huh? What do you mean?" Mom cried. She grabbed Dad's arm. "What's going on, Mr. Dove?"

"All part of the program," Mr. Dove replied. "All part of the program. I want you to be happy birds."

"Excuse me? Happy *birds*?" I demanded.

363

"It's a very old trick I learned," Mr. Dove said. "Quite easy. If you get the hedge sculpture right. Quite easy. And now you can join your feathered friends. You'll be happy. I want you to be happy."

Before we could say anything, Mr. Dove raised the hedge clippers. He pointed them at Mom and Dad. And clicked the blades together twice.

"Nooooo!" I wailed as I watched Mom and Dad shrink away — change shape — and flutter up against the cage wall.

"I turned them into lovebirds." Mr. Dove beamed. "Now they'll be happy."

"Noooo!" Another horrified wail escaped my throat as the hedge clippers clicked twice more. And as I stared in shock, not believing it, not believing it — but seeing it — my brothers were also changed into fluttering, chirping birds.

"Two mockingbirds," Mr. Dove said. "They'll like that."

He turned to me.

"No — please!" I begged. "Please don't turn me into a bird! Please!"

He smiled. "Of course not, Kim. I owe you a favor. I know you hate birds — right?"

"Please — !" I repeated. "Please — !"

"I said I'd help you pay them back," he said softly.

"No. Please — !" I begged. "Please don't — "

My family chirped and twittered, fluttering across the cage excitedly.

"I want you to be happy, Kim," Mr. Dove said.

Then he clicked the hedge clippers and changed me, too.

He changed me into — a cat.

ALIENS IN THE GARDEN

Thick, black clouds rolled across the sky as I walked toward the park. Lightning flashed and thunder rumbled in the distance.

Forget the park, Kurt, I told myself. Nobody will show up in this weather, anyway.

More thunder. Louder now. That did it. I turned around and started for home. As I hurried around the corner, I spotted Rocky up ahead of me.

I stopped — and wished I could disappear.

Rocky is a dog. A mean, vicious dog with ratty brown fur, sharp yellow fangs, and killer eyes.

I held my breath and crossed my fingers that he wouldn't come any closer. And I got lucky. Rocky sniffed in the gutter for a couple of seconds, then trotted away.

I let my breath out in a big whoosh.

"Yo, Creep-o!" a voice roared from behind me.

I sucked in my breath again. "I should have

known," I mumbled. Wherever Rocky goes, Flip won't be far behind.

Slowly, I turned around and faced him.

Flip is Rocky's owner. Flip is fourteen, two years older than I am. And he's huge, with the same ratty hair and yellow teeth as his dog.

It's hard to decide which one is meaner.

"Where do you think you're going, Kurt?" he demanded.

"Home," I told him. "A storm is coming."

"Ooh, a storm!" He sneered and pushed me backwards. "Gonna go hide under the bed?"

Flip's favorite sport is picking on me. He pushed me again, harder. I almost fell. "Get a life, Flip!" I yelled. "Go sniff gutters with your mutt!"

Flip's eyes narrowed. He clenched his big fists. You should have kept your mouth shut, I told myself. You're in major trouble now!

Just as Flip dove for me, a shaft of lightning split the clouds. Thunder boomed. More lightning flashed, and then rain poured out of the sky.

"Aah, you're not worth getting soaked for," Flip growled. Instead of pounding me to dust, he shoved me aside and took off.

Saved by a summer storm! I'd lucked out after all.

Upstairs in my bedroom, I changed into dry clothes. I could hear the wind howling outside. I ran to the window and crouched down in front of it to watch the storm. As I did, I saw something whiz past outside. Another lightning bolt split the sky. It zapped the flying object and lit it up.

I stared hard at the object. It looked like a toy spaceship.

I mashed my nose against the windowpane to see better. There! It hovered low over the backyard garden. Wobbling back and forth. Out of control.

I craned my neck to watch. The object spiraled down . . . down . . . down . . . then — *splat*! It nose-dived right into the middle of a berry bush.

I kept my eyes on that bush until the storm finally blew itself out. It wasn't a long storm, but it was one of the heaviest I've ever seen. When the rain slowed to a drizzle, I ran outside and sloshed my way into the garden.

Disaster area! Ripped leaves and broken branches covered the ground. Slimy green vegetable guts dripped down the fence. Mud slithered into my shoes and oozed between my toes.

I squished over to the berry bush and stooped down. Bloodred juice splattered onto my fingers as I pried some branches apart.

There sat the object, stuck nose-first into the ground under the bush. Wisps of hissing steam rose up from it.

I cautiously reached down and touched it.

Warm, but not too hot. The mud made a sucking sound as I tugged it loose.

I wiped the object on my shirt and stared at it.

Some kind of spaceship, for sure. Made out of metal. Cone-shaped, with three little wings at one end and a tinted window at the other. I couldn't see inside.

But it's definitely not a toy, I decided. It's too solid. And it survived the storm *and* the crash.

An awesome thought suddenly hit me. Could the little spaceship be real?

I always figured flying saucers and alien space-ships had to be huge. But I'd never seen one. How could I know for sure that I didn't have one in my hands?

I tucked the ship under my arm and hurried to the park to show it to my best friend, Jenna. I knew she would show up. Jenna loves going to the park. She practically lives there.

As I sat down on a bench, Flip burst out of some bushes and landed in front of me. Guess my luck ran out.

"Hey, Creep-o, what's that?" he asked, grab-bing for the spaceship.

I tried to push him away, but he yanked me straight off the bench and tossed me into the grass.

The ship flew from my hand and landed nearby.

Flip stared at it. His mouth hung open for a

second. Then he shook his ratty head and bellowed out a laugh. "A toy spaceship? Aren't you a little old to be playing with toys?"

As I struggled to my knees, Flip reached for the ship. I knew he'd try to smash it, so I made a grab for it.

In a flash, Flip had me in a headlock. His arm squeezed tighter around my neck. I tried to pull it away. The muscle felt like a stone. His arm didn't budge.

I gasped for air.

Flip let out another laugh.

But his laugh turned into a shriek. To my surprise, his arm dropped from my neck.

I sank to the ground. Flip shrieked again.

I sucked in air and stared up at him.

He held his face with one hand and hopped up and down, screeching in pain.

As I gazed at him, a blue light zipped past my eyes and hit Flip on his bony knee. Sparks flew from his skin. He roared and dropped to the ground. Then he rolled over, leaped up, and ran off.

Saved again! I thought. But by what? Where did that blue light come from?

I sat up and glanced around.

And gasped.

On the ground near the ship stood three small aliens.

Aliens? You're seeing things, Kurt, I told myself. Flip's choke-hold cut off your air and messed up your brain.

I glanced away. Shook my head to clear it. Blinked hard and rubbed my eyes. Slowly, I glanced back at the ground.

The aliens still stood there, not much taller than the grass. They wore puffy silver suits and round white helmets with shaded visors.

Whoa! Not only had a real spaceship crashed into the garden, but it had real aliens in it. Awesome!

I stared hard — and saw that each alien clutched a tiny gun in its hand.

Ray guns. Ray guns that shot a painful blue light!

I'm toast now! I thought, jumping to my feet.

But instead of zapping me, the aliens shoved the guns into their suits. Then they tilted their heads way back and gazed up at me.

I crouched down on my hands and knees. I stuck my face real close to one of the aliens and squinted into its visor.

A weird face with bright-red hair growing all over it. Beady little eyes. A button nose and a smile on its tiny mouth.

I heard a faint squeaking sound. I stared harder. The alien's lips flapped. It's talking! I realized. An alien is actually talking to me!

I grinned. "Hi, I'm Kurt," I told it. "Listen, thanks for zapping Flip."

371

All three aliens grabbed their helmets and cringed.

At first I didn't get it. Then I realized the problem — my voice. I'm at least a hundred times as big as these little guys, I told myself. My voice is killing their ears.

"Flip is a total bully," I whispered. "I really owe you one. I mean, you saved my life!"

I peered at the first alien again. It just shook its head and shrugged. It couldn't understand a word I said.

"Hey, Kurt what are you doing?" a voice called out from behind me. My friend Jenna's voice. The aliens stood still as she dropped onto the ground beside me.

Jenna gazed at the aliens. Then she slowly glanced at me. "Please tell me you're not playing with dolls, Kurt."

"They're not dolls," I whispered. "They're aliens."

"Alien what?"

"Alien aliens," I told her. "From outer space."

She rolled her eyes. "Give me a break!"

"Keep your voice down!" I whispered. "It hurts their ears."

"You're kidding, right?" Jenna glanced at the aliens. "Hello down there!" she cried.

The aliens grabbed their heads and cringed again.

Jenna gasped. Her green eyes grew huge.

"Kurt!" she whispered. "Please tell me you've got a remote control somewhere."

I pulled the pockets of my shorts inside out. "No remote, Jenna."

"This is unreal!" she murmured. But I could tell she believed me now. "How did they get here?"

I pointed to the ship. "The storm knocked it out of the sky, into my garden."

"Wow!" Jenna gazed at the aliens. "I never thought I'd see anything like this! I mean, there's actually life on another planet somewhere!" She bent lower and squinted closely at the first alien.

"Don't make any sudden moves," I warned. "It's got a mean ray gun. They all do. Flip tried to choke me — and they zapped him."

Jenna grinned. "If they zapped Flip, they're definitely good guys." She inspected the alien again. "I wonder where they're from."

"I don't know, but I bet they want to go home," I told her.

"After meeting Flip, who wouldn't?" Jenna muttered. "Can the ship still fly?"

Before I could answer, the aliens suddenly stiffened.

I glanced up. "Uh-oh! Flip's back!" I warned. "And he brought Drake along for company!"

Flip and his cousin Drake were tearing along the path toward the bench. Drake carried a bat. With a wild laugh, Flip vaulted the bench and landed near the spaceship.

The aliens scattered.

"Ready for some fun?" Flip roared to Drake.

Drake snickered.

"Leave them alone!" I shouted.

Flip laughed again. "Hey, Creep-o, didn't your mother ever teach you to share your toys!"

Two of the aliens scurried off in opposite directions. Drake darted after one of them, whacking his bat on the ground and laughing.

"Cut it out!" Jenna cried. She chased after Drake.

I spotted the third alien running for the ship. It tripped over a twig and fell on its face.

Flip snatched it up in his fat hand. "You're dog meat!" he snarled at it.

He pinned the alien's arms to its sides and began to squeeze.

He'll squash it! I thought. They saved me. Now it was my turn to save them!

I made a desperate leap. I crashed against Flip's knees, knocking him to the ground. The alien popped from his hand and tumbled end over end through the air.

I stretched my arms out as far as I could and caught it inches from the ground. It struggled to its feet on my palm.

"Kurt's got one!" Flip shouted to Drake, scrambling up. "Forget the others. Get Kurt!"

Drake and Flip charged at me. Jenna jumped on Flip's back, but he shook her off easily.

374

I slipped the alien into the pocket of my shorts — and ran!

I dashed along the path, scuttled through some bushes and into a clearing. As I sprinted up a grassy hill, I heard Flip and Drake crashing through the bushes after me.

I put on more speed and charged down the other side of the hill. Then I doubled back.

Gasping for breath, I crawled through the bushes again. At the edge of the path, I peeked out.

And froze.

Flip's dog, Rocky, stood on the path, his killer eyes glaring straight into mine.

My heart hammered against my chest.

Rocky's lips curled back. His yellow fangs dripped saliva. He lowered his huge, shaggy head and snarled. He pawed the ground. Snarled again.

And sprang at me!

I cried out as a blue light zapped through the air. It caught Rocky right between the eyes!

The dog yelped and dropped to the ground at my feet, looking dazed.

The blue light meant only one thing — an alien close by. I glanced around and spotted it, caught in a thicket of thorny branches.

"Thanks again!" I whispered, reaching into the bush. The tiny spacesuit ripped as I tugged the alien free. I quickly dropped it into my other pocket.

Still dazed, Rocky whined meekly as I stepped past him and bolted down the path.

"Kurt!" Jenna cried when she saw me. "Hurry!"

"I've got two of the aliens!" I gasped, running up to her. "We've got to find the other one!"

"I did," she told me. "It's in the ship. Maybe it's trying to get the spaceship working."

"Let's hope it can." I dug the other two aliens out of my pockets and set them in the open hatch of the ship.

They waved at me, then hurried inside. The tiny hatch closed.

A loud, angry bark made Jenna and me spin around. Rocky had recovered and was charging toward us. Flip and Drake raced behind him, shouting, "Get the aliens!"

I stooped down next to the spaceship. Tiny red lights flickered on, but it didn't move.

The barking and shouting grew louder.

The spaceship still didn't move.

I had to do something! I grabbed it off the ground, cocked my arm back — and *hurled* the ship as high into the air as I could!

The ship soared upward. Higher . . . higher.

Then the nose dipped.

Jenna and I both gasped.

The spaceship began to spiral down.

Rocky chased after it, barking wildly. Flip and Drake cheered.

I groaned and started to cover my eyes. But

then I saw a puff of smoke from the back of the ship. Then another. The little spacecraft leveled off — and began to climb.

"Yes!" I cheered.

Flip and Drake stared with their mouths hanging open.

More smoke billowed. The red lights twinkled. The ship kept climbing. It rose higher and higher, until all we could see was a silver dot in the sky.

"Unreal!" Jenna kept muttering as we hurried out of the park. "Real, but totally *un*real!"

"Flip and Drake still can't believe it," I said, snickering. "They're both back in the park, gaping at the sky."

She laughed. "Too bad the aliens couldn't have zapped them one last time."

"Yeah, and it's too bad they couldn't have stayed a little longer." I stared up at the sky, too. "One thing is for sure — I'll never forget them."

"I'll bet they never forget *us*, either." Jenna pointed at an ice cream truck down the street. "And I think we deserve a reward for saving them, don't you?"

"Definitely." I dug into my pockets and pulled out some coins.

I also pulled out a tiny scrap of silver material.

"Hey! It's a piece of a spacesuit," I told Jenna. "It must be from the alien that got caught in the thorn bush."

377

Jenna squinted at the scrap. "It's part of a sleeve, I think. And there's something on it. Something colorful."

We forgot about the ice cream and ran to my house. I found my magnifying glass and peered at the scrap through the lens.

"What do you see?" Jenna asked.

"I'm not sure." I closed one eye to focus better. "It's a rectangle," I told her. "With stripes going across it. Red and white stripes. The upper left-hand corner is blue. And it has a bunch of white stars on it." I counted them. "Fifty stars."

"Weird." Jenna frowned. "I wonder what it means."

"Me, too," I agreed. "Maybe it's some kind of symbol. A flag or something. From the aliens' planet." I sighed. "I guess we'll never know."

"Let's go get that ice cream," Jenna said.

I tucked the tiny cloth rectangle into my pocket and followed her out the door.

THE THUMBPRINT OF DOOM

"Let's go swimming in the lake," I suggested.

"Trisha, you already said that. Can't you think of anything else to do?" Jeremy asked. "Harold doesn't want to go swimming. He's afraid."

I was afraid too. Afraid that this was going to be the most boring summer of my life.

Usually I go to sleep-away camp in the summer — but not this year. This year I thought it would be fun to hang out with my best friend, Jeremy.

I thought wrong.

I didn't know his cousin Harold was visiting — for two whole months. Nerdy Harold. Ugh.

We're all twelve, but Harold seems a lot younger. Probably because he's really, really short. The total opposite of me and Jeremy.

"What are you afraid of, anyway?" I asked Harold, tightening my ponytail. We were walking around the block for the third time, trying to decide what to do.

"Yeah, what *are* you afraid of?" Jeremy asked.

"Fungus."

"What?" Jeremy and I shouted together.

"Fungus," Harold repeated. "You know, those tiny plants that live in the water. The ones that are so small, you can't see them."

"So what about them?" I asked.

"Well, I don't like things I can't see," Harold mumbled.

I'm doomed, I thought, staring at Harold. This really was going to be the worst summer of my life.

"How about the movies?" Jeremy suggested.

Harold said okay, so we headed for town. We had walked halfway down the block when I spotted her.

"Look," I said, turning to Jeremy. "There's the new girl. Her family moved in last week. Mom says she's our age. Let's go say hi."

I stared at the girl as we walked over. She was really pretty. Her long, shiny black hair hung down to her waist, and her skin was a beautiful olive color. She wore khaki shorts and a matching T-shirt.

"Hi!" I called when we reached her yard. "You're my new neighbor. I live over there," I said, pointing out my house.

"I'm Carla," she introduced herself, striding across the lawn in her bare feet. "We just moved in."

Carla glanced at Jeremy, then at Harold. She had the brightest green eyes I'd ever seen.

"I'm Trisha. This is Jeremy and Harold. We're going to the movies," I said. "Want to come?"

"I'd really like to," Carla started. "But I can't. My horoscope says I shouldn't go anywhere today."

"You believe in that stuff?" I asked.

"Well, I'm kind of into it. I'm pretty superstitious."

"You mean you're afraid of black cats and stuff?" Harold asked.

"Harold is only afraid of things he can't see," I told her.

Jeremy shoved his elbow into my side. Carla didn't seem to notice. She continued, "Well, I'm not afraid of black cats. But some things. Have you ever heard of the Thumbprint of Doom?"

"The Thumbprint of Doom?" I repeated. We shook our heads no.

"Well, if someone puts it on your forehead," Carla explained, lowering her voice to a whisper, "you're doomed! Something horrible will happen to you in less than twenty-four hours."

"Do you *really* believe that?" I asked.

"Yes," she replied. "Yes, I do. It's the thing I'm most afraid of."

"We — we have to go," Harold stammered. "We're going to be late for the movie."

"Okay. See you around," Carla said. The three of us hurried away.

"Boy, was she weird," Jeremy snickered.

"Totally," I agreed. Then I waved my arms over my head and started shrieking. "Oooooo! The Thumbprint of Dooooom." I jabbed my thumb onto Jeremy's forehead, hard.

Jeremy chased me down the street trying to give *me* the Thumbprint of Doom. Then we both raced after Harold. We tackled him to the ground and gave him the *Double* Thumbprint of Doom!

The next day, Jeremy and I headed down to the lake to go rowing. Harold decided to stay home — to read the dictionary. He says he wants to finish it by Christmas. He's already up to the *P*'s; I convinced him he was way behind schedule.

"You get in first," I told Jeremy when we reached the lake, "and set up the oars." Jeremy had a hard time slipping the oars into the oarlocks. They were about a hundred years old — rotted and warped.

The old wood creaked and groaned as I slid the boat into the water. I started to jump in — when I heard the scream.

A terrified scream.

"Trisha! Noooooo!"

I lost my balance and fell into the lake.

I fumbled for the side of the boat and pulled

myself up, gasping for air. Then I threw myself on the shore.

"Are you okay?" It was Carla.

I couldn't speak. I nodded.

"Hope I didn't scare you," she said. "But you can't ride a blue canoe on Tuesday!"

"Huh?" Jeremy cried, helping me up.

"It's bad luck," Carla said. "A blue canoe on Tuesday is bad luck for Wednesday."

"Carla, you scared me to death," I sputtered. "I don't believe in those weird superstitions. *And I don't believe you did such a stupid thing,*" I muttered under my breath.

While I wrung out my T-shirt and poured the water from my new sneakers, Carla apologized. Then the three of us headed home. I wanted to be mad at Carla, but I couldn't. She was convinced that she had saved my life.

"Hey! There's Harold," Jeremy pointed out on our way back. Harold was walking down the street, dodging from tree to tree. I'd seen him do that before. He was trying to avoid the dogs — if there were any.

"Hey! Guys! I finished the *P*'s!" He ran up to us. "Isn't that great, Trisha? I finished the *P*'s!" Then he shot his arms out and — he shoved me hard!

I fell to the ground and scraped my knees.

"HAROLD!" I screamed. "What did you do that for?"

"You were going to step on a crack! See," he said, pointing to the sidewalk.

"So what!"

"It's bad luck, Trisha," he explained. "Step on a crack, break your mother's back."

"Since when do you believe in superstitions?" Jeremy asked.

"Since we met Carla," Harold said, smiling at her. "I think she makes a lot of sense."

This was *definitely* going to be the worst summer of my life, I thought.

But I didn't know how right I was.

A few days later, Carla stopped by the baseball field to watch us play.

It was the bottom of the ninth, we were one run behind, and I was up at bat. We already had two outs, so I was really nervous. The game was all up to me.

I planted my feet in the batter's box and waited for the pitch. It flew past me. So did the next one. Two strikes.

"This is it, Trisha," I told myself. "Concentrate!"

My eyes were glued to the ball. It was coming — a fast ball. My favorite pitch!

I started to swing and —

"TRISHHHA!" Carla ran out onto the field. "Don't!" she shrieked, waving her arms high in the air.

384

The ball whizzed by me. "Strike three!"

"Carla!" I screamed. "What is your *problem*?"

"It's thirteen minutes after one o'clock on Friday the thirteenth," she said in a rush. "You can't hit a ball now. It would be a disaster!"

"Thanks, Carla," I grumbled. "Thanks a lot."

Carla and Harold left right after the game. Jeremy waited for me to collect my stuff from the bench. Then we walked home together.

"I can't take it anymore," I complained. "Do you know what Carla did to me yesterday?"

Jeremy shook his head no.

"She forced me to walk around the fire hydrant seven times — backwards."

"Why?" Jeremy asked.

"I don't know *why*, Jeremy. All I know is she's driving me crazy. Those superstitions are ruining my life."

Jeremy shrugged.

"We've got to show Carla that superstitions are totally dumb, Jeremy. We've got to. The question is *how*?"

Three days later, I knew how. I had a plan to cure Carla of her superstitions forever. It was sneaky. But it was good.

Friday night after dinner, Jeremy, Harold, and I stopped by her house.

"We're riding over to the Jefferson Field fairgrounds," I told her. "To check out the new carnival. You've got to come!"

Carla stood in the doorway, holding open the screen door. "Tonight?" She narrowed her eyes. Thinking. "No," she finally said. "Not tonight. The stars aren't right."

We begged and pleaded, and finally dragged her out of the house.

By the time we reached the fairgrounds, the sun had set. Jefferson Field sparkled in the dark with thousands of colored lights. They decorated a huge Ferris wheel. And a giant roller coaster. And they lit up the midway.

Carnival music blared everywhere. Bells rang out every time someone won a game.

"Wow! This is great!" Jeremy cried as we walked through the midway, tugging Carla behind us.

I spotted a small, dirty, white trailer in the back. A sign hung over the door. MADAME WANDA SEES ALL. HAVE YOUR FORTUNE TOLD.

"Come on!" I turned to Carla. "Let's see what Madame Wanda says about your future. Bet it isn't as scary as you think."

"No," Carla refused. "I'm too scared."

"We'll go in with you. It'll be a laugh. Bet she tells you some wild things."

Carla shook her head no.

"I'll stay out here with Carla," Harold offered. "You two can go in." Harold was scared, too.

386

"Harold is afraid of the future," Jeremy whispered to me, "because it's another thing he can't see!"

"We're all going in," I declared. And with that, Jeremy and I pulled Carla and Harold into Madame Wanda's trailer.

It was very dark inside, and a sweet odor filled the room. Incense, I guessed. Soft, eerie music surrounded us.

A cold green mist swirled through the air. It sent a chill down my spine. I turned to Carla. She shivered, too.

In front of us, a single candle glowed on an old table. Our shadows shifted on the walls in the flickering light.

It really was scary in here.

"H-hello," I stammered.

No answer.

I took a step forward and heard a moan.

A low moan.

My heart began to race. I glanced at the others.

Harold stood frozen in place. Jeremy looked frightened, too. In the dim light, I could see his eyes nervously dart around the room. Carla didn't move.

The moan grew louder. "Let's get out of here," I whispered.

I turned to leave. But a breeze — from nowhere — snuffed out the candle, plunging us into darkness.

387

We screamed.

And then we heard the voice.

"Come forward," it called from a darkened corner. We inched up. My legs trembled. The moaning grew closer. Closer.

"I — I want to go," Carla groaned. She bolted for the door, but a hand suddenly reached out and grabbed her.

Madame Wanda.

The woman struck a match and lit the candle. "Sit!" she commanded.

We sat.

She took her place at the table. She was dressed in a shiny black gown, and on her head she wore a dark-green turban.

I studied her face. Purple veins shot through the whites of her eyes. I couldn't stop staring at her eyes — and those lips. Dark, dramatic lips.

She grinned at me and her lips parted. Her dark eyes glowed, as if seeing right through me.

I jumped up, but she yanked me back down.

She stared deeply into our eyes. "Who will go first?" she asked slowly.

A trickle of sweat dripped down my forehead. I grabbed Carla's hand and raised it in the air. "She will!"

Carla snatched her hand back, but Madame Wanda reached out and seized it. Carla's hand trembled in Madame Wanda's.

"Do not be frightened," the fortune-teller said.

"I am only going to reveal your future. Nothing more."

Madame Wanda held Carla's hand tightly as she peered into her crystal ball. I glanced around the table. Jeremy and Harold sat perfectly still — statues with eyes glued to the crystal ball.

"Ahhhhh. I see something," Madame Wanda murmured. "Yes. It is becoming clearer!"

And then she gasped.

We all jumped.

Madame Wanda's face filled with horror. Her eyes bulged wide with fear. "No! No! I don't *believe* what I see in your future!" she cried.

"What? What is it?" Carla screamed. "Tell me!"

"I — I cannot. I have no choice! I cannot allow you to grow old and suffer!" Then she dropped Carla's hand — and pressed her thumb into Carla's forehead! "I have given you the Thumbprint of Doom!"

"Noooooo!" Carla shrieked. She knocked her chair over — and hurtled out of the trailer.

We all leaped up and ran after her. We found her leaning against the trailer. Gasping for breath. "The Thumbprint of Doom!" she murmured. She rubbed her forehead.

We laughed.

"Don't be afraid. It was all a joke," I explained. "We just wanted to show you how dumb superstitions are. Nothing bad will happen to you. You'll see. It was all a joke."

389

"Yeah," Jeremy added. "We paid Madame Wanda this morning. We paid her to say all that and press her thumb on your forehead."

"I know. I know it was a joke," Carla replied calmly. "I *knew* that woman couldn't give me the Thumbprint of Doom."

"How did you know?" I asked.

"Because only I have the power!" Carla cried. "Why do you think I believe in this stuff? Because I *know* it's all true! I know it's true — because I have the power! That's why I'm frightened of it. And now I have no choice. You know my secret. I have no choice."

Then Carla dived toward us. And before we could move, she pressed her icy thumb on our foreheads. "I've given you all the Thumbprint of Doom!" she cried.

I shrieked in horror. Carla grabbed my sleeve with an iron grip. I struggled to pull free, but she held on.

"Let me go," I cried. "Let me go!"

Carla threw back her head and laughed — a wicked laugh. She yanked on my arm. And a burning pain shot through my body.

With a burst of strength, I ripped free — and we ran.

We ran from evil Carla.

We ran from the carnival.

We ran to our doom.

*   *   *

Carla watched the three kids run off.

"That was a very mean joke, Carla," Madame Wanda said, stepping out of her trailer.

"They started it," Carla replied.

"How long do you think it will take them to realize that you have no powers? That you were just playing a trick on them?"

Carla giggled. "They'll figure it out after a day or so. Then maybe we'll all have a good laugh about it," she said. "I'm going to explore the carnival now. What time will you be home?"

"About ten," Madame Wanda replied.

"Okay," Carla said. "See you later, Mom."

R.L. STINE is the author of the series Fear Street, Nightmare Room, and Give Yourself Goosebumps, as well as the phenomenally successful Goosebumps series. His thrilling teen titles have sold more than 250 million copies internationally—enough to earn him a spot in the Guinness Book of World Records! Mr. Stine lives in New York City with his wife, Jane, and his son, Matt.